LIQUIDS AND
LIQUID MIXTURES

LIQUIDS AND
LIQUID MIXTURES

J. S. ROWLINSON

Professor of Chemical Technology
Imperial College of Science and Technology,
University of London

LONDON
BUTTERWORTH

THE BUTTERWORTH GROUP

ENGLAND: BUTTERWORTH & CO. (PUBLISHERS) LTD.
LONDON: 88 Kingsway, W.C.2B 6AB

AUSTRALIA: BUTTERWORTH & CO. (AUSTRALIA) LTD.
SYDNEY: 20 Loftus Street
MELBOURNE: 343 Little Collins Street
BRISBANE: 240 Queen Street

CANADA: BUTTERWORTH & CO. (CANADA) LTD.
TORONTO: 14 Curity Avenue, 374

NEW ZEALAND: BUTTERWORTH & CO. (NEW ZEALAND) LTD.
WELLINGTON: 49/51 Ballance Street
AUCKLAND: 35 High Street

SOUTH AFRICA: BUTTERWORTH & CO. (SOUTH AFRICA) (Pty) LTD.
DURBAN: 33/35 Beach Grove

First published 1959

Second edition 1969

Second impression (revised) 1971

Suggested U.D.C. *No.* 54–14
Suggested additional No. 541·121–14

ISBN 0 408 24191 8

Printed in Northern Ireland at The Universities Press, Belfast.

CONTENTS

PREFACE TO THE FIRST EDITION

It is unfortunate that both the theory and practice of the study of liquid mixtures have often been divorced from the study of pure liquids. I have tried, in this book, to put the two subjects together again.

There is first, in Chapters 1–3, an account of the equilibrium properties of pure liquids, and a development of reliable methods for the calculation of the thermodynamic properties of a liquid in equilibrium with its vapour. The liquid state runs from the triple point, through the normal boiling point, up to the critical point, and I have found that a satisfactory calculation of the thermodynamic properties of liquids above their normal boiling points needs equations of classical thermodynamics that are not to be found in the standard texts.

The second part of the book (Chapters 4–6) is an account of the equilibrium properties of liquid mixtures. At low vapour pressure these are summarized in the excess thermodynamic functions. This description is useless at high pressures, where the treatment given here is necessarily more qualitative. However, even a qualitative account of the equilibrium between the phases of a binary mixture reveals a variety of behaviour that is a challenge to the theorist—a challenge that has been ignored since the courageous but inevitably inadequate theories of van der Waals in 1906–1913.

The last part of this book is the interpretation of as much as possible of the experimental material in terms of the intermolecular forces. A complete account of all theories of liquids and of mixtures could not be compressed into three chapters and an appendix, but I have tried, in this space, to develop those parts of statistical thermodynamics that are common to all theories and then to restrict the account to results that can be compared directly with experiment. The theory of mixtures has been made as closely dependent as possible on the theory of pure fluids. This dependence has been a welcome feature of most theories of mixtures in the last seven years and should now, I believe, be assimilated into the text-books. The practical demands of these theories can only be met by a very detailed knowledge of the equilibrium properties of the pure liquids, and so the results of the first part of this book may serve as building bricks to those who are interested principally in mixtures.

This book is written by a physical chemist and so is primarily for chemists and physicists. The experimental parts, suitably trimmed, have been taught to honours and graduate students at Manchester, and the whole book has been the basis of two advanced courses for graduates in industry at the Royal Technical College, Salford. Much of the experimental work has been taken from the literature of chemical engineering and I hope that engineers will be able to refer to this book for a summary of our present knowledge of liquids and of the interpretation of those properties in terms of the intermolecular forces. I learnt from Professor J. O. Hirschfelder that the proper basis of chemical engineering must be molecular physics.

There are several conscious omissions. There is no account of the colligative properties of the ideal dilute solution, no account of polymer solutions, and no account of the properties of the surface of a liquid. All are discussed in standard textbooks of thermodynamics or in other monographs. I have tried throughout to keep to a minimum material that can readily be found elsewhere.

I wish to thank my colleague Mr W. B. Brown, first, for reading and criticizing the whole book in the course of innumerable discussions in the last two years, and secondly, for the use I have made of his published and unpublished work in Chapters 8 and 9. Those who are familiar with his two long papers on the theory of mixtures in the Philosophical Transactions of the Royal Society will know how much these last chapters owe to them both in content and in notation. I wish to thank also Professor G. O. Jones and Dr P. A. Walker for the loan of the latter's thesis on the properties of liquid argon, Professor R. L. Scott for sending copies of his papers on fluorocarbons before their publication, Mr E. Steiner and Dr M. J. Richardson for calculations in Chapters 2 and 9, respectively, Mrs J. Turner for typing a difficult manuscript, and my wife for her help with the proofs.

J. S. R.

Manchester

PREFACE TO THE SECOND EDITION

Much has happened in the last ten years and many parts of this book have been rewritten for this new edition.

The publication of more accurate measurements of the properties of pure liquids has led to a complete revision of the tables of Chapter 2 and to the inclusion of the properties of water. This important substance was omitted in 1958 because of some discrepancies which have now been resolved.

Our knowledge of the critical state (Chapter 3) was confused and contradictory in 1958. It is now apparently more secure and has been guided by some remarkable thermodynamic inequalities which have been discovered since 1963.

Mixtures of such simple liquids as argon, nitrogen, oxygen and the lower alkanes have been studied extensively; some doubts have been resolved and many gaps filled in Chapter 4. We now have a better appreciation of the variety of phase equilibria and critical lines that can appear in mixtures at high pressures, and of how these lines are interrelated (Chapter 6).

There was a remarkable renaissance in the theory of liquids between 1959 and 1963 and the flood of new ideas is now spilling over into the theory of mixtures. After a century of effort we are apparently within sight of an accurate theory of liquids and of liquid–vapour equilibrium. If a proper statistical theory of melting is still beyond our grasp, we can at least now discuss this phenomenon in terms of molecular parameters by using the results of computer experiments on model assemblies. Chapter 8 ends more optimistically than in the first edition.

The theory of mixtures made no real progress from 1957 until this injection of new ideas from the theory of liquids started in 1964. These ideas are reviewed in a revised Chapter 9 and, again, it seems as if quantitatively acceptable theories are now within sight. They promise to be of great practical value in the oil and gas industries where the calculation of the properties of multicomponent mixtures has long been a source of uncertainty in design work.

The scope and purpose of this book remain unchanged. It was a temptation to plunge into that rapidly growing field which is sometimes called *liquid state physics;* that is, the theoretical and experimental study of the dynamical properties of liquids. However, it was one that had to be resisted if the book was not to become much larger, later and more expensive. I have, in fact, gone further and reduced the length of those sections in which recent advances have led to a more satisfactory codification of our knowledge. 'It is no mere taste for paradox which leads one to doubt whether progress in a subject is reflected only in the increasing size of the books written about it. Encyclopaedias are very valuable works, but in some ways the ideal would be that successive editions of a book should get smaller and smaller'*.

I wish to thank many colleagues for helpful comment on the first edition: Mr P. J. Hunter for preliminary versions of some of the tables in Chapter 2, Dr I. D. Watson for some of the calculations in Chapter 9, Professors T. W. Leland and G. A. Sather for their collaboration in the work reported in Section 9.4, Dr G. S. Kell, Dr K. W. Morcom, Dr L. A. K. Staveley and Professor R. L. Scott (again) for access to unpublished work, and Mrs Frances Cole and Miss Anne Garrett for typing the manuscript.

London   J. S. R.

* C. N. Hinshelwood, Preface to *Kinetics of Chemical Change* (Oxford, 1940).

AUTHOR'S NOTE

Almost all the tables in this book have been calculated anew from the original literature and some care has been taken to ensure, first, thermodynamic consistency and, secondly, that the values quoted are the best that can be derived from all measurements so far reported. In some cases, however, use has been made of earlier compilations, and five of the most important of these are listed below. None needs any commendation here, as their reliability is generally acknowledged. They are referred to in the text only by the authors' names or abbreviated title.

F. DIN (ed.) *The Thermodynamic Functions of Gases*: Vol. 1, Ammonia, Carbon monoxide, Carbon dioxide; Vol. 2, Air, Propane, Acetylene, Ethylene, Argon; Vol. 3, Methane, Nitrogen, Ethane (Butterworth, London, 1956–1961)

K. A. KOBE and R. E. LYNN 'The critical properties of elements and compounds', *Chem. Rev.* 52 (1953) 117

J. TIMMERMANS *Physico-chemical constants of pure organic compounds*, 2 vols. (Elsevier, Amsterdam, 1950–1965)

American Petroleum Institute, Research Project 44 and Manufacturing Chemists' Association Research Project (referred to as *A.P.I.*) The first project covers hydrocarbons and related compounds, the second other inorganic and organic substances. The thermodynamic tables of each project are those in *Category A. Categories B–F* cover spectra of different kinds. Both projects are run by the Chemical Thermodynamic Properties Center, Texas A. and M. University.

National Bureau of Standards, Circular 500 'Selected values of chemical thermodynamic properties' (Washington, 1952). A new edition is being prepared, and is, at first, being issued in parts as N.B.S. Technical Note 270; that is, as 270-1, 270-2, etc.

The units of this book are the metre, kilogramme, second, kelvin, and mole, together with their multiples and sub-multiples. The first four of these are basic units of the Système international (SI) and the fifth will probably become one. The recent recommendation of the Conférence Générale des Poids et Mesures that the word *degree* be omitted and that the unit of temperature be simply the kelvin (symbol, K) has been followed.

xi

In these units we have—

Force   1 newton (N) $= 1$ kg m s^{-2}

Energy 1 joule (J) $= 1$ N m

Pressure   The fundamental unit is 1 N m^{-2}, but the practical unit is the bar, 1 bar $= 10^5$ N m$^{-2} = 10^5$ J m^{-3}. The defined but non-metric units of atm and mmHg are given exactly by 1·013 25 bar $=$ 1 atm $= 760$ mmHg.

Avogadro's constant, $N_A = 6\cdot0225 \times 10^{23}$ mol^{-1}

Molar gas constant, R $= 8\cdot3143$ J K^{-1} mol^{-1}

No units are specified in Chapter 7 when electrical entities such as a dipole are first used, but the implication of the form of the equations is that an *electrostatic system* (not SI) is being used in which a dipole is measured, for example, in debyes and in which the electrical permittivity of a vacuum is unity. For SI units we have that the force between two charges each of 1 coulomb at a separation of 1 metre is $(c^2 \cdot 10^{-7})$ newtons, where c is the numerical value of the speed of light in m s^{-1}, or 2·997 925 $\times$ 10^8. That is, the (rationalized) permittivity is $(10^7/4\pi c^2)$ F m^{-1}. This is a conflict of usage which chemists will have to resolve in the next few years.

NOTATION

The following is a list of the principal symbols:

Mathematical and Molecular Symbols

Bold type denotes a vector, **r**.
Sans-serif types denotes a tensor, **U**.
rr is a dyadic tensor.
$d\mathbf{r}$ is an element of volume, that is $dx\,dy\,dz$ or $r^2 \sin\theta\,dr\,d\theta\,d\varphi$.
Subscripts 1, 2, 3 etc. are used for individual molecules and for the different species in a mixture.
Subscripts i, j, k etc. are used for running suffixes for different molecules.
Subscripts α, β, γ etc. are used for running suffixes for different species.

u	intermolecular energy
v	intermolecular virial, (8.39)
w	derivative of v, (8.55)
$\bar{u}$	(8.61).
A	polarizability
μ	dipole moment (scalar)
q	quadrupole moment (scalar)
m, n	exponents of the Lennard-Jones potential, (7.17)
λ_2, ν_2	parameters of the Lennard-Jones potential, (7.17)
ν_3	coefficient of three-body dispersion potential (7.21)–(7.22)
σ, ϵ, r^*	collision diameter and characteristic energy of a conformal potential and, in particular, of the Lennard-Jones potential, the separation at which $u = -\epsilon$, (7.18)
b_0	$= \frac{2}{3}\pi N\sigma^3$
$X^{l_i l_j m}$	functions of r_{ij} which describe the non-central potential when multiplied by surface harmonics
λ', ν'	coefficients of the non-central part of a Lennard-Jones potential which changes with orientation, (7.25)–(7.26)
ξ, η	functions of λ' and ν', (8.161)–(8.162)
$\delta(T)$	a temperature-dependent function of ξ^2 used to represent the mean size of the non-central potential, (8.170)
$\chi(T)$	a temperature-dependent function of μ^4, (8.153)
$f_{\alpha\beta}$	ratio of $\epsilon_{\alpha\beta}$ to ϵ_{00} of a reference substance, (8.114)
$g_{\alpha\beta}$	ratio of $\sigma_{\alpha\beta}$ to σ_{00} of a reference substance, (8.114)
$h_{\alpha\beta}$	$= g_{\alpha\beta}^3$
f_x, g_x	one-fluid parameters of a substance equivalent to a mixture of composition x, (9.14)–(9.15) and (9.83)–(9.84)
f_α, g_α	mean parameters for substance α in a two-fluid mixture, (9.70)–(9.71) and (9.88)–(9.89)
$f_{\alpha\beta}^*, k_{\alpha\beta}^*$	ratios of energy and virial to those of a reference substance at separation r^*, (9.53)–(9.56)
e_{12}	$= 2f_{12} - f_{11} - f_{22}$, (9.37)
s_{12}	$= 2h_{12} - h_{11} - h_{22}$, (9.37)
d_{12}	$= 2\delta_{12} - \delta_{11} - \delta_{22}$, (9.127)
θ_{12}	$= f_{11} - f_{22}$, (9.38)
φ_{12}	$= h_{11} - h_{22}$, (9.38)

Δ_{12}	$= \delta_{11} - \delta_{22}$, (9.128)
ξ_{12}	$= f_{12}/(f_{11}f_{22})^{1/2}$, (9.95)

Thermodynamic Symbols

T^t, T^b, T^c	triple-point, normal boiling point, and critical temperature
U, H, S, A, G	energy, heat content, entropy, Helmholtz free energy, Gibbs free energy
u, h, s, a, g	molar energy, etc.
u_1, h_1, s_1	partial molar energy, etc.
u_1^0, h_1^0, s_1^0	molar energy, etc. of pure component 1
μ_1	chemical potential
μ_1', μ_1'', etc.	chemical potentials in different phases
γ_1	activity coefficient
m_1	number of moles
x_1, y_1	mole fractions in liquid and vapour
K_1	$= y_1/x_1$
α_{12}	volatility ratio, $= K_1/K_2$
$\mathcal{M}$	molar mass
σ(subscript)	derivative along the saturation line of the liquid (Section 2.1)
α_p, α_σ	coefficients of thermal expansion (Section 2.1)
β_T, β_S	coefficients of compressibility (Section 2.1)
γ_V, γ_S	thermal pressure coefficients (Section 2.1)
γ_σ	slope of vapour-pressure curve (Section 2.1–2.2)
C_p, C_V, C_σ	heat capacities at constant pressure, volume, and along the saturation line (Section 2.1 and 2.4)
C_2, C_1	heat capacities of two-phase and one-phase systems (Section 3.3 and 5.2)
G^m, G_V^m, etc.	free energy, etc. of mixing at constant pressure and constant volume (Section 4.3)
G_p^E, G_V^E, etc.	excess free energy, etc. at constant pressure and constant volume (Section 4.4)
G^*, etc.	residual free energy, etc. (Section 2.6)
G', etc.	configurational free energy, etc. (Section 2.6 and 8.2). The prime is omitted after equation (8.31) as only configurational properties are used in Chapter 8 and 9.
W	speed of sound
α, β, γ, δ, θ	indices which describe the order of the singularities at a critical point (*Tables 3.1* and *5.2*)

Statistical Symbols

$\mathcal{U}$	potential energy of an assembly in an arbitrary configuration (Section 8.2)
$\mathcal{V}$	virial of an arbitrary configuration, (8.40)
$\mathcal{W}$	(8.54)
Z	phase integral, (8.13)–(8.16)
Q	configuration integral, (8.8)–(8.12)
$f^{(1)}$, $f^{(2)}$, etc.	total molecular distribution functions (Section 8.2)
$n^{(1)}$, $n^{(2)}$, etc.	configurational molecular distribution functions (Section 8.2)
n	number density, $= N/V$
ρ	a reduced density, $= nb_0/4N$
β	$1/kT$
ψ^t, ψ^r, ψ^s	translational, rotational and vibrational molecular partition functions (Section 8.2)

$d(r)$, $e(r)$	sets of graphs (Section 8.3)
$f(r)$	(8.90)
$g(r)$	pair distribution function (8.29)
$h(r)$, $c(r)$	total and direct correlation functions (8.87)–(8.88)
$y(r)$	(8.91)
$\psi(r)$	potential of average force, (8.92)
s	(8.184)
$H(s)$, $C(s)$	Fourier transforms of $h(r)$, $c(r)$, (Section 8.6)
A_{ff}, A_{fk}, A_{kk}, etc.	fluctuation functions (Appendix and (8.63)–(8.71))
A_{fh}, A_{hh}	functions related to A_{fk}, A_{kk} (Appendix)
$A_{ff}^{(2)}$, $A_{ff}^{(3)}$, $A_{ff}^{(4)}$, etc.	molecular fluctuation integrals of pairs, triplets and quadruplets (Appendix and (8.64)–(8.83))
$A_{ff}^{(1)}$, etc.	fluctuations of 'private' energies and virials, (9.65) and (A.26)–(A.31)
Z_{hh}	(9.36) and (A.17)
$G_{\theta\theta}$, $G_{\theta\varphi}$, $G_{\varphi\varphi}$	coefficients of excess free energy, etc. in Lorentz–Berthelot mixture (9.42)
$\bar{\mathcal{U}}$, etc.	canonical average energy etc. (Section 8.2)
$\langle \mathcal{U} \rangle$, etc.	energy, etc. averaged over assignments, (9.5)

1

INTRODUCTION

1.1 The Liquid State

Everyone can recognize a liquid. It is popularly defined as a fluid which, if placed in a closed vessel, at once conforms to the shape of the vessel without necessarily filling the whole of its volume. The first property distinguishes it from a solid and the second from a gas. This simple definition is worth a closer examination for, although it is quite adequate for most purposes, it does not go very deeply into the relationship between solids, liquids and gases.

For most simple substances a clear distinction can at present be drawn between the solid state on the one hand and the fluid states, liquid and gas, on the other. If a fluid is cooled, then it changes to a solid state at a temperature which is a function of the applied pressure. At this melting, or subliming, temperature, one of the solid and one of the fluid states can exist in mutual equilibrium. Only at the triple point, a fixed temperature and pressure, can a solid phase be in equilibrium with both liquid and gas phases (*Figure 1.1*). This restriction is imposed by the phase rule of Gibbs which requires that the sum of the number of degrees of freedom and the number of phases shall be three for a pure substance. Thus in a phase-diagram of pressure as a function of temperature, one phase is represented by an area, two co-existent phases by a line, and three by the intersection of three lines at a point.

The change from solid to fluid or from one fluid phase to the other is a sharp one, at which the characteristic equilibrium properties of the substance change discontinuously. Properties such as the density, energy, heat content, heat capacities, coefficients of thermal expansion and of compressibility, refractive index and dielectric constant all have different values in the two phases. At the triple point, the change from solid to liquid is less drastic than that from liquid to gas, as is illustrated for argon in *Figure 1.2*. However, at high pressures the situation is very different, for whereas the solid–fluid discontinuities are but little affected by the pressure, the size of the liquid–gas discontinuities decreases, slowly at first, but then with increasing rapidity as the two states finally become indistinguishable at the *gas–liquid critical point* (*C* in *Figure 1.1*). The eventual fate of the solid–fluid transition is not known. It has been followed, for example, to 7400 bar and 50 K for helium and to

1

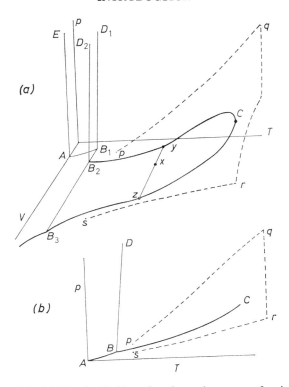

Figure 1.1. (*a*) The (*p, V, T*) surface for a given mass of a simple
substance, and (*b*) the (*p, T*) projection of this surface
A volume of the solid at absolute zero
AB₁ vapour-pressure curve of the solid
B_1, B_2, and B_3 volumes of the solid, liquid and gas at the triple point
BD and *BC* melting curve of the solid and vapour-pressure curve of
the liquid; the latter ends at the critical point *C*

12 000 bar and 330 K for argon without changing its character in
any way[1]. These pressures and temperatures are well above the
gas–liquid critical point of 2 bar and 5 K for helium and 49 bar and
151 K for argon.

Other substances have similarly failed to show a solid–fluid
critical point at the highest pressures reached, and measurements of
the densities and entropies of the two co-existent phases do not
suggest that they are approaching such a point.

It is likely, therefore, that the solid states of matter are always
distinct from the fluid states and are separated from them at all
temperatures by a first-order transition of the kind shown in

Figure 1.2. This tentative conclusion is unaffected by any phase changes that may occur between different solid states. Most substances have more than one solid phase, each being stable over a definite range of pressure and temperature. The transitions between these phases may be far from simple but, at a given pressure, there is one which, on heating, passes into the fluid at a simple first-order

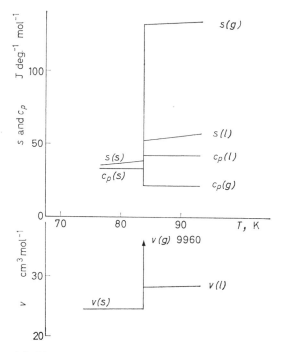

Figure 1.2. Changes of molar entropy (*s*), heat capacity (c_p) and volume (*v*) at the triple point of argon. The entropy is measured from an arbitrary zero

transition. However, the behaviour of some substances composed of large molecules—and particularly of polymers—is not so simple. One kind of complication, the formation of a glass, is discussed briefly at the end of this Section.

The second of the common criteria above, which distinguishes a liquid from a gas, implies that the term liquid is properly restricted to a fluid which is in equilibrium with its vapour.

Figure 1.1a represents the volume of a given amount of a substance, say one mole, as a function of pressure and temperature.

If this amount is placed in a vessel of the pressure, volume and temperature represented by the point x, then the vessel will contain liquid characterized by the point y and gas (or vapour) characterized by the point z. That is, the liquid and gas have, respectively, the pressure, temperature and volume per mole of these points. Since the overall molar volume is that of the vessel, x, it follows that the ratio of the masses of the two phases (m_y/m_z) is the ratio of the lengths (xz/xy).

A line that joins two coexistent phases in such a way that the position of a point on the line is a measure of the relative amounts of the phases is called a *tie-line*. Thus all points on the line B_2C are liquid states, for they are states of the fluid in equilibrium with infinitesimal amounts of gas. All points on the curved surface to the right of B_2D_2 represent the fluid state, which cannot be divided into liquid and gas in any but an arbitrary way except for points along the continuous curve B_2CB_3. Thus a fluid at point p, which might be said to be 'obviously' a liquid, can be changed to point s, 'obviously' a gas, first by heating at constant volume to q, expanding at constant temperature to r, and then cooling at constant volume to s. At no point in this three-stage transformation has a change of phase occurred, and no dividing meniscus, such as that which separates y and z, would have been observed in the vessel.

There is, in fact, no qualitative physical test that could distinguish fluid at point p from that at point s without making a change of pressure, volume or temperature that brings the fluid into the two-phase region of B_2CB_3. The two fluids differ only in degree. At higher temperatures and pressures, any attempt to divide the fluid state must be even more artificial. One arbitrary distinction that is sometimes used is to call a fluid of low density a vapour if it can be liquefied by isothermal compression, and a gas if it cannot. More common is the use of the word gas to describe a fluid of low density, whatever the temperature.

It would be pedantic to describe all states except B_2C and B_3C as fluids every time they are mentioned, and so in this book the word liquid is used freely for fluids on or near the line B_2C and the word gas for fluids of low density, in contexts where the meaning is clear. This line is usually called the *orthobaric liquid curve* or the *saturation curve*. The latter term is conveniently applied both to B_2C (a saturated liquid) and to B_3C (a saturated gas).

This unity, or continuity, of the fluid state of matter contrasts with the apparent lack of continuity between the fluid and the solid state. It is, of course, impossible to prove experimentally the negative proposition that the lines B_1D_1 and B_2D_2 of *Figure 1.1(a)* never meet at a critical point. However, the present position is that continuity

4

between the liquid and the gas phases has been known since Caignard de la Tour discovered the critical point of ethyl ether in 1822*, whilst continuity of the fluid and solid phases has never been observed and probably does not exist. There is throughout this book, therefore, the frequent mention of gases, but less of solids.

The view that liquids were more akin to gases than to solids was commonplace at the end of the last century, and although it later fell out of favour, is now to the fore again. The principal reason for not emphasizing the continuity of the fluid state and for thinking of liquids as disordered solids was the similarity of structure revealed by their x-ray diffraction patterns. The immediate neighbours of a molecule in a liquid have a disposition similar to those about a molecule in a solid. This similarity is a necessary consequence of the small difference in the density of the two phases. Gases at low density have no x-ray diffraction patterns, apart from those due to the internal structure of the molecules. If they are compressed, above or below the critical temperature, to a density comparable with that of the solid, then a pattern typical of a saturated liquid appears[3]. There have, however, been few studies on compressed gases and it is only the unfamiliarity of such patterns that has led to the comparison, *faute de mieux*, of the liquid patterns with those of solids.

A second factor which has supported the view that a liquid is akin to a solid has been the intensive development in the last twenty years of statistical theories of the liquid state that have been based on this analogy. These theories are greatly simplified if the liquid is supposed to be divided into a number of cells arranged regularly on a lattice, each containing one molecule. This approximation is tractable and has been moderately successful in practice. However, it is neither the only approach nor even the most successful numerically and its influence on the theory of mixtures, as apart from pure liquids, has often been unhelpful.

The restriction of the term liquid to fluids on the saturation line B_2C still allows the discussion of their properties over wide ranges of pressure and temperature. The temperatures of the triple points† of substances extend from 14 K for hydrogen to temperatures too

---

* For references to the early history of the study of liquids and gases see the work of J. R. Partington[2].

† The triple point differs slightly from the melting point in the presence of air at one atmosphere, both because of the slope of B_2D_2 in *Figure 1.1*, which represents the change of the melting point with pressure, and because of the solubility of air in the liquid. The former effect is usually the larger, and for water lowers the melting point by 0·010 K. The triple point is more reproducible than the normal melting point, and that of water is now accepted as a thermometric fixed point.

high for accurate measurement for substances such as diamond. Triple-point pressures are never very high, that of carbon dioxide being one of the highest known at 5·2 bar. Higher pressures have been reported only for the elements carbon, phosphorus and arsenic[4], for which the triple points are not well established. Most pressures are only of the order of 10^{-3} bar and a few, such as that of n-pentane, are as low as 10^{-7} bar.

The critical temperatures, the upper limits of the liquid state, also extend over an enormous range, starting with that of helium at 5 K and rising to temperatures well beyond measurement.

The critical pressures are much more uniform; the majority are about 50 bar, that of water being unusually high at 221 bar and those of helium and hydrogen being unusually low at 2 bar and 13 bar, respectively.

The *normal liquid range* of a substance is sometimes defined as the temperature interval between the normal melting point and the normal boiling point; that is, the temperature at which the vapour pressure is 1 atmosphere. This, however, is another artificial definition which has little to recommend it. As may be seen from the range of triple-point and critical pressures quoted above, a pressure of 1 atmosphere has no fundamental significance and obviously refers to quite different relative conditions for different substances.

The subject of this book is the liquid state as a whole, and no undue emphasis is placed on that part which happens to lie below 1 atmosphere pressure.

These wide variations in the properties of liquids make it useful to attempt some classification of liquids before discussing any property in detail. A satisfactory classification can be made only in terms of the intermolecular forces (Chapter 7), for it is these forces that are the sole determinants of all the physical properties discussed in this book. At low temperatures, the strength and symmetry of these forces determine the properties of the crystal. In the fluid states at higher temperatures the symmetry becomes less important.

The equilibrium properties of a substance, whether it is solid or fluid, are the result of the balance of the cohesive or potential energy on the one hand, and the kinetic energy of the thermal motions on the other. The translational kinetic energy is the same for all molecules at a given temperature—the classical principle of the equipartition of energy—and so it is solely the differences in the strength and types of the intermolecular energies that cause the properties of one liquid to differ from those of another at this fixed temperature. If liquids are compared not at the same temperature but at the same fraction of, say, their critical temperatures, then it is found that it is differences in type and symmetry of the inter-molecular energies that are responsible for the differences. To anticipate, therefore, the discussion of Chapter 7, the following classes of liquids may be distinguished, in increasing order of complexity:

(*1*) *The inert gases*—The molecules are monatomic and so, in isolation, spherically symmetrical. The force between a pair of molecules is entirely central; that is, the force acts through the centres of gravity, and neither molecule exerts a torque on the other.

(*2*) *Homonuclear diatomic molecules* such as hydrogen, nitrogen, oxygen and the halogens, and *heteronuclear diatomic molecules with negligible dipole moments*, such as carbon monoxide—The internuclear distances are here much smaller than the mean separation of the molecules in the liquid, and so the intermolecular forces do not depart greatly from spherical symmetry.

(*3*) *The lower hydrocarbons and other simple non-polar substances such as carbon tetrachloride*—The lower hydrocarbons are comparable in symmetry with the diatomic molecules, but as the chain length increases, the maximum internuclear distance within one molecule ceases to be small when compared with the mean intermolecular separation. That is, the forces depart greatly from spherical symmetry.

(*4*) *Simple but polar substances* such as sulphur dioxide and the hydrogen and methyl halides—These molecules have a direct electrostatic interaction between permanent dipole moments super-imposed on a force field which is otherwise reasonably symmetrical. Molecules with large quadrupole moments, such as carbon dioxide and acetylene, are few in number but must be included in this class.

(*5*) *Molecules of great polarity or electrical asymmetry*—Water and ammonia are in this class. The polarity is often localized in one part of the molecule, as in organic alcohols, amines, ketones and nitriles.

These divisions are rather arbitrary but do place in a rough order of increasing complexity many of the substances discussed in this book. As far as possible, examples will be chosen from the earlier substances in this list, since these illustrate more clearly many of the essential properties of the liquid state without the complications introduced by the polarity and shape of the larger molecules. This choice is not always possible, as much of the best experimental work has been done on the less simple substances.

The complications of shape and polarity are discussed explicitly in some Sections, as, for example, the mixtures of substances from class (*5*) above which are discussed in Chapter 5, but where the property under discussion is exhibited by the simple as well as by the complex molecules, then the former have been chosen as examples.

This policy will, it is hoped, excuse the frequency of the references to liquid argon in the Chapters that follow.

There are several important omissions from this list of liquids. One is helium, which must be excluded from the first class because of the peculiarity of its liquid structure; a second is that class of liquids, mainly of high molecular weight, which form glasses on cooling; and a third those rare liquids which form an ordered fluid

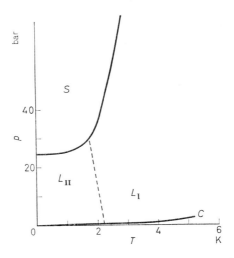

Figure 1.3. The phase diagram of normal helium. The melting point of the solid is at 24 bar or above. The liquid state is divided into two liquids L_I and L_{II} by a second-order transition which is shown by the dashed line. C is the critical point. Compare this diagram with *Figure 1.1b*

phase on cooling, the so-called *liquid crystals*. None is discussed here, since each has received a monograph to itself[5-7]. However, it may be useful to indicate briefly how these three classes of liquids depart from normality.

The phase diagram of helium is shown in *Figure 1.3*. There is no triple point at which gas, liquid and solid are in equilibrium, since the solid is stable only at pressures above 24 bar. There is, however, a second liquid phase, of most unusual dynamical properties, which is formed on cooling the normal liquid in equilibrium with the vapour.

This behaviour is partly a consequence of the fact that ^{4}He obeys Bose–Einstein statistics, but mainly due to the light mass and weak intermolecular forces. The mass (and moments of inertia) of a molecule are not determinants of the equilibrium properties of fluids that obey the laws of classical statistical mechanics—a consequence of the equipartition of energy—but are relevant to the quantal description of the system. The importance of the mass is measured by the size of the ratio $(h^2/m\sigma^2\epsilon)$ where h is Planck's constant, m the mass of the molecule, and σ and ϵ a distance and energy proportional to the size of the molecule and the greatest energy of interaction of the molecules[8].

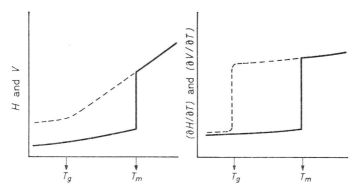

Figure 1.4. The glassy state: H and V, and their derivatives, change on passing from the liquid state (above T_m) to the solid state (full line), to the supercooled liquid (dashed line) and, below T_g, to the glassy state (dashed line)

The departure from classical behaviour is large for helium, since m, σ and ϵ are all small. Liquid hydrogen, deuterium and neon show much smaller departures, which are usually called the *quantum corrections*, and all other liquids are adequately described by classical theory.

The simplest physical picture of this quantum effect is a zero-point energy of the molecule vibrating in a 'cage' of its nearest neighbours in the liquid and solid states. A low mass leads to a high frequency of vibration and so to a large zero-point energy. At zero pressure and temperature, the cohesive forces of helium are not strong enough to restrain the zero-point vibrations of the solid lattice. Only when an additional restraint of 24 bar external pressure is applied does the liquid crystallize to a normal solid.

The glassy state is rarely met in simple substances but is common with polymers and with substances such as polyalcohols and sugars. Their liquids can be readily cooled below the normal or true melting points and eventually harden to a glass. The hardening is not sharp but is usually confined to a range of 10–20 K. *Figure 1.4* is a sketch of the volume and heat content of a substance in the solid, liquid and glassy states. The transition from super-cooled liquid to glass is usually reversible in experiments that last no more than a few hours, but the glasses themselves are prone to crystallization (or devitrification) if kept for a long time just below the glass point, T_g. The glassy state is metastable with respect to the crystalline but is usually sufficiently reproducible for the meaningful measurement of its thermodynamic functions. It has all the properties of a liquid except that of obvious mobility. It is isotropic, has no ordered crystalline structure, no cleavage planes, flows slowly under stress, and has no sharp melting point but softens gradually to a normal liquid without the absorption of a latent heat.

Liquid crystals are a rare state of matter, formed by some complex organic molecules which can pack together in roughly parallel sheets or columns without losing mobility or forming a true crystalline phase. The transitions from liquid crystal to normal liquid, on the one hand, and to true solid crystal on the other, are simple first-order transitions. The liquid crystal is found sometimes only at high pressures.

REFERENCES

[1] Holland, F. A., Huggill, J. A. W. and Jones, G. O. *Proc. R. Soc.* A207 (1951) 268; Robinson, D. W. A225 (1954) 393; Lahr, P. H. and Eversole, W. G. *J. chem. Engng Data* 7 (1962) 42; Babb, S. E. *Rev. mod. Phys.* 35 (1963) 400

[2] Partington, J. R. *An Advanced Treatise on Physical Chemistry:* Vol. 1, *The Properties of Gases;* Vol. 2. *The Properties of Liquids,* London (Longmans) 1949–51

[3] Pings, C. J., in *The Physics of Simple Liquids* (ed. Temperley, H. N. V., Rowlinson, J. S. and Rushbrooke, G. S.) Chapter 10, Amsterdam (North-Holland) 1968

[4] Zernike, J. *Chemical Phase Theory,* p. 23, Antwerp (Kluwer) 1956; Bundy, F. P. *J. chem. Phys.* 38 (1963) 631

[5] Mendelssohn, K. *Handbuch der Physik* (ed. Flügge, S.), Vol. 15, pp. 370–416, Berlin (Springer) 1956

[6] Jones, G. O. *Glass,* London (Methuen) 1955; Mackenzie, J. D. (ed.) *Modern Aspects of the Vitreous State,* Vol. 1–3, London (Butterworth) 1961–4

[7] Gray, G. W. *Molecular Structure and the Properties of Liquid Crystals,* New York (Academic Press) 1962; Porter, R. S. and Johnson, J. F. (ed.) *Ordered Fluids and Liquid Crystals,* Washington (Am. Chem. Soc.) 1967

[8] De Boer, J. and Bird, R. B., in Hirschfelder, J. O., Curtiss, C. F. and Bird, R. B. *Molecular Theory of Gases and Liquids,* Ch. 6, New York (Wiley) 1954; De Boer, J. *Progress in Low Temperature Physics* (ed. Gorter, C. J.), Vol. 2 Ch. 1, Amsterdam (North-Holland) 1957

2

THE THERMODYNAMIC PROPERTIES

2.1 SUMMARY OF THERMODYNAMIC RELATIONS

The more important of the thermodynamic equations used in this book are set out in this Section but they are not in the order in which they occur in formal textbooks of thermodynamics, as this Section is in no way intended as a substitute for such books*. Many of these equations are well known, but those describing the change of thermodynamic functions along the saturation curve of a liquid are derived and discussed in greater detail than usual, since these are the derivatives which are most readily measured for a liquid. The equations in this Section are applicable to pure substances and to mixtures of fixed composition. The change of thermodynamic functions with composition is discussed in Chapter 4.

Small changes in the energy U, the heat-content (or enthalpy) H, the Helmholtz free energy A, and the Gibbs free energy G are given by the following four fundamental equations for systems of constant composition and total mass:

$$dU = \quad T\,dS - p\,dV \tag{2.1}$$
$$dH = \quad T\,dS + V\,dp \tag{2.2}$$
$$dA = -S\,dT - p\,dV \tag{2.3}$$
$$dG = -S\,dT + V\,dp \tag{2.4}$$

where S is the entropy. It follows that

$$(\partial U/\partial V)_S = (\partial A/\partial V)_T = -p \tag{2.5}$$
$$(\partial H/\partial p)_S = (\partial G/\partial p)_T = V \tag{2.6}$$
$$(\partial A/\partial T)_V = (\partial G/\partial T)_p = -S \tag{2.7}$$

The changes of U, H, S, A and G with temperature are related to the heat capacities at constant volume and at constant pressure

$$C_V = T(\partial S/\partial T)_V = (\partial U/\partial T)_V = -T(\partial^2 A/\partial T^2)_V \tag{2.8}$$
$$C_p = T(\partial S/\partial T)_p = (\partial H/\partial T)_p = -T(\partial^2 G/\partial T^2)_p \tag{2.9}$$
$$U = A - T(\partial A/\partial T)_V \tag{2.10}$$
$$H = G - T(\partial G/\partial T)_p \tag{2.11}$$

* Two of the most suitable for the subject of this book are cited in ref. 1.

The isothermal changes of U, H, S, A and G with volume or pressure can be expressed solely in terms of pressure, volume, temperature and their mutual derivatives, as, for example, in (2.5) and (2.6). Similar equations for the entropy (Maxwell's equations) can be obtained by the differentiation of (2.5)–(2.7). Thus

$$-(\partial^2 A/\partial V\,\partial T) = (\partial S/\partial V)_T = (\partial p/\partial T)_V \qquad (2.12)$$

$$-(\partial^2 G/\partial p\,\partial T) = (\partial S/\partial p)_T = -(\partial V/\partial T)_p \qquad (2.13)$$

Similar equations for U and H are obtained by differentiation of the Gibbs–Helmholtz equations, (2.10) and (2.11).

$$(\partial U/\partial V)_T = -p + T(\partial p/\partial T)_V \qquad (2.14)$$

$$(\partial H/\partial p)_T = V - T(\partial V/\partial T)_p \qquad (2.15)$$

whence

$$(\partial C_V/\partial V)_T = T(\partial^2 p/\partial T^2)_V \qquad (2.16)$$

$$(\partial C_p/\partial p)_T = -T(\partial^2 V/\partial T^2)_p \qquad (2.17)$$

The pair of equations (2.14) and (2.15) are known as the *thermodynamic equations of state*.

It is usually unprofitable to express U, A and C_V as functions of the pressure or H, G and C_p as functions of the volume, but such equations can readily be obtained if they are needed. However, one 'cross-relation' of this kind is useful—that for the difference between C_p and C_V

$$\left(\frac{\partial H}{\partial T}\right)_p = \left(\frac{\partial (U + pV)}{\partial T}\right)_p$$

$$= \left(\frac{\partial U}{\partial T}\right)_V + \left(\frac{\partial U}{\partial V}\right)_T \left(\frac{\partial V}{\partial T}\right)_p + p\left(\frac{\partial V}{\partial T}\right)_p \qquad (2.18)$$

whence, from (2.14),

$$C_p - C_V = T\left(\frac{\partial p}{\partial T}\right)_V \left(\frac{\partial V}{\partial T}\right)_p \qquad (2.19)$$

This difference is equal to the 'work of expansion' only if $(\partial U/\partial V)_T$ is zero, as, for example, in a perfect gas. However, for liquids the second term on the right-hand side of (2.18) is far from negligible and is generally larger than the third. Eqn. (2.19) may be put into two other forms by using an identity connecting the three mutual derivatives of p, V and T. The specification of any two of these determines the third in a system of one phase and of fixed composition. Hence

$$\mathrm{d}p = (\partial p/\partial V)_T\,\mathrm{d}V + (\partial p/\partial T)_V\,\mathrm{d}T \qquad (2.20)$$

or

$$\left(\frac{\partial V}{\partial p}\right)_T \left(\frac{\partial T}{\partial V}\right)_p \left(\frac{\partial p}{\partial T}\right)_V = -1 \qquad (2.21)$$

The alternative forms of (2.19) are therefore

$$C_p = C_V - T\left(\frac{\partial V}{\partial T}\right)_p^2 \Big/ \left(\frac{\partial V}{\partial p}\right)_T \qquad (2.22)$$

$$C_p = C_V - T\left(\frac{\partial p}{\partial T}\right)_V^2 \Big/ \left(\frac{\partial p}{\partial V}\right)_T \qquad (2.23)$$

Eqn. (2.21) may be compared with the identity connecting the three mutual derivatives along a fixed line on the p, V, T surface as, for example, along a line of constant entropy, or along the saturation (or orthobaric) curve which is denoted here by the subscript σ. For such derivatives

$$\left(\frac{\partial V}{\partial p}\right)_\sigma \left(\frac{\partial T}{\partial V}\right)_\sigma \left(\frac{\partial p}{\partial T}\right)_\sigma = +1 \qquad (2.24)$$

The three mutual derivatives of p, V and T are named as follows:

$(1/V)(\partial V/\partial T)_p$ is the coefficient of thermal expansion and is denoted here by α_p. However, if a saturated liquid is heated, its vapour pressure increases, and so the volume increase of a pure substance in contact with its own vapour is not that at constant pressure. The measured derivative is that along the saturation curve and is denoted here by α_σ. This is equal to $(1/V)(\partial V/\partial T)_\sigma$. The difference between the two coefficients of thermal expansion is shown in *Figure 2.1*. It is usually negligible below the normal boiling point but is appreciable at higher vapour pressures. It follows directly from the rules of partial differentiation (or from this figure) that

$$\left(\frac{\partial V}{\partial T}\right)_p = \left(\frac{\partial V}{\partial T}\right)_\sigma - \left(\frac{\partial V}{\partial p}\right)_T \left(\frac{\partial p}{\partial T}\right)_\sigma \qquad (2.25)$$

where $(\partial p/\partial T)_\sigma$ is the rate of increase of vapour pressure with temperature. This equation, like most of those involving derivatives with a subscript σ, is formally applicable to any fixed line on the p, V, T surface, including that of the saturated vapour, if the meaning of σ is suitably extended.

$(-1/V)(\partial V/\partial p)_T$ is the isothermal coefficient of bulk compressibility and is denoted here by β_T. The coefficient β_σ is of little importance. It is usually negative and much larger than β_T. Such a coefficient can be useful in the discussion of a solid–fluid boundary.

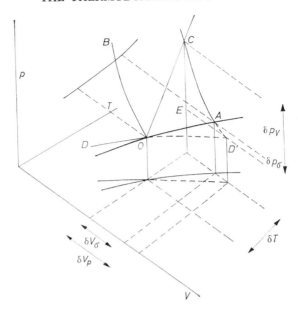

Figure 2.1. The change of the orthobaric volume of a liquid with p, V and T is shown by OA. The slopes of its projections on the (V, T) and (p, T) planes are $(\partial V/\partial T)_\sigma$ and $(\partial p/\partial T)_\sigma$. OB and AC represent the isothermal compression of the liquid, and OC represents the heating at constant volume, with a slope of $(\partial p/\partial T)_V$. DOD' is an isobar whose slope at O is $(\partial V/\partial T)_p$. Eqn. (2.25) is readily derived from this figure

$(\partial p/\partial T)_V$ is the thermal pressure coefficient and is denoted here by γ_V. It follows that the slope of a vapour-pressure curve, $(\partial p/\partial T)_\sigma$, may be written γ_σ—a notation which will be used whenever it is necessary to contrast this derivative with γ_V. At the critical point γ_V and γ_σ become equal. This fact was known to van der Waals and has been 'rediscovered' several times since then[2].

The change of α_p with pressure is the complement of the change of β_T with temperature

$$\left(\frac{\partial}{\partial p}\right)_T\left(\frac{\partial V}{\partial T}\right)_p = \left(\frac{\partial}{\partial T}\right)_p\left(\frac{\partial V}{\partial p}\right)_T; \qquad \left(\frac{\partial \alpha_p}{\partial p}\right)_T = -\left(\frac{\partial \beta_T}{\partial T}\right)_p \quad (2.26)$$

Experimental results are often expressed in terms of these coefficients, and it is therefore useful to rewrite some of the equations above in the following forms

$$\alpha_p = \beta_T \gamma_V \tag{2.27}$$

$$\alpha_\sigma = \alpha_p - \beta_T \gamma_\sigma = \alpha_p \left(1 - \frac{\gamma_\sigma}{\gamma_V} \right) \tag{2.28}$$

$$\gamma_V - \gamma_\sigma = \alpha_\sigma / \beta_T \tag{2.29}$$

$$(\partial S / \partial V)_T = \alpha_p / \beta_T = \gamma_V \tag{2.30}$$

$$(\partial S / \partial p)_T = -V \alpha_p \tag{2.31}$$

$$(\partial U / \partial V)_T = -p + T \alpha_p / \beta_T = -p + T \gamma_V \tag{2.32}$$

$$(\partial H / \partial p)_T = V(1 - T \alpha_p) \tag{2.33}$$

$$C_p = C_V + T V \alpha_p \gamma_V \tag{2.34}$$

$$= C_V + T V \alpha_p^2 / \beta_T \tag{2.35}$$

$$= C_V + T V \beta_T \gamma_V^2 \tag{2.36}$$

In practice, C_p (like α_p) is not usually measured directly for a liquid on its saturation curve, as an increase of temperature at constant pressure causes complete evaporation. A heat capacity more closely related to experiment is C_σ, that of a liquid which is maintained at all temperatures in equilibrium with an infinitesimal amount of vapour. This heat capacity is the amount of energy supplied per unit rise of temperature to heat a liquid along its saturation curve, and therefore is given by

$$T \left(\frac{\partial S}{\partial T} \right)_\sigma \equiv C_\sigma = T \left(\frac{\partial S}{\partial T} \right)_V + \left(\frac{\partial S}{\partial V} \right)_T \left(\frac{\partial V}{\partial T} \right)_\sigma \tag{2.37}$$

$$= C_V + T \left(\frac{\partial p}{\partial T} \right)_V \left(\frac{\partial V}{\partial T} \right)_\sigma \tag{2.38}$$

This equation may be combined with (2.34)–(2.36) to give several equations, of which the most useful are

$$C_\sigma = C_V + T V \alpha_\sigma \gamma_V = C_V + T V \alpha_p (\gamma_V - \gamma_\sigma) \tag{2.39}$$

$$= C_p - T V \alpha_p \gamma_\sigma = C_p - T V (\alpha_p - \alpha_\sigma) \gamma_V \tag{2.40}$$

The second pair of equations shows that the difference between C_p and C_σ is often negligible at low vapour pressures. Neither C_p nor C_σ is, in general, equal to the change of heat content with temperature along the saturation curve. This is given by

$$\left(\frac{\partial H}{\partial T} \right)_\sigma = \left(\frac{\partial H}{\partial T} \right)_p + \left(\frac{\partial H}{\partial p} \right)_T \left(\frac{\partial p}{\partial T} \right)_\sigma \tag{2.41}$$

$$= C_p + V(1 - T \alpha_p) \gamma_\sigma = C_\sigma + V \gamma_\sigma \tag{2.42}$$

Similarly

$$\left(\frac{\partial U}{\partial T} \right)_\sigma = \left(\frac{\partial H}{\partial T} \right)_\sigma - \left(\frac{\partial (pV)}{\partial T} \right)_\sigma = C_\sigma - p V \alpha_\sigma \tag{2.43}$$

If the product $(T\alpha_p)$ is positive but less than unity, as it generally is near the normal boiling point, then

$$\left(\frac{\partial H}{\partial T}\right)_\sigma > C_p > C_\sigma > \left(\frac{\partial U}{\partial T}\right)_\sigma > C_V \qquad (2.44)$$

The differences between the first four of these quantities are generally much less than that between the fourth and fifth.

These equations apply also to the saturated-gas boundary, but here the difference between C_p and C_σ may never be ignored, as $(V\alpha_p)$ is always large and, indeed, may be large enough to make C_σ negative. In practice, this heat capacity of the saturated gas is positive for large molecules, for which that of the perfect gas is above about $80\ \mathrm{J\ K^{-1}\ mol^{-1}}$, and negative for the saturated vapours of substances such as argon, carbon dioxide, ammonia and steam.

The adiabatic coefficient of bulk compressibility is defined by

$$\beta_S = -\frac{1}{V}\left(\frac{\partial V}{\partial p}\right)_S \qquad (2.45)$$

It is related to the speed of sound in a fluid by

$$W^2 = v/\mathcal{M}\beta_S \qquad (2.46)$$

where W is the speed, v the molar volume and $\mathcal{M}$ the molar mass. The speed *defined* by this equation is, of course, a purely thermodynamic quantity. The experimental speed is equal to this speed over a wide range of frequencies and amplitudes for most fluids, and so may be regarded as an equilibrium property. However, it is sometimes larger than the speed defined by (2.46) at very high frequencies where the thermal properties of a fluid depend on the rate of heating. This anomalous speed is discussed in Section 2.5.

The ratio of β_T to β_S may be derived as follows

$$\mathrm{d}S = (\partial S/\partial V)_p\,\mathrm{d}V + (\partial S/\partial p)_V\,\mathrm{d}p \qquad (2.47)$$

whence

$$\left(\frac{\partial V}{\partial p}\right)_S = -\frac{(\partial S/\partial p)_V}{(\partial S/\partial V)_p} = -\frac{(\partial S/\partial T)_V(\partial T/\partial p)_V}{(\partial S/\partial T)_p(\partial T/\partial V)_p} = \frac{C_V}{C_p}\left(\frac{\partial V}{\partial p}\right)_T \qquad (2.48)$$

or

$$\beta_T/\beta_S = C_p/C_V \qquad (2.49)$$

The equilibrium speed of sound is, therefore, given by

$$W^2 = (C_p/C_V)(v/\mathcal{M}\beta_T) \qquad (2.50)$$

16

An expression for the difference between β_T and β_S follows from (2.49) and the equations for the difference between C_p and C_V

$$\beta_T - \beta_S = TV\alpha_p^2/C_p \tag{2.51}$$

or

$$(1/\beta_S) - (1/\beta_T) = TV\gamma_V^2/C_V \tag{2.52}$$

The adiabatic thermal pressure coefficient, γ_S, is given by

$$\gamma_S \equiv \left(\frac{\partial p}{\partial T}\right)_S = -\frac{(\partial S/\partial T)_p}{(\partial S/\partial p)_T} = \frac{C_p}{T(\partial V/\partial T)_p} \tag{2.53}$$

Alternative forms for this last equation are

$$\gamma_S = \frac{C_p}{TV\alpha_p} = \frac{\alpha_p}{\beta_T - \beta_S} = \gamma_V + \frac{C_V}{TV\alpha_p} = \gamma_\sigma + \frac{C_\sigma}{TV\alpha_p} \tag{2.54}$$

The third adiabatic coefficient, α_S, is of little importance. It is generally negative and is given by

$$\alpha_S \equiv \frac{1}{V}\left(\frac{\partial V}{\partial T}\right)_S = -\frac{C_V}{TV\gamma_V} = -\beta_S\gamma_S \tag{2.55}$$

The chemical potential is an intensive property which may be defined by the equations

$$\mu = (\partial G/\partial m)_{p,T} = g \tag{2.56}$$

(where m is the number of moles) for a one-component system maintained at constant pressure and temperature. The condition for equilibrium between two or three phases is that the three quantities, pressure, temperature and chemical potential, shall be equal in each phase.

The requirements of thermal and mechanical stability impose limitations on the signs and sizes of many of these thermodynamic functions. Consider a system of energy U, entropy S and volume V, which may be represented as a point on a surface in a three-dimensional (U, S, V) space. The surface itself represents all possible states of the system, and for a small displacement on such a surface,

$$\delta U = \left(\frac{\partial U}{\partial S}\right)_V(\delta S) + \left(\frac{\partial U}{\partial V}\right)_S(\delta V) + \tfrac{1}{2}\left(\frac{\partial^2 U}{\partial S^2}\right)_V(\delta S)^2$$

$$+ \left(\frac{\partial^2 U}{\partial S\,\partial V}\right)(\delta S)(\delta V) + \tfrac{1}{2}\left(\frac{\partial^2 U}{\partial V^2}\right)_S(\delta V)^2 + \ldots \tag{2.57}$$

Now, for equilibrium at a point on this surface it is necessary[3] that the surface lies above the tangent plane at that point. The surface is therefore essentially convex and

$$\left(\frac{\partial^2 U}{\partial S^2}\right)_V > 0 \qquad \left(\frac{\partial^2 U}{\partial V^2}\right)_S > 0 \tag{2.58}$$

$$\left(\frac{\partial^2 U}{\partial S^2}\right)_V \left(\frac{\partial^2 U}{\partial V^2}\right)_S - \left(\frac{\partial^2 U}{\partial S \, \partial V}\right)^2 > 0 \tag{2.59}$$

From (2.1)

$$(\partial U/\partial S)_V = T \qquad (\partial U/\partial V)_S = -p \tag{2.60}$$

and so (2.58) becomes

$$(\partial T/\partial S)_V > 0 \qquad \text{or} \qquad (T/C_V) > 0 \tag{2.61}$$

and

$$-(\partial p/\partial V)_S > 0 \qquad \text{or} \qquad (1/V\beta_S) > 0 \tag{2.62}$$

The first of these conditions, (2.61), is the condition of thermal stability, namely that $1/C_V$ is positive. The second can be called the condition of mechanical stability, namely that $1/\beta_S$ is positive, but this expression is used also for the stronger condition that follows from (2.59). This may be written

$$-\left(\frac{T}{C_V}\right)\left(\frac{\partial p}{\partial V}\right)_S - \left(\frac{\partial T}{\partial V}\right)_S^2 > 0 \tag{2.63}$$

By substitution from (2.52) and (2.55)

$$-\left(\frac{C_V}{T}\right)\left(\frac{\partial p}{\partial V}\right)_T > 0 \tag{2.64}$$

that is

$$-(\partial p/\partial V)_T > 0 \qquad \text{or} \qquad (1/\beta_T) > 0 \tag{2.65}$$

The condition of (isothermal) mechanical stability can be derived more simply by considering the (A, V, T) surface, rather than the more primitive surface of (U, S, V). If local fluctuations of volume are to lead to an increase of A in an isothermal system, then

$$(\partial^2 A/\partial V^2)_T > 0 \tag{2.66}$$

which leads at once to (2.65). However, this surface, which has one intensive variable and only two extensive variables, is not so powerful an instrument as the (U, S, V) surface. It is, for example, impossible to derive the condition of thermal stability from the (A, V, T) surface, since the only states that may be represented on such a surface are those of uniform temperature.

These conditions of stability are necessary but not sufficient in a multi-component system. In these there is a further condition, that of material stability, which is discussed in Chapter 5.

There are no restrictions on the signs of α_p or γ_V except the obvious consequence of (2.65) that both coefficients have the same sign. They are generally positive. The coefficient γ_σ is always positive for liquid–gas equilibrium and usually positive for solid–fluid equilibrium. It follows from (2.49) and (2.52) that

$$C_p \geqslant C_V \qquad \text{and} \qquad \beta_T \geqslant \beta_S \qquad (2.67)$$

These conditions are equalities only if α_p, and therefore γ_V, are zero. The coefficient γ_S has the same sign as γ_V and its modulus is larger.

2.2 VAPOUR PRESSURE

The vapour pressure of a pure liquid is a function only of temperature, since a system of one component and two phases has only one degree of freedom. If a gas is compressed isothermally, at a temperature below the critical, the pressure rises until the vapour pressure is reached and the first drop of liquid is formed. This pressure and volume define the *dew-point* for that temperature. The pressure remains constant at p_σ until the last trace of gas disappears at the *bubble-point*, and then rises rapidly in the liquid phase. The volumes of the gas and liquid at the dew- and bubble-points are called the orthobaric volumes. The absence of a change of pressure between these points is often a sensitive test of purity and is used to demonstrate the absence of dissolved air from a liquid.

S. Young, who was always a careful worker, was one of the first to demonstrate this equality of dew- and bubble-point pressures for a pure substance, and to use it as a criterion of purity. Timmermans, a disciple of Young, recommends that a difference of one part in 600 of p_σ is the maximum that should be tolerated in samples of liquid which are to be used for accurate physical measurements. Unfortunately, this is a test that cannot be made in most types of apparatus that are used for measuring vapour pressures below 1 atmosphere.

The process of condensation described above is that for a fluid which is always at equilibrium. It is sometimes possible to compress a gas to a pressure greater than p_σ without producing immediate condensation, as the liquid phase is formed readily only in the presence of suitable nuclei about which the liquid drops can grow. Such nuclei are generally foreign particles, such as dust, and so the cleaner the gas the more readily is this non-equilibrium state produced. The state is usually described as *supercooled*, since it may also be produced by cooling at constant pressure a gas which is near to its saturation curve.

It is similarly possible, although less easy, to over-expand or *superheat* a liquid. It is even possible by confining the liquid in a capillary to carry this expansion into the region of negative pressures without evaporating the liquid. This is best done by applying tension to the liquid by spinning the capillary in a centrifuge. In this way negative pressures of −270 bar have been reached in water, and −310 bar in chloroform[4]. Other methods of stretching

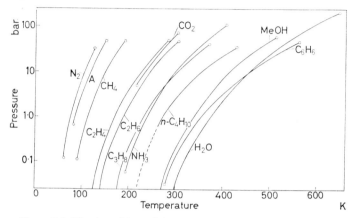

Figure 2.2. The logarithm of the vapour pressures of twelve liquids as functions of the absolute temperature. The circles mark the triple and critical points

the liquid lead to smaller and less reproducible negative pressures. In the complementary process of direct superheating, a temperature of 270°C has been achieved[5] for liquid water at 1 bar.

The variation with temperature of the vapour pressures of some liquids is shown in *Figure 2.2**. Such graphs form a remarkably regular family of curves and it is rare for two of them to cross. Such a crossing (a *Bancroft point*) occurs only when the molecules in the two liquids are dissimilar in chemical type or in shape. In *Figure 2.2* the logarithm of the pressure is plotted against the temperature. Such a graph is satisfactory for direct reading. The logarithm of the pressure is, however, much closer to a linear function of the reciprocal of the absolute temperature than to this itself, and so can be represented by the well known equation

$$\log_{10} p_\sigma = a - b/T \qquad (2.68)$$

This representation is shown in *Figure 2.3* for benzene.

* Critical tables of vapour pressures are to be found in the four sources cited on p. xi. An extensive but uncritical collection has been made by Jordan[6] and over 1000 references are to be found in the *Handbook of Chemistry and Physics*[6].

Although it is widely used, and is generally quite satisfactory, this equation cannot fit measurements of the highest accuracy even over small ranges of temperature. It is therefore often supplemented by a deviation graph in which the right-hand side of (2.68), with suitable values of a and b, is chosen as a datum line and the small deviations

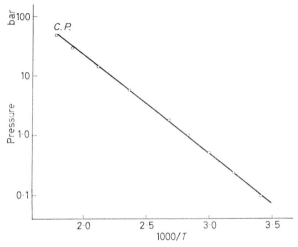

Figure 2.3. The logarithm of the vapour pressure of benzene as a function of the reciprocal of the absolute temperature. The points are those of *Table 2.3* below, the highest (*C.P.*) being the critical point. The straight line has the equation

$$\log_{10}(p/\text{bar}) = 4\cdot6757 - 1660\ \text{K}/T$$

from it of the experimental points are shown as a function of temperature. Such a graph is shown in *Figure 2.4*. The choice of a and b is not very critical if the equation is to be used with a deviation graph, otherwise it is customary to choose the parameters by the method of least squares in which $(1/T)$ is the independent and $(\log p)$ the dependent variable. This choice of variables assumes that the experimental error in $(1/T)$ is negligible compared to that in $(\log p)$—which is probably wrong for many measurements below room temperature. The accuracy of this simple equation may be improved by adding further parameters, as, for example, in the equation of Antoine[7]

$$\log_{10} p_\sigma = a - b/(T + c) \qquad (2.69)$$

where c is a temperature which is small compared to T. Forziati, Norris and Rossini[8] have used this equation to represent their accurate measurements of the vapour pressures of the hydrocarbons

21

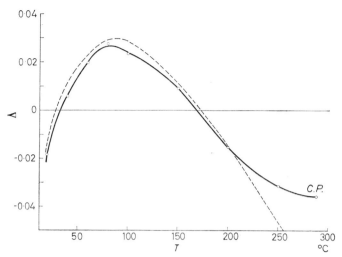

Figure 2.4. The deviation, $\Delta\ [= \log_{10}(p_{obs}/p_{cal})]$, of the vapour pressure of benzene from the line in *Figure 2.3*. The dashed curve is the Antoine equation[8]

$$\log_{10}(p/\text{bar}) = 4\cdot03699 - 1214\cdot645/(221\cdot205 + t\,°\text{C})$$

(*Figure 2.4*). As it stands, this equation has the disadvantage that it is not linear in the three parameters which cannot, therefore, be determined easily by the method of least squares. However, by substituting

$$a = a', \qquad b = -(a'c' + b'), \qquad c = -c' \qquad (2.70)$$

the equation may be written[8]

$$a'T + b' + c' \log_{10} p_\sigma - T \log_{10} p_\sigma = 0 \qquad (2.71)$$

The best values of a', b' and c' may now be found by minimizing the sum, over all experimental points, of the squares of the left-hand side of this equation.

The slope of the vapour-pressure curve is the important coefficient γ_σ, and is proportional to the latent heat of evaporation. It is readily found if an equation such as (2.68) or (2.69) has been fitted to the experimental points and supplemented, if necessary, with a deviation graph, or it may be found by numerical differentiation. The relation of this slope to the latent heat may be derived by the following argument. Let the pressure and temperature of a two-phase system be changed from p and T to $p + \delta p$ and $T + \delta T$ in such a way that neither phase, liquid or gas, disappears. The

22

condition for the preservation of this equilibrium is

$$\mu^l(p, T) = \mu^g(p, T) \tag{2.72}$$

$$\mu^l(p + \delta p, T + \delta T) = \mu^g(p + \delta p, T + \delta T) \tag{2.73}$$

or

$$\left[\left(\frac{\partial \mu^l}{\partial p}\right)_T - \left(\frac{\partial \mu^g}{\partial p}\right)_T\right]\delta p + \left[\left(\frac{\partial \mu^l}{\partial T}\right)_p - \left(\frac{\partial \mu^g}{\partial T}\right)_p\right]\delta T = 0 \tag{2.74}$$

The chemical potential is equal to the molar Gibbs free energy in a system of one component, and so, from (2.6) and (2.7)

$$\left(\frac{\partial p}{\partial T}\right)_\sigma = \gamma_\sigma = \frac{S^g - S^l}{V^g - V^l} \tag{2.75}$$

The difference $(S^g - S^l)$ is denoted ΔS and is equal to $\Delta H/T$, so giving *Clapeyron's equation*

$$(\partial p/\partial T)_\sigma = \Delta S/\Delta V = \Delta H/T\Delta V \tag{2.76}$$

This equation is exact and is applicable to liquid–gas, to solid–fluid and to solid–solid phase boundaries with, of course, the appropriate extension of meaning of the suffix σ. However, for the liquid–gas equilibrium, the volume difference takes a particularly simple form at low pressures. In the limit, V^g differs from its value in a perfect gas by an amount that is small compared to V^g, and V^l approaches a constant value that is similarly small. Hence

$$(\partial p/\partial T)_\sigma = (p\Delta h)/(RT^2) \tag{2.77}$$

or

$$\left(\frac{\partial \ln p}{\partial(1/T)}\right)_\sigma = -\frac{\Delta h}{R} \tag{2.78}$$

This approximation, the *Clapeyron–Clausius equation*, has been widely used for calculating latent heats from the slopes of vapour-pressure curves, but such use is dangerous without considering carefully the validity of the two assumptions necessary for its deduction from the exact equation (2.76).

Consider, for example, the vapour-pressure curve of benzene*. At the normal boiling point the observed slope[8,9] is 23·41 mmHg K^{-1}. The unit of pressure (mmHg) is defined[11] as 133·322 N m^{-2}, and therefore

$$(\partial p/\partial T)_\sigma = 1·102_6 \text{ J cm}^{-3} = \Delta h/\Delta v$$

* For other examples see ref. 10.

Hence, from the approximate equation (2.78), and with a gas constant of $8 \cdot 314$ J K^{-1} mol^{-1},

$$\Delta h = 31\ 960 \text{ J mol}^{-1}$$

However, a better estimate of Δh may be obtained by correcting the gas volume by means of the virial equation of state which, to the second term, may be written

$$v^g = RT/p + B \tag{2.79}$$

The second virial coefficient of benzene[12] at 80°C is approximately -960 cm^3 mol^{-1} and the molar volume of the liquid[13] is 96 cm^3 mol^{-1}. The difference between corrected gas and liquid volumes, calculated from eqn. (2.79), gives

$$\Delta h = 30\ 800 \text{ J mol}^{-1}$$

The difference between the two calculated heats is due almost entirely to the neglect of the departure of the vapour from the perfect-gas laws in the derivation of (2.78). The measured latent heat[14] is

$$\Delta h = 30\ 780 \text{ J mol}^{-1}$$

with which the heat calculated from (2.76) agrees, within the experimental errors of $(\partial p/\partial T)_\sigma$ and B. The departure of a *saturated* vapour from the perfect-gas laws increases with increasing temperature and vapour pressure.

A calculation of this kind can be reversed and experimental values of Δh and $(\partial p/\partial T)_\sigma$ be used to calculate the second virial coefficient, as, in fact, has been done in the case of benzene[15,16] and of acetone[17]. However, such calculations are not very accurate, since B is rarely more than 5 per cent of Δv, which is the quantity that is calculated directly.

Eqn. (2.78) can be integrated to give the empirical vapour-pressure equation (2.68) if it is assumed that the latent heat is independent of temperature—an assumption which is never exactly correct. Thus a derivation of (2.68) can be made only after making three assumptions that are reasonable near the triple-point but quite incorrect at high vapour pressures. The fact that this simple equation holds quite well over the whole of the liquid range means that both Δh and Δv change with temperature in such a way that, fortuitously, the slope $[\partial \ln p/\partial(1/T)]_\sigma$ remains almost constant. Both Δh and Δv vanish at the critical point but their ratio remains finite. The change of Δh with temperature is given by

$$\left(\frac{\partial(\Delta h)}{\partial T}\right)_\sigma = \left(\frac{\partial(T\Delta s)}{\partial T}\right)_\sigma \tag{2.80}$$

$$= \Delta c_\sigma + \Delta s = \Delta c_\sigma + \gamma_\sigma \Delta v \tag{2.81}$$

$$= \Delta c_p + \gamma_\sigma \Delta[(\partial h/\partial p)_T] = \Delta c_p + \gamma_\sigma \Delta[v - T(\partial v/\partial T)_p] \tag{2.82}$$

The first pair of equations, (2.81), is of little use, as c_σ of the gas is not experimentally accessible, but the second pair, (2.82), reduces to the simple equation

$$[\partial(\Delta h)/\partial T]_\sigma = \Delta c_p \tag{2.83}$$

at low temperatures where γ_σ is negligible. The coefficient of γ_σ in these equations is non-zero down to the lowest temperatures, as it is the difference between the isothermal Joule–Thomson coefficients, $(\partial h/\partial p)_T$, of the gas and liquid phases. This coefficient is non-zero and negative in a real gas in the limit of zero density, and non-zero and positive in a liquid at low temperatures. It is zero for a liquid at the temperature at which the inversion curve cuts the vapour-pressure curve. This temperature, at which α_p is equal to $(1/T)$, is near the critical.

The normal boiling point of a liquid is the temperature at which the vapour pressure is 1 atm. It does not differ measurably from the temperature at which the liquid boils freely in dry air at a pressure of 1 atm. The process of boiling expels the dissolved air from the system, so that equilibrium is set up between pure liquid and pure vapour. In this respect, the boiling point differs from the melting point which is affected by air dissolved in the liquid phase.

The entropy of evaporation of a liquid at its normal boiling point usually lies between $9R$ and $14R$, where R is the gas constant—a much smaller range than is covered by the latent heats and the temperatures separately. The range of entropies is even less for those common organic solvents whose boiling points lie between 30°C and 150°C. This rough constancy is embodied in *Trouton's rule*[18] which is now usually stated that the molar entropy of evaporation of a liquid at its normal boiling point (the *Trouton constant*) is about 10–11R.

Table 2.1 shows the Trouton constants of some common liquids which have been classified into the five groups proposed in Chapter 1 (page 7).

Some simple substances have been excluded from this list because of known abnormalities. Hydrogen and helium are not comparable with the other liquids in classes 1 and 2 because of the large size of the 'quantum corrections'. Those substances that exist as strongly

Table 2.1. Entropies of evaporation at the normal boiling point (Trouton's constant) divided by the gas constant, R (from N.B.S. and *A.P.I.*44)

Class 1		Class 2		Class 3		Class 4		Class 5	
Ar	9·0	N_2	8·7	N_2O	10·8	HCl	10·3	NH_3	11·7
Kr	9·1	O_2	9·1	CH_4	8·8	HBr	10·3	H_2O	13·1
Xe	9·2	Cl_2	10·3	C_2H_6	9·6	H_2S	10·6	CH_3OH	12·6
Rn	9·4	CO	8·9	C_3H_8	9·8	SO_2	11·4	C_2H_5OH	13·2
				n-C_4H_{10}	9·9	CH_3Cl	10·4		
				i-C_4H_{10}	9·8	$CHCl_3$	10·6		
				n-C_7H_{16}	10·3	$(CH_3)_2O$	10·4		
				c-C_6H_{12}	10·2				
				C_6H_6	10·5				

bound dimers (or higher groups) in either gaseous or liquid states have been excluded. Substances that are strongly dimerized in the liquid have unusually large Trouton's constants, as, for example, nitric oxide* with a value of $13·7R$. If the gas is also dimerized, then the constant is low, as with acetic acid (7·5) and hydrogen fluoride (3·1).

The variations shown by the more normal substances in *Table 2.1* are not immediately explicable. The most useful generalization that can be made from these figures is that Trouton's constant increases with the increasing complexity of the intermolecular forces, and so with the increasing class number as set out in Chapter 1. Superimposed on this increase is the tendency noted by Barclay and Butler[20] for the Trouton's constants of chemically similar substances to increase with increasing boiling point. These generalizations cover a much wider range of substances than can be cited here, but even for this limited sample it is seen that the constants of non-polar liquids are distributed fairly evenly from 8·5 to $11R$ and do not all lie in the usually quoted range of 10–$11R$. The latter is that covered by the non-polar common laboratory solvents.

2.3 MECHANICAL PROPERTIES

It is convenient to discuss together the coefficients of thermal expansion, α_p, of isothermal compressibility, β_T, and of thermal pressure, γ_V, which are interrelated by (2.27). These coefficients and those along the saturation curve, α_σ and γ_σ, may be called the *mechanical coefficients* of a liquid, and may be contrasted with the *adiabatic coefficients*, β_S, γ_S and W (the speed of sound), to which they are related through the *thermal coefficients*, C_V, C_p and C_σ.

The name *mechanical* is not entirely appropriate, since the adiabatic coefficients can also be measured by purely mechanical means; that is, by experiments in which there are no measurements of

* For the evidence for the dimerization of liquid nitric oxide, see ref. 19.

quantities of heat. It is only the equations which relate the two classes that contain the thermal coefficients. The most useful distinction is to be found at the molecular level where it will be shown that the mechanical coefficients are determined, to a high degree of accuracy, solely by the intermolecular forces, whilst the adiabatic and the thermal coefficients depend also on the internal properties of the molecules.

In practice, knowing the adiabatic coefficients is of little use without a knowledge of either the thermal or the mechanical coefficients. The measurement of both the adiabatic and the mechanical coefficients is a way of measuring heat capacities without measuring a quantity of heat, as, for example, in the method of Lummer and Pringsheim (the measurement of γ_S) and in the determination of heat capacities from the speed of sound.

In this Section, there is first a discussion of the mechanical coefficients, the methods of measuring them and the accuracy with which they are known, and then a short critical review of the properties of two common liquids, benzene and n-heptane, for which the coefficients are reasonably consistent. For most other liquids it is necessary to consider together both the mechanical and adiabatic coefficients in order to determine the 'best' set of coefficients. Discussion of these is, therefore, deferred until Section 2.5.

The coefficient that is most easily measured is α_σ which may be determined from measurements of the orthobaric liquid density over the whole liquid range. Measurements of the density of a liquid in contact with air at 1 atm probably give a coefficient which is nearer to α_p than to α_σ, but they are only possible at low vapour pressures where the difference between these coefficients is negligible. If the orthobaric density of the pure liquid is known to 1 part in 10^5 at intervals of 5 K, then it is not difficult to obtain α_σ to about $\frac{1}{2}$ per cent by some suitable method of differentiation.

Such tables of density are common in works of reference (see, for example, p. xi), but particular attention may be drawn to the measurements of S. Young, as these are very reliable and generally extend from room temperature to the critical points. Their accuracy at room temperature is often a little less than that of the best modern results, but the latter rarely cover such wide ranges of temperature. Most of Young's work is quoted by Timmermans. Several empirical equations can be used to represent the change of α_σ with temperature, the most common at low temperatures being a linear or quadratic equation. The coefficient becomes infinite at the critical point.

The isothermal compressibility is not so readily measured. It is usually about 10^{-4} bar^{-1} for a liquid near its triple point but decreases rapidly with increasing pressure (at constant temperature), often falling to half its initial value at 500 bar.

Measurements of β_T have been made by two methods. The first, and more reliable, is to observe the changes of volume when the pressure is increased in steps of about 100 bar to pressures of 1000 bar or more. The value of β_T at the vapour pressure is obtained by an extrapolation of the mean values over these large changes of pressure. Such an extrapolation needs very great care if it is to give accurate values of β_T at low pressures.

With such measurements, there is little difficulty in measuring the changes of volume, which are comparatively large, nor is there much trouble in performing the compression isothermally. If a liquid is suddenly compressed to, say, 200 bar, then its temperature rises by about 5 K. (The amount of the increase is given by the adiabatic coefficient, γ_S.) This rise of temperature is soon dissipated if the liquid is enclosed in a metal vessel in a thermostat, and so the final (isothermal) change of volume is soon observable.

In the second method, an attempt is made to measure directly the limiting value of β_T at zero pressure by observing the small change of volume following a pressure change of about 1 bar. It is now very difficult to conduct the experiment isothermally, for the initial (adiabatic) rise of temperature is only about 10^{-2} K and such an increase will not be dissipated smoothly unless the thermostat is maintained constant to 10^{-3} or 10^{-4} K. This is technically very difficult, and it is rare for truly isothermal changes to have been measured by this method. In a successful measurement of an isothermal compressibility it is clear that a necessary condition is

$$\Delta p \cdot \beta_T \gg \delta T \cdot \alpha_p \qquad (2.84)$$

where Δp is the experimental change of pressure and δT the size of the temperature fluctuations of the thermostat. It is interesting to notice that most of the results published by Quincke[21] in 1883 as isothermal compressibilities are within 2 per cent of the now accepted adiabatic coefficients but are up to 30 per cent below the true isothermal compressibilities. His pressure change was rarely more than $\frac{1}{2}$ bar.

Direct measurement of β_T is, therefore, best based on measurements of volume as a function of pressure up to several hundred bars. The calculation of β_T from such observations is made by fitting the results to an empirical equation, and the two most commonly used are those of Tait and of Hudleston.

Tait[22] sought an equation to represent the compressibility of sea-water, the density of which had been measured from the oceanographic research vessel H.M.S. Challenger, and proposed

$$\frac{V_0 - V}{V_0 p} = \frac{A}{B + p} \tag{2.85}$$

where V_0 is the volume at zero pressure and A and B are positive parameters. This equation was later interpreted, apparently first

Table 2.2. The relative volumes of water at 0°C

p (atm)	1	501	1001	1501	2001	2501	3001
V (obs. Amagat)	1·000 00	0·976 68	0·956 45	0·939 24	0·923 93	0.910 65	0·898 69
V (calc. Tait)	1·000 00	0·976 57	0·956 52	0·939 16	0·923 99	0·910 62	0·898 75

by Tamann[23], as a differential equation which could be written

$$\left(\frac{\partial V}{\partial p}\right)_T = -\frac{A}{B + p} \tag{2.86}$$

and integrated to give

$$V - V_0 = A \ln [B/(B + p)] \tag{2.87}$$

which for practical purposes is usually written

$$\frac{V - V_0}{V_0} = C \log_{10}\left[\frac{B}{B + p}\right] \tag{2.88}$$

This substitution was detected first by Kell[24] and independently by Hayward[25]. Both observe that Tait's original equation (2.85) is generally more accurate and more convenient than the modified equation (2.88) to which his name is now most commonly attached. *Table 2.2* shows Tait's original fitting of (2.85) to Amagat's measurements of the volume of water.

Hudleston[26] proposed the equation

$$\ln\left[\frac{pV^{2/3}}{V_0^{1/3} - V^{1/3}}\right] = A + B(V_0^{1/3} - V^{1/3}) \tag{2.89}$$

and this has been widely used to represent the best modern measurements of the compression of hydrocarbons. For these it is superior to Tait's equation, although it is less accurate for water. It is also less convenient to use than either form of Tait's equation, but this is of little moment if the fitting is done by computer.

The earliest measurements of β_T that are of more than historical interest are those of Amagat[27] in 1893. He measured volume as a function of pressure and temperature for twelve common liquids to 3000 atm and, in some cases, to 200°C. The accuracy of his measurements is good, even by modern standards, and their range has rarely been surpassed. He calculated α_p and β_T from his results—generally mean values over 20°C and 50 atm, respectively—and, from their ratio, found the thermal pressure coefficient, γ_V.

He was followed by Bridgman[28] who, in 1913, studied almost the same twelve liquids up to 12 kbar but not to such high temperatures. He again measured volume as a function of pressure and temperature. Twenty years later he published three papers[29] in which he reported similar measurements, up to 95°C, on a very wide range of organic liquids—hydrocarbons, halides, alcohols, glycols and esters—and in 1942 he extended his pressure range to 50 kbar in a search for a solid–fluid critical point[30]. This series of papers and the book[30] in which they are summarized are still an important source of knowledge of the volumetric behaviour of fluids at very high pressures.

Other substantial sets of measurements on liquids are those on organic liquids of Gibson[31] (who used the pseudo-Tait equation), those on hydrocarbons of Doolittle[32] (who used Hudleston's equation) and of several other groups[33], and those on water of Kell and Whalley[34].

The third mechanical coefficient, γ_V, is more easily measured than β_T, but such measurements are surprisingly scarce and until recently were almost entirely confined to the work of Hildebrand and his colleagues[35,36]. Their apparatus is essentially a constant-volume thermometer. The liquid is confined to a glass bulb with a capillary neck in which its level may be maintained at a fixed point by an electrical contact to a mercury interface. The coefficient γ_V is found directly as the slope of a graph of pressure against temperature for a liquid in such an apparatus.

This graph is always close to a straight line, even at the critical point, and so its slope is easily measured. For example, Amagat's measurements of α_p and β_T for ethyl ether at 20°C give the following figures for the slope and curvature of the isochores

$$\left(\frac{\partial p}{\partial T}\right)_V = 9 \cdot 0 \text{ bar K}^{-1}; \qquad \left(\frac{\partial^2 p}{\partial T^2}\right)_V = -0 \cdot 009 \text{ bar K}^{-2}$$

Thus, in a typical experiment to measure γ_V directly, in which the temperature is raised by 5 K, the pressure would increase by 45 bar. The change in γ_V over this range would be only 0·05 bar K^{-1}, about 0·6 per cent, and so the curvature of a plot of p against T would be almost undetectable.

The sign of the second derivative is important since it determines the change of C_V with pressure or density (2.16). Unfortunately measurements of this derivative are rare, but those of β_T by Gibson and co-workers[31] confirm that it is small and negative for organic liquids at temperatures near their normal boiling point. A negative derivative implies an increase of C_V with pressure. Such an increase

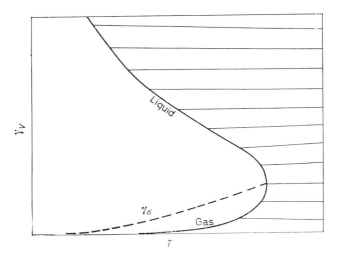

Figure 2.5. The variation of the thermal-pressure coefficient with temperature for the saturated gas and liquid, and for the homogeneous fluid at temperatures above saturation

has been observed directly for ethanol by Bryant and Jones[37], but such calorimetric evidence of the sign of the derivative is probably harder to obtain than the mechanical evidence.

The thermal-pressure coefficient changes smoothly with temperature on passing along the co-existence curve from liquid to gas through the critical point. At this point it is equal to γ_σ, the limiting slope of the vapour-pressure curve.

The relation between the two coefficients is shown in *Figure 2.5*. The full line passing through the critical point represents γ_V along the co-existence curve. The shape of the $(p,\,V,\,T)$ surface near this point makes it clear that here the change of γ_V with saturation temperature is infinitely rapid. The full lines to the right of this curve show γ_V along a set of isochores, for each of which the volume is the orthobaric volume at the temperature at which the line cuts the saturation curve.

The slopes of these lines are always small, as indicated by the figure. The slope of the vapour-pressure curve, γ_σ, is shown by the dashed line which crosses the two-phase region and cuts the co-existence curve at the critical point. It is seen that γ_V is a much more convenient function for interpolation or extrapolation than α_p or β_T, as it remains finite up to the critical point where its value is easily determined from vapour-pressure measurements.

It is of interest to examine the experimental values of α_p, β_T and γ_V for benzene and n-heptane, to see how accurately and consistently these are known over the whole of the liquid range and so to describe a systematic sequence for obtaining the best values of all the coefficients. These liquids are typical of non-polar substances.

It is best to start by deriving the coefficients α_σ from the orthobaric volumes, which are here assumed to be above suspicion. The isobaric coefficients, α_p, are calculated from these by using approximate values of β_T or γ_V in (2.28) or (2.29). No great accuracy is needed in the calculation of the correction terms at low temperature where they are small.

Measurements of γ_V are usually more accurate than those of β_T, and so it is best, for purposes of comparison, to convert the latter into the former by dividing it into α_p. The several experimental measurements of γ_V and β_T can then be compared directly on one plot of γ_V as a function of temperature. The extrapolation of this graph to the critical point may be made by using the limiting slope of the vapour-pressure curve. Such a graph is strongly recommended for smoothing and reconciling measurements of β_T and γ_V.

Benzene

The vapour pressure has been measured recently with great accuracy over the whole of the liquid range by Ambrose, Broderick and Townsend[9] whose results confirm many earlier measurements. The orthobaric densities found by Young, and quoted by Timmermans, yield reliable values of α_σ. The compressibility β_T has been measured several times[31,38] at temperatures below the normal boiling point, and these measurements, together with those of β_S, are reviewed by Holder and Whalley[38]. The adiabatic coefficient has been measured also by Fort and Moore[39]. Bridgman[29] measured the compression at 95°C, and a value of β_T of 1.77×10^{-4} bar^{-1} on the saturation curve can be obtained from his results by fitting them to Tait's equation. The thermal pressure coefficient, γ_V, has been measured repeatedly below the normal boiling point. There is good agreement between the recent work of Allen, Gee and Mangaraj[36] and the earlier work of Westwater, Frantz and Hildebrand[35]. The results of Bianchi, Agabio and Turturro[36] appear to be a little high.

The results of these measurements, reduced where necessary to values of γ_V, are shown in *Figure 2.6*. It is seen that a reasonable, if somewhat long, interpolation can be made to give γ_V over the whole of the liquid range. The smoothed values of γ_V are used, in their turn, to calculate smooth values of β_T, etc. The recommended

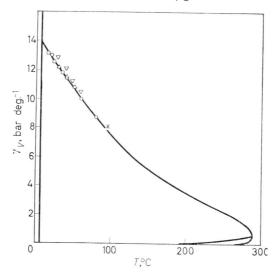

Figure 2.6. Thermal pressure coefficient of benzene

○ from measurements of β_T (see Holder and Whalley[38])
△ from γ_V by Allen, Gee and Mangaraj[36]
▽ from γ_V by Bianchi, Agabio and Turturro[36]
□ from γ_V by Westwater, Frantz and Hildebrand[35]
✕ from β_T by Bridgman[29]

values are shown in *Table 2.3*. (The heat capacities are discussed below.)

n-*Heptane*

Young (quoted by Timmermans) has measured the vapour pressure and orthobaric densities up to the critical point. Densities below room temperature are to be found in A.P.I. 44. The compressibility, β_T, has been measured several times[32-3,40], and γ_V by Westwater, Frantz and Hildebrand[35]. The measurements of Doolittle[32] are the most valuable at temperatures above the normal boiling point. These results were treated in the same way as those for benzene, and the smoothed coefficients are shown in *Table 2.4*.

The difference between α_σ and α_p is well shown in *Tables 2.3* and *2.4*. It is important at high vapour pressures and may not be

Table 2.3. Benzene

T °C	p_σ bar	v cm³ mol⁻¹	$\alpha_\sigma \times 10^3$ K⁻¹	α_p K⁻¹	$\beta_T \times 10^4$ bar⁻¹	β_s bar⁻¹	γ_σ bar K⁻¹	γ_v K⁻¹	C_σ J K⁻¹ mol⁻¹	C_p J K⁻¹ mol⁻¹	C_v	$v^2(\partial u/\partial v)_T$ J m³ mol⁻²
5·524^t	0·0480	87·34	1·20	1·20	0·86	0·59	0·0025	14·0	132	132	91	2·980
20	0·0995	88·86	1·22	1·22	0·95	0·66	0·0048	12·9	134·9	134·9	93·9	2·980
40	0·2439	91·08	1·25	1·25	1·10	0·78	0·0102	11·4	139·2	139·3	98·7	2·960
60	0·5220	93·46	1·29	1·29	1·29	0·93	0·0187	10·0	144·2	144·3	104·1	2·910
80	1·0105	95·90	1·35	1·35	1·55	1·13	0·0305	8·7	149	149	109	2·830
100	1·801	98·53	1·44	1·45	1·93	—	0·0486	7·5	—	—	—	2·720
150	5·823	106·9	1·79	1·83	3·5	—	0·1186	5·2	—	—	—	2·510
200	14·25	118·3	2·43	2·60	7·4	—	0·2296	3·5	—	—	—	2·300
250	29·88	—	—	—	—	—	0·399	2·2	—	—	—	—
288·94^c	48·98	256	∞	∞	∞	∞?	0·617	0·617	∞	∞	∞?	1·950

t = triple point, c = critical point

34

Table 2.4. n-Heptane

T °C	p_σ bar	v cm³ mol⁻¹	α_σ	α_p × 10³ K⁻¹	β_T	β_s × 10⁴ bar⁻¹	γ_σ	γ_v bar K⁻¹	C_σ	C_p J K⁻¹ mol⁻¹	C_v	$v^2(\partial u/\partial v)_T$ J m³ mol⁻²
−90.60†	—	129·5	—	—	—	—	—	—	203·1	203·1	—	—
−80	—	130·9	—	—	—	—	—	—	201·7	201·7	—	—
−60	—	133·6	—	—	—	—	—	—	202·0	202·0	—	—
−40	—	136·6	—	—	—	—	—	—	205·1	205·1	—	—
−20	—	139·7	—	—	—	—	—	—	209·9	209·9	—	—
0	0·0153	143·0	1·211	1·211	1·20	0·95	—	10·1	216·0	216·0	168·2	5·550
20	0·0473	146·6	1·234	1·234	1·40	1·11	—	8·8	223·0	223·0	176·3	5·540
40	0·1227	150·3	1·29	1·29	1·65	1·31	—	7·8	230·6	230·6	183·2	5·520
60	0·2765	154·4	1·36	1·36	1·97	1·57	—	6·9	238·8	238·9	190·6	5·490
80	0·5687	158·8	1·45	1·45	2·38	1·90	—	6·1	247·4	247·6	198·0	5·420
100	1·060	163·6	1·57	1·58	3·03	2·38	0·030	5·2	256·8	257·1	206·9	5·240
150	3·712	179·0	2·03	2·08	5·9	4·8	0·079	3·5	282·5	283·7	229	4·730
200	9·681	202·3	3·03	3·28	15·6	12·4	0·162	2·1	313	318	252	4·030
250	21·31	259	9·1	12	110	70	0·301	1·1	400	450	280	—
267·1ᶜ	27·24	430	∞	∞	∞	∞?	0·35	0·35	∞	∞	∞?	3·080

entirely negligible at low ones. At the normal boiling point it is 0·6 per cent for n-heptane and a little less for benzene. The difference becomes infinite at the critical point.

2.4 HEAT CAPACITIES

None of the three heat capacities, C_V, C_p or C_σ, can conveniently be measured directly for a liquid on its saturation curve.

A direct measurement of C_V is difficult at low temperatures where γ_V is large, since it is impossible to make a vessel strong enough to confine the liquid to constant volume as the temperature is raised. However, with good design the correction for the expansion of the vessel need not be large, and Jones and his colleagues have attempted such measurements with some success[37,41]. Their accuracy at low temperatures (high γ_V) is less than that of the best measurements of C_σ. Direct measurements of C_V are more practicable near the critical point where γ_V is very much smaller.

The heat capacity at constant pressure, C_p, may be measured directly for a fluid at a pressure a little greater than the saturation vapour pressure by using a flow calorimeter, but such measurements are now rarely made for liquids of appreciable vapour pressure. The direct measurement of C_p of a saturated liquid is clearly impossible, since the application of heat at constant pressure simply evaporates the liquid.

The third heat capacity, C_σ, is more closely related to experiment and could, in principle, be measured directly in a calorimeter whose volume at each temperature was adjusted to be that of the saturated liquid. This would, however, be difficult to realize experimentally.

In practice, it is customary not to attempt the direct measurement of any of these but to measure the heat capacity at constant *total* volume of a liquid in equilibrium with a small amount of its vapour. In a two-phase system, this is closely related to C_σ of the liquid and less related to C_p. At zero vapour pressure it is clearly equal to both.

The differences at high vapour pressure were first discussed as problems of practical importance when heat capacities were required for liquid ammonia, carbon dioxide and methyl chloride, all of which are substances used in the refrigeration industry. Osborne and van Dusen[42] and Babcock[43] made full analyses of the heat capacity of the two-phase system in order to derive C_σ and C_p for liquid ammonia. However, their methods are lengthy and their equations are not always in the simplest form. A later treatment by Hoge[44] is clearer and more concise, but he derives only C_σ.

It is simple to obtain both C_σ and C_p from the heat capacity of the two-phase system at constant total volume by using the equations already derived for α_σ and C_σ. Let there be m^l moles of liquid (molar volume, v^l) and m^g moles of vapour (molar volume, v^g) in a closed vessel of total volume V. Let δm be the number of moles that evaporate when the temperature is raised δT. The total volume is unchanged, and so

$$m^l v^l + m^g v^g = (m^l - \delta m)v^l(1 + \alpha_\sigma^l \delta T) + (m^g + \delta m)v^g(1 + \alpha_\sigma^g \delta T)$$

(2.90)

or

$$\frac{\mathrm{d}m^g}{\mathrm{d}T} = - \frac{m^l v^l \alpha_\sigma^l + m^g v^g \alpha_\sigma^g}{\Delta v}$$

(2.91)

where Δv is $(v^g - v^l)$.

The coefficient α_σ^g is large and negative, and so $(\mathrm{d}m^g/\mathrm{d}T)$ may have either sign, according to the size of the ratio (m^l/m^g). If this ratio is large, as is generally the case in a calorimeter, then $(\mathrm{d}m^g/\mathrm{d}T)$ is negative—that is, vapour condenses on raising the temperature and saturation pressure.

The heat capacity of the two-phase system is composed of three parts—the saturation heat capacity of the liquid, that of the gas, and the heat required to evaporate (δm) moles of liquid. That is

$$C = m^l c_\sigma^l + m^g c_\sigma^g - T\gamma_\sigma(m^l v^l \alpha_\sigma^l + m^g v^g \alpha_\sigma^g)$$

(2.92)

where $(T\gamma_\sigma)$ has been substituted for $(\Delta h/\Delta v)$ by using Clapeyron's equation. This equation is formally symmetrical in the properties of the liquid and gas and may be used as it stands. It is more convenient, however, to eliminate c_σ^g in favour of $(\partial^2 p/\partial T^2)_\sigma$ by using (2.81).

This gives

$$C = m(c_\sigma^l - T\gamma_\sigma v^l \alpha_\sigma^l) + m^g T\Delta v(\partial^2 p/\partial T^2)_\sigma$$

(2.93)

$$= m[c_p^l - T\gamma_\sigma v^l(2\alpha_p^l - \beta_T^l \gamma_\sigma)] + m^g T\Delta v(\partial^2 p/\partial T^2)_\sigma$$

(2.94)

where m is the total number of moles.

The first of these equations is a combination of two of Hoge, with the minor difference that he replaces $m^g \Delta v$ by the more easily observable difference $(V - mv^l)$. It is seen from this equation that C does not approach (mc_σ^l) in the limit of zero vapour space ($m^g \to 0$). The heat capacity changes discontinuously at the phase boundary from the value given by (2.93) with m^g equal to zero, to the heat capacity at constant volume of the homogeneous liquid. The change at the boundary is equal to $[Tv\alpha_\sigma(\gamma_V - \gamma_\sigma)]$ and is negative at both bubble- and dew-points. This is illustrated by plotting entropy as a function of ln T in *Figure 2.7*. The slopes of an isochore on such a graph are C_V, of an isobar, C_p and of the saturation curve, C_σ. This figure shows that $C_V < C_\sigma < C_p$ for the saturated liquid, that C_V of the two-phase system is a little less than C_σ, and that C_p of the two-phase system is infinite. In this figure, C_σ is small but negative on the gas boundary.

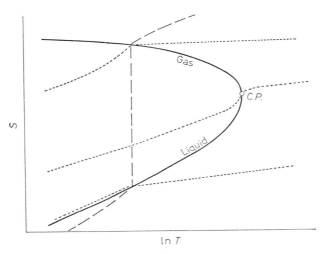

Figure 2.7. The change of entropy with ln T along the saturation curve (full line), along one isobar (dashed line), and along three isochores (dotted lines), the second of which passes through the critical point

The relative sizes of the terms in (2.93) may be illustrated by considering a calorimeter of 10 cm³ internal volume containing 9·5 cm³ of liquid benzene and 0·5 cm³ of benzene vapour at the normal boiling point of 80°C. The three terms on the right-hand side of this equation are here 14·87, −0·01 and +0·01 J K⁻¹, respectively. That is, the 'vapour correction' to be applied to the measured C to obtain (mc_σ^l) is negligible for this filling. The heat capacity (mc_p^l) is larger than (mc_σ^l) by 0·1 per cent (2.94). At higher vapour pressures these corrections rapidly become more important. For example, the difference between C_p and C_σ for ammonia[42] at 30°C where the vapour pressure is 11 bar is 1 per cent of C_σ. The correction for nitrogen at this vapour pressure is 5 per cent (see below).

It is seen from these two equations that C_σ is more easily obtained from the two-phase heat capacity than is C_p. The correction to obtain C_σ requires a knowledge of α_σ, but that to obtain C_p requires also a knowledge of β_T which, as shown in the previous Section, is not so readily available.

Many of the published heat capacities are at such low vapour pressures that the distinction between C_σ and C_p is negligible. Some authors distinguish between the two and tabulate both, but others omit to do so even where the difference is not entirely negligible. It is reasonable to assume that papers in which there is no mention of the correction to obtain C_p (that is, of β_T or equivalent information) are, in fact, reporting measurements of C_σ. If the heat capacities are to be used for computing entropies of the saturated liquid, then C_σ is the correct one to use. Most of the best measurements have been made for this purpose, and it is therefore rare to find good measurements above 25°C, the standard temperature at which entropies are usually computed.

The measurement of the heat capacity of the two-phase system is made by supplying electrically a small amount of heat to a closed vessel nearly full of liquid and observing the rise in temperature. The thermal capacity of the calorimeter may be calculated from the known heat capacity of the material used in its construction or, more usually, is determined from a second experiment with a liquid of known heat capacity in the calorimeter. Comparatively simple equipment will give the heat capacity to about 1 per cent, but if a higher accuracy is needed, then the equipment can become quite elaborate. Harrison and Moelwyn-Hughes[45] have pointed out that modern measurements of the heat capacity of a common liquid such as carbon tetrachloride differ by more than 1 per cent.

The best practice is to use an 'adiabatic' calorimeter in which the heat loss to the surroundings is eliminated by ensuring that a shield around the vessel containing the liquid is maintained, at all times, at the same temperature as the liquid. The experimental arrangements are described in a recent book[46]. Timmermans tabulates C_p for most common organic liquids.

The heat capacities quoted in *Tables 2.3* and *2.4* are mainly those of Huffman and his colleagues[47]. Those of n-heptane are particularly accurate, since it has been chosen[48] as a calorimetric sub-standard. The values of C_V and β_S in these Tables have been calculated from C_σ and β_T. Values of β_S observed directly, or derived from the speed of sound, agree with these to within 1–2 per cent. However, β_S is usually known more accurately than β_T, since W can be measured to 1 part in 1000. In these cases it is better to use β_S in the earliest stages of the calculations and to treat β_T as the derived property Such calculations are discussed in the next Section.

2.5 ADIABATIC PROPERTIES

The most important of the adiabatic coefficients is β_S, the bulk compressibility. It can be measured directly or can be calculated from the speed of sound by using (2.46). The direct measurements are usually made by compressing the liquid in a glass bulb to a pressure about 1 bar above atmospheric. The isentropic volume change on suddenly releasing the excess pressure is about 10^{-4} of the total volume and may easily be observed if the vessel has a capillary neck. A small correction must be made to the apparent value of β_S for the compressibility of the glass vessel.

Such measurements were first made for common organic liquids by Tyrer[49] in 1913, but his work was not followed up until 1952. Since then, Staveley and his colleagues[50] have measured β_S for a considerable number of liquids and binary mixtures up to 70°C, and more recently similar measurements have been made by Harrison and Moelwyn-Hughes[45]. These results and those of Tyrer agree well and are apparently accurate to about 1 per cent.

Much more common are values of β_S derived from the speed of sound. The accurate measurement of this speed is very inconvenient for sound of audible frequency owing to its long wavelength and the consequent large size of the apparatus. However, measurements at frequencies above the audible (ultrasonic frequencies) are readily made on samples of liquid of about 100 cm³ or less. Such sound waves are generated by applying an alternating electric field of suitable frequency to a crystal of quartz which is thereby set into resonant longitudinal oscillations (the piezoelectric effect). Ultrasonic waves are generated from the free surface of such an oscillating crystal, and their wavelength can be measured by setting up standing waves in the liquid between the crystal surface and a parallel reflector. By this and similar methods using the oscillating quartz, the speeds and sometimes the coefficients of absorption have been measured for several hundred liquids.

Most of the measurements have been at or near room temperature, but fortunately the simple liquids such as argon, nitrogen and oxygen have been adequately studied. The frequency used by Freyer, Hubbard and Andrews[51], the pioneers in this field, was 0·4 MHz (that is $0\cdot4 \times 10^6$ s⁻¹) and most of the more recent work has been at this, or even higher frequencies. A full description of the apparatus and methods, and many of the results, are given in recent reviews[52-3].

At these frequencies it is necessary to consider carefully whether the observed speed of sound is the equilibrium speed. At low frequencies, W is independent of the frequency ν, and the small coefficient of absorption per unit length, α, increases as ν^2. This absorption is due to the 'classical' effects of the shear and bulk viscosity and the thermal conductivity of the fluid. These values of W are correctly related to the static compressibility, β_S, by (2.46).

However, many fluids show dispersion (that is, change of W with ν) at high frequencies due to relaxation effects[54]. W increases slowly with ν, often over several decades, and α contains a 'non-classical' component with a peak at a frequency of $(1/2\pi\tau)$, where τ is the time of relaxation of the physical process that is responsible for the dispersion. When ν is large compared with τ^{-1}, then W resumes a constant but higher value that is not directly related to the static compressibility. These relaxation effects are due to processes of equipartition of energy or change of internal structure in the fluid whose times of relaxation are generally less than 10^{-6} s. Such processes have, in the past, been described formally as a bulk viscosity, and this is, indeed, a valid mathematical description if a frequency-dependent coefficient of viscosity is admitted. However, the name is not a helpful one and disguises the nature of the processes responsible. Until recently there was some doubt about the existency of true (frequency-independent) bulk viscosity in a monatomic fluid, but good evidence for it in liquid argon has been obtained recently by Naugle[55].

It is usually not difficult to be sure that measurements are made at a frequency below the relaxation region, and so to obtain the static β_S. One very powerful test has been developed recently by comparing W at a frequency of, say, 10^6 s^{-1} with that of hypersonic waves at frequencies at upwards of 10^{10} s^{-1}. If these speeds are the same, then it is unlikely that any relaxation process is occurring.

These hypersonic speeds are found indirectly from the Brillouin scattering of light from a laser beam. The fluctuations of density that are inevitably present in a liquid can be regarded, after Fourier analysis, as a set of random hypersonic waves propagated at frequencies of the order of 10^{10} s^{-1}, which are so highly damped that each wave moves only a distance of a few molecular diameters. Nevertheless, such a wave can act as a diffraction grating for a monochromatic beam of light and can produce a line at the appropriate Bragg angle. Since the 'grating' is moving, the spectrum consists of a closely spaced doublet on each side of the Rayleigh line. The separation of the doublet is a result of the Doppler difference between waves moving in opposite directions but otherwise identical, and so is a measure of the speed of (hyper)sound. Since the speed of light is large compared with that of sound, the Doppler spacing is small (ca. 0·2 cm^{-1}) and can only be observed accurately with the highly monochromatic light from a laser (line width, ca. 0·04 cm^{-1}).

This type of scattering was first predicted by Brillouin[56] and has been much used in the last few years for studying the dynamical properties of fluids[53,57]. Thus the separation of the doublet gives the speed of sound, the width of the Brillouin lines is a measure of the length of the 'grating' and so of the coefficient of absorption, α, and the ratio of the intensity of the Brillouin and Rayleigh lines is a function of β_T/β_S.

For the purpose of this Chapter, however, the valuable feature of these results is that they can show convincingly that dispersion is absent in many liquids below 10^{10} s^{-1}. Thus Comley[58] has shown that there is no relaxation in aliphatic hydrocarbons, but that it is present in benzene. Chiao and Fleury[57] have demonstrated its presence also for carbon disulphide, toluene and acetic acid.

Conventional ultrasonic methods cover the range 10^5 to 10^8 s^{-1} which is often sufficient to show if there is a relaxation process with a time longer than 10^{-9} s. Thus the results on argon, discussed below, cover a frequency range of 10^2, and the essentially constant speed found is good evidence for the absence of relaxation. Indeed, it would be hard to imagine a mechanism that could produce it.

The measurements of Heasell and Lamb[59] on 94 liquids from 100 to 200 MHz have shown that absorption, and therefore dispersion, is negligible up to these frequencies for most alcohols, amines, ethers and alkyl halides. Heavy absorption was found in esters, benzene, ethylene dichloride and in amines[60], and has been reported by others at much lower frequencies for some branched paraffins[61], for cyclohexane derivatives[62] (0·2 MHz) and for toluene[63] (0·1 MHz).

It is clear that as soon as one leaves argon and comes to much more complicated liquids, it is difficult to predict the frequency range in which any given liquid will show dispersion. The two cases that have been most thoroughly investigated are those of carbon disulphide[57,64] and acetic acid[57,65]. Their study has led to some elucidation of the processes responsible for dispersion in liquids.

In the case of carbon disulphide, it is clear that it is the vibrational energy of the molecules which is responsible for the dispersion. Such energy can here only be acquired from translational energy after a lag of about 10^{-6} s, and it is this lag which is responsible for the failure of the vibrational energy to follow the heating and cooling of the adiabatic acoustical cycle. Such lags are known to be responsible for the dispersion of sound in gases—a phenomenon which is much better understood than dispersion in liquids.

Ethylene dichloride is probably similar to carbon disulphide but is unusual in showing two regions of thermal dispersion in both gas and liquid states[53,54,66].

With acetic acid, it is probable that there are two independent mechanisms: a thermal relaxation below 7 MHz which is similar to that in carbon disulphide, and a lag in the equilibration of monomers and dimers above 15 MHz. This interpretation is not yet beyond doubt, although it is certain that structural as well as thermal relaxation can occur in hydrogen-bonded liquids.

A third process of which the relaxation can occasionally be observed is that of chemical reaction. The classic example amongst gases is the dimerization of nitrogen dioxide. In liquids, the association of acetic acid can be regarded as a chemical reaction, but a clearer example is the acid–base equilibrium in an aqueous solution of an amine[67].

However, even when the mechanism of relaxation is obscure, there is usually no mistaking its presence, and no difficulty in choosing values of the speed of sound which are unaffected by it. Such values lead to accurate values of β_S and are our principal source of knowledge of this coefficient.

The principal use of values of β_S is to calculate β_T, the isothermal coefficient. This may be done directly by (2.51), if α_p and C_p are known. However, in the absence of any independent knowledge of β_T it is only α_σ and C_σ that are generally available. It is therefore necessary to combine equations (2.28), (2.39), (2.40), (2.49) and (2.51) to give the following equation for β_T

$$\beta_T = \frac{\beta_S C_\sigma + TV\alpha_\sigma(\alpha_\sigma + \beta_S\gamma_\sigma)}{C_\sigma - TV\gamma_\sigma(\alpha_\sigma + \beta_S\gamma_\sigma)} \tag{2.95}$$

This, fortunately explicit, equation for β_T is the most direct way of calculating the isothermal coefficient from the adiabatic coefficient and the three experimentally accessible coefficients C_σ, α_σ and γ_σ. The values of β_T so derived are those for the saturated liquid, as the pressures used in measuring β_S, either directly or from the speed of sound, are always low. Once β_T is known, all the other coefficients α_p, γ_V, C_p and C_V may readily be derived.

This calculation is illustrated for the six liquids, argon, nitrogen, oxygen, methane, carbon tetrachloride and water. The speed of sound has been accurately measured in all these liquids in conditions where it is clear that there is no dispersion. The adiabatic compressibility has also been measured directly for carbon tetrachloride and water.

Argon

Measurements on this substance are unusually extensive, since it is the most commonly chosen 'model' substance used to test theories

43

of the liquid state. It suffices to indicate by references the values chosen for the triple-point temperature[68] and pressure[68,69], the saturated vapour pressure[68,70,71], the critical constants[70] and orthobaric volumes[70,72]. Earlier measurements of the last three properties are reviewed by Din. The heat capacity, C_σ, has been measured by Jones and Walker[41,73], and C_V along the critical isochore by Voronel' and his colleagues[74]. These last results can be converted to C_V of the orthobaric liquid by using (2.19) and (2.94).

These results lead to reliable values of α_σ and γ_σ, whilst other measurements in the same papers[41,70,72] yield β_T and γ_V. However, accurate values of β_S are of more value in determining the remaining thermodynamic properties. Concordant measurements of the speed of sound have been made by Liepmann[75], Galt[76], Dobbs and

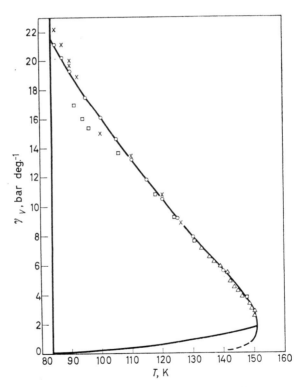

Figure 2.8. Thermal pressure coefficient of argon

○ from measurements of β_s from the speed of sound[75-78]
△ from γ_V by Michels *et al.*[70]
□ from γ_V by Walker[41]
× from β_T by van Itterbeek *et al.*[72]

Finegold[77] and by van Itterbeek and his colleagues[78]. Earlier results of van Itterbeek were up to 2 per cent above those now used, and the resolution of this discrepancy (ascribed by them to an impurity) is most welcome, since the latest set of measurements covers the whole liquid range, up to the critical point. The accuracy of all these measurements is about 1 part per thousand in W, or 2 parts in β_S.

The reconciliation of all these results is again done by converting β_T and β_S to γ_V and smoothing the resulting set of points. This is done in *Figure 2.8* in which it is seen that agreement is generally good between the modern results. There are, however, some recent measurements of β_T by two different methods, at Oxford[79], which are equivalent to values of γ_V 10–15 per cent larger than those shown at 115–130 K. This discrepancy is hard to resolve.

The heat capacities are shown in *Figure 2.9*, and smoothed values of all functions in *Table 2.5*.

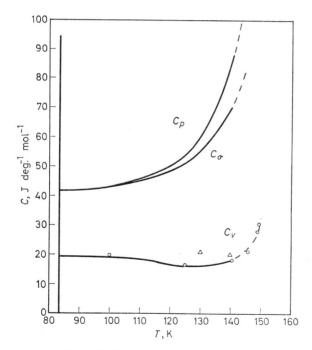

Figure 2.9. The heat capacities of liquid argon

○ C_V from measurements of Walker[41]

△ C_V obtained indirectly from measurements along the critical isochore by Voronel' et al.[74]

45

Table 2.5. Argon

T K	p_σ bar	v cm³ mol⁻¹	$\alpha_\sigma \times 10^3$ K⁻¹	α_p K⁻¹	$\beta_s \times 10^4$	β_T bar⁻¹	γ_σ bar K⁻¹	γ_v K⁻¹	C_σ	C_p J K⁻¹ mol⁻¹	C_v	W m s⁻¹
83·81ᵃ	0·68905	28·19	4·37	4·39	0·948	2·033	0·080	21·6	41·8	41·9	19·5	863
85	0·789	28·34	4·40	4·42	0·970	2·089	0·087	21·2	41·9	42·0	19·5	855
87·29ᵇ	1·013	28·66	4·47	4·49	1·022	2·217	0·107	20·3	42·1	42·2	19·4	838
90	1·336	29·00	4·55	4·58	1·077	2·37	0·133	19·3	42·2	42·4	19·3	821
95	2·149	29·67	4·75	4·80	1·211	2·74	0·193	17·5	42·4	42·7	19·0	783
100	3·25	30·38	5·00	5·08	1·363	3·16	0·256	16·1	43·1	43·5	18·7	747
105	4·73	31·15	5·29	5·41	1·556	3·71	0·333	14·6	44	45	19	708
110	6·67	32·03	5·7	5·9	1·80	4·47	0·435	13·2	45	46	18	667
120	12·17	34·25	7·3	7·8	2·49	7·40	0·670	10·5	49	51	17	587
130	20·28	37·50	10	11	3·99	14·1	0·965	7·9	55	60	17	485
140	31·67	42·42	16	21	7·59	38	1·32	5·6	70	86	18	374
150·86ᶜ	48·98	74·6	∞	∞	∞?	∞	1·8	1·8	∞	∞	∞?	0?

Nitrogen

The triple point[80], orthobaric density[72,81,82] and vapour pressure[83,84] are well established. The critical constants recommended by Kobe and Lynn are still acceptable. There are three good sets of measurements[83,85,86] of C_σ. The speed of sound has been measured by Liepmann[75] and, on several occasions, by van Itterbeek, whose most recent set[78] extends almost to the critical point. He and his colleagues have also measured β_T directly[72,82], although probably with less accuracy. *Figure 2.10* shows γ_V as a function of temperature.

The smoothed results are displayed in *Table 2.6*.

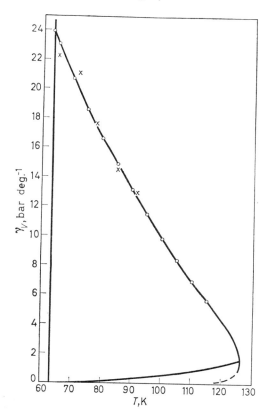

Figure 2.10. Thermal pressure coefficient of nitrogen

○ from measurements of β_s from the speed of sound[75,78]
× from β_T by van Itterbeek *et al.*[72,82]

Table 2.6. Nitrogen

T K	p_σ bar	v cm³ mol⁻¹	$\alpha_\sigma \times 10^3$ K⁻¹	α_p K⁻¹	$\beta_s \times 10^4$ bar⁻¹	β_T bar⁻¹	γ_σ bar K⁻¹	γ_v K⁻¹	C_σ J K⁻¹ mol⁻¹	C_p	C_v	W m s⁻¹
63·18ᵗ	0·1253	32·25	4·73	4·73	1·16	1·98	0·023	23·9	56·1	56·1	33·0	995
65	0·174	32·53	4·86	4·87	1·22	2·11	0·030	23·1	56·3	56·3	32·6	975
70	0·387	33·37	5·15	5·16	1·39	2·49	0·057	20·7	56·7	56·8	31·8	925
75	0·763	34·35	5·48	5·51	1·60	2·95	0·096	18·6	57·2	57·3	31·0	875
77·35ᵇ	1·013	34·70	5·65	5·69	1·71	3·22	0·118	17·7	57·5	57·7	30·6	851
80	1·364	35·22	5·87	5·92	1·86	3·56	0·148	16·6	57·8	58·0	30·3	823
85	2·271	36·30	6·35	6·45	2·17	4·34	0·218	14·9	58·5	58·9	29·3	773
90	3·58	37·53	6·97	7·14	2·58	5·43	0·307	13·1	59·4	60·1	28·5	720
95	5·41	39·0	7·9	8·2	3·18	7·15	0·418	11·5	61·1	62·4	27·6	662
100	7·82	40·7	9·0	9·5	4·04	9·67	0·542	9·8	63·2	65·3	27·3	600
105	10·88	42·6	10·3	11·2	5·2	13·4	0·685	8·4	65·7	69·1	27·0	540
110	14·71	45·1	12·6	14·3	7·1	20·6	0·851	6·9	70	76	27	477
115	19·42	48·7	16	20	10·7	35	1·04	5·6	76	88	27	403
120	25·17	53·2	23	31	19	73	1·26	4·3	—	—	—	314
126·1ᶜ	33·9	90·1	∞	∞	∞?	∞	1·6	1·6	∞	∞	∞?	0?

48

Oxygen

The liquid range of oxygen is unusually long, from the triple point at 54 K to the critical point at 155 K, and it is unfortunate that so many precise measurements have been confined to the range of temperature below the normal boiling point at 90 K. The triple point, vapour pressure and critical constants were measured accurately by Hoge[87]. These measurements of the vapour pressure and others more recent have been analysed by Mullins, Ziegler and Kirk[88], whose recommendations are followed here. The orthobaric volumes were measured many years ago by Baly and Donnan[81] and by Mathias and Onnes[89], with excellent agreement. Their work is confirmed by van Itterbeek and Verbeke[90]. However, Stewart[91], who relies on recent unpublished measurements of L. A. Weber, has proposed volumes that are larger by 0·5 per cent and lead to a minimum in α_σ near 70 K. Liquids with unusually low triple points often have exceedingly low coefficients of thermal expansion, and it would be interesting to have confirmation, or otherwise, of a minimum. Meanwhile, the older results are used here.

The heat capacity, C_σ, has been measured by Clusius[85] and by Giauque and Johnston[92]. The latter are preferred since they show less scatter, agree well with some early measurements of Eucken and cover a wider range of temperature. The coefficient γ_V can be obtained from the isotherms of van Itterbeek and Verbeke[90] and from the isochores of Timrot and Borisoglebskii[93]. The latter results are not very accurate (the orthobaric volumes are too large at low temperatures), but they are valuable because they are direct measurements and the only ones available above the normal boiling point. The speed of sound has been measured several times by van Itterbeek, whose most recent results[78] are again used here.

The smoothing of these results is shown in *Figure 2.11* and the derived properties in *Table 2.7*.

Methane

The triple point, vapour pressure, and critical temperature and pressure were measured, or reviewed, in 1955 by Armstrong, Brickwedde and Scott[94]. Later measurements of the vapour pressure at low temperatures by Cutler and Morrison[95] agree well, and those of Hestermans and White[96] at high temperatures do so moderately well, but are probably high at pressures near 1 bar. The triple point and normal boiling point of Armstrong *et al.* have been confirmed by Clusius, Endtinger and Schleich[97]. The orthobaric volumes are not as certain as might be expected, in spite of several recent sets of measurements at both low[98] and high[99, 72] temperatures. The most probable values are shown in *Table 2.8*.

Table 2.7. Oxygen

T K	p bar	v cm³ mol⁻¹	$\alpha_\sigma \times 10^3$ K⁻¹	$\alpha_p \times 10^3$ K⁻¹	$\beta_s \times 10^4$ bar⁻¹	$\beta_T \times 10^4$ bar⁻¹	γ_σ bar K⁻¹	γ_v bar K⁻¹	C_σ J K⁻¹ mol⁻¹	C_p	C_v	W m s⁻¹
54·35[t]	0·001 52	24·42	3·33	3·33	—	—	—	—	53·1	53·1	—	—
55	0·001 84	24·47	3·35	3·35	—	—	—	—	53·1	53·1	—	—
60	0·007 30	24·91	3·48	3·48	0·597	0·94	0·001 84	37·1	53·2	53·2	33·9	1142
65	0·023 24	25·35	3·60	3·60	0·650	1·05	0·004 98	34·3	53·3	53·3	33·0	1104
70	0·062 26	25·81	3·75	3·75	0·710	1·19	0·011 33	31·5	53·4	53·4	32·1	1066
75	0·1449	26·30	3·90	3·90	0·778	1·34	0·022 70	29·1	53·6	53·6	31·2	1028
80	0·3006	26·82	4·06	4·07	0·857	1·51	0·040 90	27·0	53·8	53·8	30·2	989
85	0·5682	27·38	4·32	4·33	0·952	1·76	0·067 67	24·6	54·0	54·1	29·3	948
90	0·9943	27·99	4·58	4·60	1·06	2·04	0·1046	22·5	54·3	54·4	28·3	907
90·18[b]	1·0133	28·02	4·59	4·61	1·07	2·05	0·1062	22·5	54·4	54·5	28·2	906
95	1·633	28·65	4·87	4·90	1·20	2·39	0·1528	20·5	55	55	28	865
100	2·542	29·40	5·2	5·2	1·36	2·83	0·2133	18·4	56	56	27	822
110	5·434	31·1	5·8	5·9	1·80	3·85	0·3742	15·3	57	58	27	734
120	10·21	33·1	6·7	7·0	2·52	5·5	0·5919	12·3	60	62	27	641
130	17·28	35·6	8·2	9·0	3·83	9·3	0·8712	9·6	64	68	27	539
140	27·87	39·5	13	16	6·93	24	1·219	6·7	75	85	27	422
150	42·19	47·4	—	—	19·7	—	1·669	—	—	—	—	274
154·77[c]	50·8	75·0	∞	∞	∞ ?	∞	1·97	1·97	∞	∞	∞ ?	0 ?

Table 2.8. Methane

T K	p_σ bar	v cm³ mol⁻¹	α_σ × 10³ K⁻¹	α_p K⁻¹	β_s × 10⁴ bar⁻¹	β_T bar⁻¹	γ_σ bar K⁻¹	γ_v bar K⁻¹	C_σ	C_p J K⁻¹ mol⁻¹	C_v	W m s⁻¹
90·66[t]	0·1169	35·3	2·95	2·95	0·891	1·42	0·0150	20·8	53·1	53·1	33·3	1577
95	0·199	36·00	3·06	3·06	0·941	1·54	0·0231	19·9	53·4	53·4	32·6	1544
100	0·345	36·57	3·18	3·19	1·006	1·69	0·0359	18·8	53·7	53·7	31·8	1505
105	0·565	37·17	3·31	3·32	1·078	1·87	0·0533	17·7	54·1	54·2	31·3	1466
110	0·882	37·80	3·44	3·46	1·155	2·06	0·0760	16·8	54·6	54·7	30·6	1428
111·66[b]	1·013	38·00	3·48	3·50	1·183	2·13	0·0844	16·4	54·9	55·0	30·5	1415
120	1·923	39·20	3·72	3·75	—	2·53	0·1354	14·8	56·2	56·4	30·5	—
130	3·67	40·75	4·07	4·14	—	3·23	0·219	12·8	58·2	58·7	30·4	—
140	6·40	42·55	4·60	4·74	—	4·31	0·332	11·0	61	62	31	—
150	10·40	44·70	5·40	5·70	—	6·3	0·471	9·0	64	66	31	—
160	15·92	47·5	6·8	7·4	—	10·0	0·640	7·4	69	73	30	—
170	23·31	51·4	9·3	10·8	—	18·3	0·841	5·9	76	84	29	—
180	32·87	57·6	14	18	—	40	1·08	4·5	86	116	31	—
190·6[c]	45·8	99	∞	∞	∞?	∞	1·42	1·42	∞	∞	∞?	0?

51

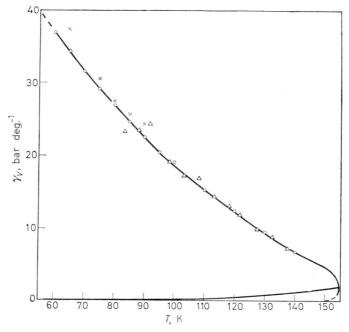

Figure 2.11. Thermal pressure coefficient of oxygen

○ from measurements of β_s from the speed of sound[78]
△ from γ_V by Timrot and Borisoglebskii[93]
× from β_T by van Itterbeek and Verbeke[90]

The heat capacity, C_σ, is well established at low temperatures[95,100] and has been measured twice at high temperatures[86,96]. Here the more recent work of Hestermans and White is perhaps to be preferred, but there must be some doubt. The heat capacity, C_p, and the coefficient γ_V can be obtained from the measurements of van Itterbeek, Verbeke and Staes[72], whilst β_S at low temperatures can be found from the speed of sound[101]. *Table 2.8* summarizes these results.

Carbon tetrachloride

There is a wealth of information on this liquid at room temperature. The density and vapour pressure are discussed adequately in works of reference, notably in that by Timmermans. The coefficient γ_V has been measured directly many times[35,36]; β_T has been measured directly, and earlier measurements of it reviewed, by Holder and Whalley[38]; β_S has been measured directly[49,102] and can be derived from the many measurements of the speed of

Table 2.9. Carbon tetrachloride

t °C	p bar	v cm³ mol⁻¹	$\alpha_\sigma \times 10^3$ K⁻¹	α_p	$\beta_s \times 10^4$ bar⁻¹	β_T	γ_σ bar K⁻¹	γ_v	C_σ, C_p J K⁻¹ mol⁻¹	C_v	W m s⁻¹
−22.96^t	0·0108	91·7	1·14	1·14	0·51	0·75	0·0006	15·2	130	90	1090
−20	0·0133	92·1	1·14	1·14	0·53	0·77	0·0008	14·9	130	90	1076
−10	0·0250	93·1	1·16	1·16	0·568	0·821	0·0015	14·1	130	90	1040
0	0·0442	94·23	1·18	1·18	0·616	0·890	0·0024	13·2	130	91	1005
10	0·0742	95·35	1·196	1·196	0·665	0·960	0·0036	12·5	131	91	971
20	0·1194	96·50	1·218	1·219	0·718	1·035	0·0055	11·8	132	91	939
30	0·1861	97·69	1·240	1·242	0·778	1·120	0·0080	11·1	132	91	906
40	0·2812	98·90	1·266	1·268	0·841	1·22	0·0111	10·4	133	92	876
50	0·4120	100·17	1·290	1·292	0·917	1·33	0·0150	9·7	133	92	845
60	0·5853	101·50	1·320	1·323	1·01	1·45	0·0202	9·1	134	93	816
70	0·8183	102·87	1·342	1·346	1·10	1·59	0·0263	8·4	134	94	790
80	1·115	104·3	1·39	—	—	—	0·0329	—	—	—	—
100	1·942	107·3	1·49	—	—	—	0·0509	—	—	—	—
200	14·57	129·4	2·6	—	—	—	0·228	—	—	—	—
283·2^c	45·6	276	∞	∞	∞?	∞	0·58	0·58	∞	∞?	0?

sound[39,51,103-5]. The measurements of Nozdrev[106] at temperatures up to 170°C are unfortunately too inaccurate to be of much use. The heat capacity, C_σ, is well established at low temperatures[45,50,107]. *Table 2.9* summarizes these results.

Water

The density of water is at a maximum at 4°C, and at this temperature

$$\alpha_\sigma = 0; \qquad \alpha_p \simeq 0; \qquad \gamma_V = \gamma_\sigma \qquad (2.96)$$

$$\beta_T \simeq \beta_S \qquad (2.97)$$

$$C_\sigma = C_V \simeq C_p \qquad (2.98)$$

It is clear that at the temperature at which α_σ is zero, α_p and γ_V are not exactly zero, since neither β_T nor γ_σ is zero. However, the temperature at which α_p and γ_V are zero lies very close to that at which α_σ is zero and, for all practical purposes, the relations (2.96)–(2.98) may all be taken to be equalities.

It is only within the last few years that there have been made extensive and consistent sets of measurements which satisfy these equations. Many properties can now be taken, with confidence, from one of the recent sets of 'Steam Tables' that conform to the International Skeleton Table of 1963. The one chosen here is that prepared by the National Engineering Laboratory[108] and this has been supplemented with further results obtained from it and other sources by Gibson and Bruges[109]. These sources lead to accurate values of the orthobaric volume, vapour pressure and critical constants. The heat capacities, C_σ and C_p have been measured many times (see de Haas[110]); at high temperatures, they can be found by differentiation of S_σ (from the N.E.L. Tables) and from the measurements of Ginnings and Furukawa[111]. The coefficient β_T has been measured recently by Diaz Peña and McGlashan[112] and by Kell and Whalley[34]; at low temperatures, β_S follows from unusually accurate measurements of the speed of sound[113,114]. *Table 2.10* summarizes these results.

The second adiabatic coefficient is the thermal pressure coefficient, γ_S. This is related to C_p by (2.54), and most of its measurements have had as their object the determination of the heat capacity. This method of measurement was quite common for gases, where it was introduced by Clément and Desormes and, in a more direct form, by Lummer and Pringsheim. It has not been used so often for liquids and has little to commend it. *Table 2.11* compares the measured and calculated values of γ_S.

Table 2.10 Water

t °C	p_σ bar	v_σ cm³ mol⁻¹	$\alpha_\sigma \times 10^3$ K⁻¹	α_p	$\beta_T \times 10^4$ bar⁻¹	β_s	γ_σ bar K⁻¹	γ_v	C_σ	C_p J K⁻¹ mol⁻¹	C_v	W m s⁻¹
0·01ᵗ	0·006 112	18·019	−0·0685	−0·0685	0·508	0·508	0·000 443 7	−1·35	75·99	75·99	75·94	1403
10	0·012 271	18·021	+0·0880	+0·0880	0·478	0·477	0·000 822 1	+1·84	75·55	75·55	75·47	1448
20	0·023 368	18·048	0·207	0·207	0·4586	0·4556	0·001 447	4·52	75·35	75·35	74·86	1482·8
40	0·073 750	18·158	0·386	0·386	0·4423	0·4310	0·003 931	8·73	75·28	75·28	73·36	1529·2
60	0·199 19	18·323	0·523	0·523	0·4448	0·4226	0·009 220	11·82	75·38	75·38	71·62	1551·3
80	0·473 59	18·538	0·641	0·642	0·4614	0·4257	0·019 18	13·91	75·60	75·61	69·76	1554·8
100	1·0133	18·799	0·750	0·752	0·490	0·438	0·036 17	15·35	75·85	75·87	67·80	1543
150	4·7597	19·648	1·027	1·035	0·621	0·506	0·1276	16·7	77·5	77·6	63·2	—
200	15·551	20·835	1·34	1·37	0·87	0·64	0·3254	15·7	80·6	81·0	60	—
250	39·776	22·54	1·85	1·95	1·47	0·95	0·6717	13·3	86·1	87·6	57	—
300	85·917	25·29	2·90	3·3	3·3	1·8	1·211	10·0	98	104	56	—
350	165·37	31·36	6·8	9·8	15	5	2·029	6·5	143	182	57	—
374·2ᶜ	221·2	55·9	∞	∞	∞	∞?	2·64	2·64	∞	∞	∞?	0?

55

Table 2.11. The adiabatic thermal pressure coefficient

Substance	t °C	γ_S (obs.) bar K^{-1}	Ref.	γ_S (calc.)† bar K^{-1}
Benzene	20	42·7	115	42·4
	40	38·9	115	39·0
n-Heptane	20	41·8	116	42·1
Carbon tetrachloride	20	37·9	116	38·3
		39·0	117	
	40	33·7	116	33·9
		35·0	117	

† The last column is calculated from Tables 2.3, 2.4 and 2.9.

The measurements of Damköhler[117] were made at a mean pressure of 26 bar and have been corrected to the saturation pressure. The correction may be calculated by differentiating the right-hand side of (2.54) with respect to pressure, and reduces his original results by 0·7 bar K^{-1}. Nevertheless, his results are probably still too high, and so his calculated values of C_p are too big.

2.6 Residual and Configurational Properties

Changes in energy can be measured experimentally, but no absolute value can be given to such a quantity, for it can only be reckoned from an arbitrary zero. A natural choice of the zero is the state of the fluid when each molecule has no kinetic energy, is in its ground level of rotational, vibrational and electronic energy, and is separated from all other molecules by an infinite distance. This is the state of a gas at the absolute zero of temperature and at zero density.

Another possible choice is that of the crystal at absolute zero. This differs from the former state by the lattice energy (or latent heat) of the crystal—an energy that is the sum of the intermolecular energies of the molecules and the zero-point energies of oscillation.

Both these conventional zeros are widely used and both have their advantages, but neither is the most convenient reference state if one is studying the properties of a fluid as a manifestation of its intermolecular forces. The energy difference of a given fluid from that of the perfect gas at absolute zero is made up of two parts. These may be related to the energy changes of the two steps of the most natural path leading from the reference state of zero temperature and infinite volume to the state (T, V) of the given fluid.

First the perfect gas may be heated from 0 to T whilst the volume remains infinite. The energy needed for this change is a purely molecular energy; that is, it is that needed to increase the internal energies and the translational kinetic energies of the molecules to those appropriate to the temperature T. If the fluid is now compressed to the volume V at constant temperature T, there will be a further change in its energy which is due solely to the effects of the intermolecular forces.

It is this second energy change which is here called the *residual energy*, as it is the energy of the fluid, less that of the same substance as a perfect gas at the same temperature. The name *internal energy* is sometimes chosen for this quantity, but this usage can lead to confusion, as the name is also used for the total energy U above that of the gas at absolute zero. More formally, the residual value of any function X may be denoted $X^*(V, T)$ and defined[118,119]

$$X^*(V, T) = \int_{\infty}^{V} \left[\left(\frac{\partial X}{\partial V} \right)_T - \left(\frac{\partial X}{\partial V} \right)_T^{\text{perfect gas}} \right] \mathrm{d}V \qquad (2.99)$$

The measurement of a residual property of a liquid is made in two steps. First, the integral of (2.99) is evaluated from infinite volume to V^g, the orthobaric vapour volume. Secondly, there is added to this quantity the change in X on isothermal condensation, less the change (if any) in this property on compressing a perfect gas from V^g to V^l. The most informative of the residual functions are U^*, H^*, C_V^* and C_p^*. The energies are calculated by the two-step process just described, but the heat capacities may be found more simply.

These are absolute quantities, and so the residual heat capacities are obtained by subtracting the absolute values for the liquid and for the perfect gas. The latter are most conveniently calculated for simple molecules from a knowledge of the frequencies of their normal modes of vibration[120,121]. Direct calorimetric values of C_V or C_p must be used for more complex molecules for which no certain assignment of frequencies can be made. These must be corrected for departures from the perfect-gas laws[119]. Such departures are usually far from negligible even at the normal boiling point.

The first of the two terms in the residual heat content, H^*, is that of the saturated gas. At low vapour pressures this is given by

$$H_{\text{gas}}^* = p_\sigma[B - T(\mathrm{d}B/\mathrm{d}T)] \qquad (2.100)$$

where p_σ is the vapour pressure and B the second virial coefficient. The calculation of H^* for the gas at higher vapour pressures, and particularly near the critical point, can only be made if the equation of state has been well established or, more rarely, from direct measurements of the isothermal Joule–Thomson coefficient, $(\partial H/\partial p)_T$. If the volume of the gas is known as a function of temperature and pressure, then

$$H^*_{\text{gas}} = \int_{\infty}^{V} \left[T\left(\frac{\partial p}{\partial T}\right)_V + V\left(\frac{\partial p}{\partial V}\right)_T \right] dV = \int_{0}^{p} \left[V - T\left(\frac{\partial V}{\partial T}\right)_p \right] dp$$

(2.101)

of which (2.100) is a special case. The second term in H^* of the orthobaric liquid is the latent heat of evaporation, ΔH, which, as shown above, may be obtained either by direct measurement or from the slope of the vapour-pressure curve. This second term is usually much the larger part of the residual heat content. A typical graph of the variation of H^* with temperature is shown in *Figure 2.12*.

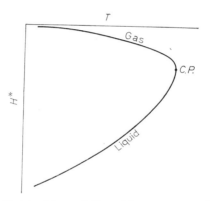

Figure 2.12. Sketch of the variation with temperature of the residual heat content of orthobaric gas and liquid. The difference between the two curves is the latent heat of evaporation

The molar residual energy, u^*, and the molar residual heat capacities are related to h^* by

$$h^* = u^* + pv - RT$$

(2.102)

$$(\partial h^*/\partial T)_p = c^*_p; \qquad (\partial u^*/\partial T)_V = c^*_v$$

(2.103)

These equations follow from (2.99). The slope $(\partial h^*/\partial T)_\sigma$ is not equal to c^*_p but approaches it closely at low vapour pressures.

The residual properties are, perhaps, the most direct measures of the effects of the intermolecular forces, but in the statistical theory of fluids it is more convenient to work with slightly different functions—the *configurational properties* (see below, Chapter 8). The differences between the two sets of functions are trivial. They are the configurational properties of the perfect gas, and it will be shown that these vanish for u and c_v. If the configurational properties are denoted h', u', etc., then

$$u' = u^*; \qquad c_v' = c_v^* \qquad (2.104)$$

$$h' = h^* + RT; \qquad c_p' = c_p^* + R \qquad (2.105)$$

Argon (Table 2.12)

The values of Δh, the latent heat of evaporation, of h' and u' shown in *Table 2.12* have been obtained from the tables of Din and

Table 2.12. Configurational properties of liquid argon

T K	Δh	h' J mol^{-1}	u'	c_p' J K^{-1} mol^{-1}	c_v'
83·81[a]	6610	−5940	−5940	29·4	7·0
85	6570	−5910	−5910	29·5	7·0
87·29[b]	6517	−5840	−5840	29·7	6·9
90	6440	−5760	−5760	29·9	6·8
95	6290	−5590	−5590	30·2	6·5
100	6110	−5420	−5430	31·2	6·2
105	5900	−5230	−5240	32	6
110	5660	−5030	−5050	34	5
120	5100	−4630	−4670	39	5
130	4350	−4170	−4250	48	5
140	3350	−3610	−3750	74	6
150·86[c]	0	−2030	−2400	∞	∞ ?

from the more recent work of Michels[70]. The heat capacities, c_p' and c_v', follow directly from *Table 2.5* by subtracting the molar heat capacity of the perfect gas, which is $3R/2$ for argon.

Nitrogen (Table 2.13)

The latent heat of evaporation has been measured at the boiling point by Giauque and Clayton[83] and from 65–80 K by Furukawa and McCoskey[80]. Their results agree at the boiling point to 0·2 per cent. The combination of γ_σ of *Table 2.6* and the orthobaric densities of Mathias, Onnes and Crommelin[81] gives a latent heat about 1–2 per cent greater than these. The residual heat content of

Table 2.13. Configurational properties of liquid nitrogen

T K	Δh	h' J mol^{-1}	u'	c_p' J K^{-1} mol^{-1}	c_v'
63·18[t]	6100	−5580	−5580	35·3	12·2
65	6050	−5520	−5520	35·5	11·8
70	5850	−5300	−5300	36·0	11·0
75	5670	−5100	−5100	36·5	10·2
77·35[b]	5590	−5020	−5020	36·9	9·8
80	5500	−4930	−4930	37·2	9·5
90	5150	−4560	−4570	39·3	7·7
100	4660	−4190	−4210	44·5	6·5
110	3920	−3700	−3770	55	6

the gas may be estimated from its density[81, 82] and from a calculated value of the second virial coefficient based upon a Lennard-Jones potential. The contribution of this residual heat to that of the liquid is only 2 per cent at 80 K, and so any error in choosing the second virial coefficient cannot contribute appreciably to the final error. The heat capacities are taken from Table 2.6. That of the perfect gas at constant volume is $5R/2$ at all relevant temperatures.

Oxygen (Table 2.14)

The latent heat has been measured at the boiling point by Giauque and Johnston[92], by Frank and Clusius[122] and Clusius and Konnertz[123], and from 65–95 K by Furukawa and McCoskey[80]. All

Table 2.14. Configurational properties of liquid oxygen

T K	Δh	h', u' J mol^{-1}	c_p' J K^{-1} mol^{-1}	c_v'
65	7490	−6950	32·5	12·2
70	7380	−6800	32·6	11·3
75	7260	−6650	32·8	10·4
80	7120	−6480	33·0	9·4
85	6980	−6310	33·3	8·5
90	6830	−6140	33·6	7·5
95	6680	−5940	34	7

agree within 0·2 per cent. The residual heat content of the gas has been estimated from the vapour pressure and an estimated second virial coefficient. The heat capacities are from *Table 2.7*.

Methane (Table 2.15)

The latent heat has been measured directly at 99·5 K by Frank and Clusius[122] (8521 J mol⁻¹). Other, but less exact, values can be

Table 2.15. Configurational properties of liquid methane

T K	Δh	h'	c_p'	c_v'
	J mol⁻¹		J K⁻¹ mol⁻¹	
90·66[t]	8730	−8000	28·2	8·4
95	8640	−7870	28·4	7·7
100	8540	−7750	28·7	6·9
105	8440	−7620	29·2	6·4
110	8320	−7480	29·8	5·7
111·66[b]	8270	−7420	30·1	5·6
120	8040	−7180	31·4	5·6
130	7730	−6870	33·7	5·5
140	—	—	37	6
150	—	—	41	5
160	—	—	48	5
170	—	—	59	4

calculated from γ_σ, the volume of the orthobaric liquid and, at low temperatures, a value of the volume of the orthobaric gas calculated from the vapour pressure and an estimated second virial coefficient. The heat capacities are taken from *Table 2.8*. That of the perfect gas at constant volume is $3R$ at all relevant temperatures.

Carbon dioxide (Table 2.16)

The results are derived from the table compiled by D. M. Newitt, M. U. Pai, N. R. Kuloor and J. A. W. Huggill (Din, Vol. 1). The values of c_p' are only approximate as they are $(\partial h'/\partial T)_\sigma$.

Ethylene (Table 2.17)

The latent heat has been measured at the boiling point by Egan and Kemp[124] and from 143–254 K by Clusius and Konnertz[123]. The

Table 2.16. Configurational properties of liquid carbon dioxide (Units of J, K and mol)

t °C	−56·60^t	−50	−40	−30	−20	−10	0	5	10	15	20	25	30	31·04^e
Δh	15 340	14 850	14 130	13 360	12 500	11 510	10 320	9550	8720	7820	6740	5330	2720	0
h'	—	−13 820	−13 260	−12 660	−12 040	−11 380	−10 650	−10 250	−9810	−9330	−8770	−8020	−6730	−5000
c_p'	56	58	61	64	70	80	—	—	—	—	—	—	—	∞

Table 2.17. Configurational properties of liquid ethylene (Units of J, K and mol)

T K	110	120	130	140	150	160	169·4^b	170	180	190	200
Δh	—	—	—	14 400	14 100	13 800	13 500	13 500	13 100	12 600	12 100
h'	—	—	—	−13 400	−12 900	−12 500	−12 100	−12 100	−11 700	−11 300	−10 900
c_p'	43·9	43·3	42·7	42·2	41·8	41·3	41·3	41·3	—	—	—

former is 1 per cent above the latter. The residual heat content of the gas may be calculated with reasonable confidence from the vapour pressure (Din) and the second virial coefficient up to 200 K, where the pressure is 4 bar. The heat capacity of the liquid has been measured by Egan and Kemp, and that of the gas may be calculated from the spectroscopic frequencies[125].

Water (*Table 2.18*)

The values shown are derived from *Table 2.10*, the N.E.L. Tables[108] and spectroscopic values of C_V for the perfect gas[125].

Table 2.18. Configurational properties of liquid water

t °C	Δh	h' J mol^{-1}	u'	c_p'	c_v' J K^{-1} mol^{-1}
0·01^t	45 053	−42 780	−42 780	50·82	50·77
10	44 628	−42 290	−42 290	50·34	50·26
20	44 204	−41 790	−41 790	50·10	49·61
40	43 348	−40 820	−40 820	49·94	48·02
60	42 478	−39 800	−39 800	49·93	46·17
80	41 585	−38 780	−38 780	50·03	44·18
100	40 655	−37 790	−37 790	50·15	42·08
150	38 090	−35 250	−35 260	51·5	37·1
200	34 960	−32 610	−32 640	54·4	33
250	30 900	−29 740	−29 830	61	30
300	25 300	−26 430	−26 650	75	27
350	16 090	−21 970	−22 490	150	27
374·2^c	0	−15 220	−16 460	∞	∞ ?

Propane (*Table 2.19*)

The values are derived from the tables of N. R. Kuloor, D. M. Newitt and J. S. Bateman (Din, Vol. 2). Their values of c_v are not used, as they are said to be good to only 10 per cent.

The values of the configurational heat capacities following the Table are derived from the sources indicated (units: J K^{-1} mol^{-1}).

Table 2.19. Configurational properties of liquid propane (Units of J, K and mol)

T K	200	220	$231 \cdot 10^b$	240	260	280	300	320	340	360	$370 \cdot 0^c$
Δh	20 200	19 300	18 790	18 400	17 300	16 100	14 700	12 800	10 500	6600	0
h'	−18 900	−17 700	−17 120	−16 700	−15 700	−14 80)	−13 900	−12 700	−11 300	−9320	−6040
c'_p	—	—	48	46	44	46	53	64	—	—	∞

64

Carbon Monoxide

(from A. S. Leah (Din, Vol. 1))

T K	$68 \cdot 09^t$	70	80	$81 \cdot 63^b$	84
c_p'	39·3	39·4	39·6	39·7	39·7

Ethane

(*Liquid*, Witt and Kemp[126]; *Gas*, Heuse; Eucken and Parts; Eucken and Weigert[127]; see also H. E. Tester (Din, Vol. 3))

T K	90	100	120	140	160	180	$184 \cdot 1^b$
c_p'	36	37	37	38	39	41	42

Ammonia

(from P. Davies (Din, Vol. 1))

T K	200	250	300	320	340	360	380	400	$405 \cdot 6^c$
c_p'	48	50	54	57	63	74	95	—	∞
c_v'	—	—	—	20	16	15	16	26	∞ ?

Carbon disulphide

(from the measurements of Brown and Manov[128] and Staveley, Hart and Tupman[50])

t°C	-108	-80	-60	-40	-20	0	20	40
c_p'	48	45	43	42	41	39	39	38
c_v'	23	20	18	16	15	13	12	12

Carbon tetrachloride

(Staveley, Hart and Tupman[50], *Table 2.9* and Albright, Galegar and Innes[129])

t°C	-20	-10	0	10	20	30	40	50	60
c_p'	—	—	—	—	57	57	56	56	56
c_v'	20	19	18	17	16	16	15	15	15

Chloroform

(Harrison and Moelwyn-Hughes[45], Staveley, Hart and Tupman[50] and Gelles and Pitzer[130])

t°C	-30	-20	-10	0	10	20	30	40	50
c_p'	58·3	57·9	57·4	56·9	56·5	56·3	56·3	56·5	56·6
c_v'	22·6	21·6	20·7	20·1	19·6	19·0	18·5	17·9	17·4

Acetone

(Pennington and Kobe[17])

t°C	20	50
c_p'	62	62

Benzene

(Staveley, Hart and Tupman[50])

$t°C$	20	30	40	50	60	70
c'_p	63	61	60	59	59	59
c'_v	22	20	19	18	18	17

Toluene

(Staveley, Hart and Tupman[50])

$t°C$	−88	−80	−60	−40	−20	0	20	40	60	80
c'_v	41	36	32	29	27	25	23	22	20	19

These figures show that c'_p and c'_v both increase with the complexity of the molecules. The former rises monotonically with temperature for simple substances towards its infinite value at the critical point. For complex and polar liquids it first falls with increasing temperature, passes through a flat minimum and then joins the upward movement to the critical point. The heat capacity at constant volume falls with rising temperature for all liquids until a temperature close to the critical is reached, when it rises sharply. The group of aliphatic alcohols conforms qualitatively to this pattern but the minima in c'_p lie at unexpectedly low temperatures[50,131]. This may be due to the fact that, unlike the other molecules discussed, their polar groups are flexibly attached to the carbon skeleton.

2.7 VAN DER WAALS'S EQUATION

The empirical equation of van der Waals[132] played an important part in the early development of theories of the liquid state and of solutions. It is still not entirely without interest, as it is the simplest form of equation that gives a qualitatively adequate account of the process of condensation (including the metastable states) and of the properties of the liquid. Its merits are that it is easy to manipulate and that it never predicts physically absurd results. It may be used in theoretical work for a quick qualitative examination of a new problem. Some of the properties of a 'van der Waals fluid' are summarized here, others are discussed in the next Chapter.

The equation is

$$(p + a/v^2)(v - b) = RT \tag{2.106}$$

where v is the molar volume, R is the gas constant, and a and b are parameters which change from one substance to another. They may be expressed in terms of two of the critical constants p^c, v^c and T^c, as

is shown in any elementary text. The equation obtained by eliminating a and b in favour of the critical constants is in *reduced form*;
that is, it is a function only of the dimensionless ratios p/p^c, v/v^c and
T/T^c. The vapour pressure and orthobaric volumes may be found
by equating the temperature, pressure and chemical potential of the
two coexisting phases*. The coefficients α_p, β_T and γ_V are readily
derived by differentiation. The last is particularly simple, as it is a
function only of density

$$\gamma_V = \frac{R}{v-b}; \qquad \frac{\gamma_V T^c}{p^c} = \frac{8(v^c/v)}{3-(v^c/v)} \qquad (2.107)$$

Figure 2.13 shows that, qualitatively, the vapour pressure, orthobaric densities and γ_V behave correctly. The prediction that γ_V is
independent of T (that is, that the isochores are linear) is a good

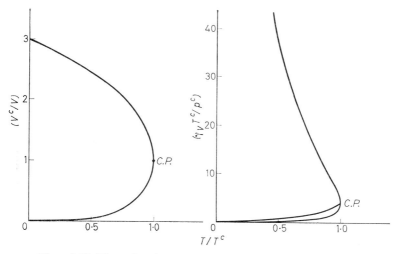

Figure 2.13. The reduced orthobaric densities, slope of the vapour-
pressure curve, and thermal pressure coefficient for van der Waals's
equation

approximation, but is not exactly true, as shown above and in the
next Chapter. At very low temperatures the equation becomes less
realistic, as it does not predict the occurrence of a solid phase. The
limiting values for the orthobaric liquid at zero temperature, of the
three dimensionless coefficients $(\alpha_p T^c)$, $(\beta_T p^c)$ and $(\gamma_V T^c/p^c)$ are,
respectively, $(8/27)$, 0 and ∞.

* See ref. 119. The method of solution used there is not original but was devised
(though not published) by Gibbs[133].

There are two other consequences of this equation of state that are fulfilled approximately by many real liquids. These are not entirely independent but are best considered separately. The first is that the function $v^2(\partial u/\partial v)_T$ should be a constant[50,134]. In practice, it is not exactly constant but does not change very much over the whole of the fluid range. It is necessarily finite both at the critical point and in the limit of zero gas density, where it is equal to $RT^2(\mathrm{d}B/\mathrm{d}T)$. It is therefore not surprising that it is a well-behaved function along both branches of the orthobaric curve. It may be related to γ_V by the thermodynamic equation of state (2.14). Its calculation is sensitive to small errors in γ_V and, near the critical point, in V. Some typical values are shown in *Figure 2.14*. The

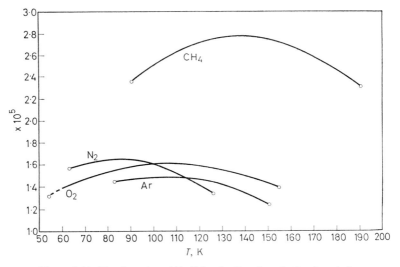

Figure 2.14. The function $v^2(\partial u/\partial v)_T$, in J cm³ mole⁻²; the circles mark the triple and critical points (see also *Tables 2.3* and *2.4*)

variations shown cannot be dismissed as experimental error.

The second simple consequence[134] of van der Waals's equation is that, at low temperatures,

$$(\partial u/\partial v)_T = \Delta u/v^l \qquad (2.108)$$

where Δu is the energy of evaporation. This equation follows directly from the facts that van der Waals's equation requires the residual energy to be a linear function of density, and that the orthobaric vapour density may be neglected at low temperatures. The energy of evaporation at low temperatures is given by

$$\Delta u = \Delta h - p_\sigma \Delta v \tag{2.109}$$

Figure 2.15 shows the closeness with which equation (2.108) is obeyed

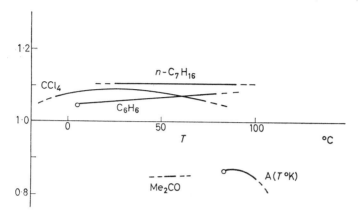

Figure 2.15. The ratio $[v(\partial u/\partial v)_T/\Delta u]$ at low temperatures. The circles mark the triple points

by some of the liquids discussed above. The figures for carbon tetrachloride are those of Benninga and Scott[35]. The agreement is poor for argon and nitrogen and for all polar liquids. Water is, as often, anomalous, as the left-hand side of (2.108) vanishes at 4°C.

A discussion of all empirical equations proposed since that of van der Waals would be out of place here. However, one of these deserves mention because of its wide use in chemical engineering. This is the equation of Redlich and Kwong[135]

$$p = \frac{RT}{v - b} - \frac{a}{T^{1/2}v(v + b)} \tag{2.110}$$

It is clearly based on that of van der Waals and has much of its simplicity. However, its greater numerical accuracy, particularly when modified[135] to allow for departures from the principle of corresponding states, makes it of great practical value.

Both (2.106) and (2.110) are readily extended to mixtures by treating a as a quadratic function and b as a linear function of mole fraction (see Chapter 9).

REFERENCES

[1] Prigogine, I. and Defay, R. *Chemical Thermodynamics*, Vol. 1 (trans. Everett, D. H.), London (Longmans) 1954; Guggenheim, E. A., *Thermodynamics*, 5th Ed., Amsterdam (North-Holland) 1967

[2] Keesom, W. H. *Communs phys. Lab. Univ. Leiden* No. 75 (1901)

[3] Gibbs, J. W. *Collected Works*, Vol. 1, p. 42, Yale (New Haven) 1928; see also [1]

[4] Briggs, L. J. *J. appl. Phys.* 21 (1950) 721; *J. chem. Phys.* 19 (1951) 970; Donoghue, J. J., Vollrath, R. E. and Gerjuoy, E. 19 (1951) 55; Hayward, A. T. J. *NEL Rep.* No. 158 (1964)

[5] Kenrick, F. B., Gilbert, C. S. and Wismer, K. L. *J. phys. Chem.* 28 (1924) 1297

[6] Jordan, T. E. *Vapor Pressures of Organic Compounds*, New York (Interscience) 1954; *Handbook of Chemistry and Physics* (Chemical Rubber Publishing Co., annual)

[7] Antoine, C. *C. r. hebd. Séanc. Acad. Sci.*, Paris 107 (1888) 681, 778

[8] Forziati, A. F., Norris, W. R. and Rossini, F. D. *J. Res. natn. Bur. Stand.* 43 (1949) 555; Willingham, C. B., Taylor, W. J., Pignocco, J. M. and Rossini, F. D. 35 (1945) 219

[9] Ambrose, D., Broderick, B. E. and Townsend, R. *J. chem. Soc.* A (1967) 633

[10] Andon, R. J. L., Cox, J. D., Herington, E. F. G. and Martin, J. F. *Trans. Faraday Soc.* 53 (1957) 1074

[11] *Br. Stand.* 2520, 3763; *Misc. Publs Bur. Stand.* 253 (1963)

[12] Lambert, J. D., Roberts, G. A. H., Rowlinson, J. S. and Wilkinson, V. J. *Proc. R. Soc.* A196 (1949) 113

[13] *A.P.I.* 44

[14] Fiock, E. F., Ginnings, D. C. and Holton, W. B. *Bur. Stand. J. Res.* 6 (1931) 881

[15] Curtiss, C. F. and Hirschfelder, J. O. *J. chem. Phys.* 10 (1942) 491

[16] Scott, D. W., Waddington, G., Smith, J. C. and Huffman, H. M. *J. chem. Phys.* 15 (1947) 565

[17] Pennington, R. E. and Kobe, K. A. *J. Am. chem. Soc.* 79 (1957) 300

[18] Trouton, F. *Phil. Mag.* 18 (1884) 54

[19] Rice, O. K. *J. chem. Phys.* 4 (1936) 367; Smith, A. L., Keller, W. E. and Johnston, H. L. 19 (1951) 189; Guggenheim, E. A. *Molec. Phys.* 10 (1966) 401; 11 (1966) 403; Scott, R. L. 11 (1966) 399, 503

[20] Barclay, I. M. and Butler, J. A. V. *Trans. Faraday Soc.* 34 (1938) 1445

[21] Quincke, G. *Annln Phys.* 19 (1883) 401

[22] Tait, P. G. *Voyage of H.M.S. Challenger*, Vol. 2 (1889), Part 4, p. 1–76 (esp. p. 33); *Scientific Papers* Vol. 2, Papers 61 and 107, Cambridge Univ. Press, 1900

[23] Tamann, G. *Z. phys. Chem.* 17 (1895) 620

[24] Kell, G. S. Private communication (1964)

[25] Hayward, A. T. J. *Br. J. appl. Phys.* 18 (1967) 965

[26] Hudleston, L. J. *Trans. Faraday Soc.* 33 (1937) 97; Bett, K. E., Weale, K. E. and Newitt, D. M. *Br. J. appl. Phys.* 5 (1954) 243

REFERENCES

[27] Amagat, E.-H. *Annls Chim.* (*Phys.*) 29 (1893) 505

[28] Bridgman, P. W. *Proc. Am. Acad. Arts Sci.* 49 (1913) 1

[29] Bridgman, P. W. *Proc. Am. Acad. Arts Sci.* 66 (1931) 185; 67 (1932) 1; 68 (1933) 1

[30] Bridgman, P. W. *Proc. Am. Acad. Arts Sci.* 74 (1942) 399; see also *idem, Physics of High Pressure*, London (Bell) 1949, with Suppl. and *Collected Papers*, Oxford (Pergamon) 1966

[31] Gibson, R. E. and Kincaid, J. F. *J. Am. chem. Soc.* 60 (1938) 511; Gibson, R. E. and Loeffler, O. H. 61 (1939) 2515, 2877; 63 (1941) 898; *J. phys. Chem.* 43 (1939) 207

[32] Doolittle, A. K., Simon, I. and Cornish, R. M. *A.I.Ch.E.Jl* 6 (1960) 150; Doolittle, A. K. and D. B. *ibid.* 153, 157; Doolittle, A. K. *Chem. Engng Prog. Symp. Ser.* 59 (1963) No. 44, 1

[33] Jessup, R. S. *Bur. Stand. J. Res.* 5 (1930) 985; Dow, R. B. and Fenske, M. R. *Industr. Engng Chem.* 27 (1935) 165; Dow, R. B. and Fink, C. E. *J. appl. Phys.* 11 (1940) 353; Smith, L. B., Beattie, J. A. and Kay, W. C. *J. Am. chem. Soc.* 59 (1937) 1587; Felsing, W. A. and Watson, G. M. 64 (1942) 1822; 65 (1943) 780; Eduljee, H. E., Newitt, D. M. and Weale, K. E. *J. chem. Soc.* (1951) 3086, 3092; Cutler, W. G., McMickle, R. H., Webb, W. and Schiessler, R. W. *J. chem. Phys.* 29 (1958) 727; Lowitz, D. A., Spencer, J. W., Webb, W. and Schiessler, R. W. 30 (1959) 73

[34] Kell, G. S. and Whalley, E. *Phil. Trans. R. Soc.* A258 (1965) 565; Kell, G. S. *J. chem. Engng Data* 12 (1967) 66

[35] Westwater, W., Frantz, H. W. and Hildebrand, J. H. *Phys. Rev.* 31 (1928) 135; Hildebrand, J. H. 34 (1929) 649; with Carter, J. M. *J. Am chem. Soc.* 54 (1932) 3592; Alder, B. J., Haycock, E. W., Hildebrand, J. H. and Watts, H. *J. chem. Phys.* 22 (1954) 1060; Benninga, H. and Scott, R. L. 23 (1955) 1911; Smith, E. B. and Hildebrand, J. H. 31 (1959) 145

[36] Allen, G., Gee, G. and Mangaraj, D. *Polymer* 1 (1960) 467; Bianchi, U., Agabio, G. and Turturro, A. *J. phys. Chem.* 69 (1965) 4392; Orwoll, R. A. and Flory, P. J. *J. Am. chem. Soc.* 89 (1967) 6814

[37] Bryant, M. O. and Jones, G. O. *Proc. phys. Soc. Lond.* B66 (1953) 421

[38] Holder, G. A. and Whalley, E. *Trans. Faraday Soc.* 58 (1962) 2095

[39] Fort, R. J. and Moore, W. R. *Trans. Faraday Soc.* 61 (1965) 2102

[40] Boelhouwer, J. W. M. *Physica* 26 (1960) 1021

[41] Jones, G. O. and Walker, P. A. *Conférence de Physique des Basses Températures* (Paris, 1955); *Proc. phys. Soc. Lond.* B69 (1956) 1348; Walker, P. A., *Ph.D. Thesis*, London, 1956

[42] Osborne, N. S. and Van Dusen, M. S. *Bull. Bur. Stand., Wash.* 14 (1918) 397

[43] Babcock, H. A. *Proc. Am. Acad. Arts Sci.* 55 (1920) 323 (see p. 392)

[44] Hoge, H. J. *J. Res. natn. Bur. Stand.* 36 (1946) 111

[45] Harrison, D. and Moelwyn-Hughes, E. A. *Proc. R. Soc.* A239 (1957) 230

[46] McCullough, J. P. and Scott, D. W. (Ed.) *Experimental Thermodynamics*, Vol. 1, *Calorimetry of Non-reacting Systems*, London (Butterworth) 1968

[47] Oliver, D. G., Eaton, M. and Huffman, H. M. *J. Am. chem. Soc.* 70

(1948) 1502 (benzene); Huffman, H. M., Gross, M. E., Scott, D. W. and McCullough, J. P. *J. phys. Chem.*, 65 (1961) 495 (n-heptane)

[48] Douglas, T. B., Furukawa, G. T., McCoskey, R. E. and Ball, A. F. *J. Res. natn. Bur. Stand.* 53 (1954) 139

[49] Tyrer, D. *J. chem. Soc.* 103 (1913) 1675; 105 (1914) 2534

[50] Staveley, L. A. K. and Parham, D. N. *Changements de Phases*, p. 366, Paris (Soc. chim. Phys.) 1952; Staveley, L. A. K., Hart, K. R. and Tupman, W. I. *Discuss. Faraday Soc.* 15 (1953) 130; Staveley, L. A. K., Tupman, W. I. and Hart, K. R. *Trans. Faraday Soc.* 51 (1955) 323

[51] Freyer, E. B., Hubbard, J. C. and Andrews, D. H. *J. Am. chem. Soc.* 51 (1929) 759

[52] Barone, A. *Handbuch der Physik*, Vol. 11, Part 2 (ed. Flügge, S.), Berlin (Springer) 1962; Schaaffs, W., *Molekularakustik*, Berlin (Springer) 1963; Mason, W. P. (ed.) *Physical Acoustics, Principles and Methods*, Vol. 1, Part A, New York (Academic Press) 1964

[53] Sette, D., in *Physics of Simple Liquids* (ed. Temperley, H. N. V., Rowlinson, J. S. and Rushbrooke, G. S.), Amsterdam (North-Holland) 1968

[54] Herzfeld, K. F. and Litovitz, T. A. *Absorption and Dispersion of Ultrasonic Waves*, New York (Academic Press) 1959; Sette, D. *Handbuch der Physik* (ed. Flügge, S.) Vol. 11, Part 1, Berlin (Springer) 1961; Bauer, H. J. (p. 48) and Lamb, J. (p. 203) in Mason, W. P. (ed.) *Physical Acoustics, Principles and Methods*, Vol. 2, Part A, New York (Academic Press) 1964

[55] Naugle, D. G., with Squire, C. F. *J. chem. Phys.* 42 (1965) 3725; 44 (1966) 741; with Lunsford, J. H. and Singer, J. R. 45 (1966) 4669

[56] Brillouin, L. *Annls Phys.* 17 (1922) 88

[57] Chiao, R. Y. and Stoicheff, B. P. *J. opt. Soc. Am.* 54 (1964) 1286; Rank, D. H., Kiess, E. M., Fink, U. and Wiggins, T. A. 55 (1965) 925; Chiao, R. Y. and Fleury, P. in *Physics of Quantum Electronics* (ed. Kelley, P. L. Lax, B. and Tannenwald, P. E.), New York (McGraw-Hill) 1966; Mountain, R. D. *J. Res. natn. Bur. Stand.* 70A (1966) 207; *Rev. mod. Phys.* 38 (1966) 205

[58] Hakim, S. E. A. and Comley, W. J. *Nature, Lond.* 208 (1965) 1082; Comley, W. J. *Br. J. appl. Phys.* 17 (1966) 1375

[59] Heasell, E. L. and Lamb, J. *Proc. phys. Soc. Lond.* B69 (1956) 869

[60] Heasell, E. L. and Lamb, J. *Proc. R. Soc.* A237 (1956) 233; Krebs, K. and Lamb, J. A244 (1958) 558

[61] Young, J. M. and Petrauskas, A. A. *J. chem. Phys.* 25 (1956) 943

[62] Karpovich, J. *J. chem. Phys.* 22 (1954) 1767

[63] Moen, C. J. *J. acoust. Soc. Am.* 23 (1951) 62

[64] Andreae, J. H., Heasell, E. L. and Lamb, J. *Proc. phys. Soc. Lond.* B69 (1956) 625

[65] Lamb, J. and Pinkerton, J. M. M. *Proc. R. Soc.* A199 (1949) 114; Piercy, J. E. and Lamb, J. *Trans. Faraday Soc.* 52 (1956) 930; Maier, W. and Rudolph, H. D. *Z. phys. Chem. Frankf. Ausg.* 10 (1957) 83 (benzoic acid)

[66] Andreae, J. H. *Proc. phys. Soc. Lond.* B70 (1957) 71

[67] Blandamer, M. J., Clarke, D. E., Hidden, N. J. and Symons, M. C. R. *Trans. Faraday Soc.* 63 (1967) 66

REFERENCES

[68] Michels, A., Wassenaar, T., Sluyters, T. and de Graaff, W. *Physica* 23 (1957) 89; Pool, R. A. H., Shields, B. D. C. and Staveley, L. A. K. *Nature, Lond.* 181 (1958) 831

[69] Flubacher, P., Leadbetter, A. J. and Morrison, J. A. *Proc. phys. Soc. Lond.* 78 (1961) 1449; Thomaes, G. and van Steenwinkel, R. *Molec. Phys.* 5 (1962) 307; Weir, R. D., *Ph.D. Thesis*, London, 1966

[70] Michels, A. Levelt, J. M. and de Graaff, W. *Physica* 24 (1958) 659; Michels, A., Levelt, J. M. and Wolkers, G. J. *ibid.* 769

[71] van Itterbeek, A., de Boelpaep, J., Verbeke, O., Theeuwes, F. and Staes, K. *Physica* 30 (1964) 2119; Lurii, L. I. and Rabinovitch, V. A. *Russ. J. phys. Chem.* 40 (1966) 379

[72] van Itterbeek, A. and Verbeke, O. *Physica* 26 (1960) 931; with Staes, K. 29 (1963) 742; Pool, R. A. H., Saville, G., Herrington, T. M., Shields, B. D. C. and Staveley, L. A. K. *Trans. Faraday Soc.* 58 (1962) 1692

[73] Clusius, K. *Z. phys. Chem.* B31 (1936) 459

[74] Bagatskii, M. I., Voronel', A. V. and Gusak, V. G. *Soviet Phys. JETP* 16 (1963) 517

[75] Liepmann, H. W. *Helv. phys. Acta* 12 (1939) 421

[76] Galt, J. K. *J. chem. Phys.* 16 (1948) 505

[77] Dobbs, E. R. and Finegold, L. *J. acoust. Soc. Am.* 32 (1960) 1215

[78] van Dael, W., van Itterbeek, A., Cops, A. and Thoen, J. *Physica* 32 (1966) 611

[79] Davies, R. H., Duncan, A. G., Saville, G. and Staveley, L. A. K. *Trans. Faraday Soc.* 63 (1967) 855; Streett, W. B. and Staveley, L. A. K., private communication (1966)

[80] Furukawa, G. T. and McCoskey, R. E. *NACA tech. Note* 2969 (1953)

[81] Baly, E. C. C. and Donnan, F. G. *J. chem. Soc.* 81 (1902) 907; Mathias, E., Onnes, H. K. and Crommelin, C. A. *Communs phys. Lab. Univ. Leiden* No. 145c (1914)

[82] van Itterbeek, A. and Verbeke, O. *Cryogenics* 2 (1961–62) 79

[83] Giauque, W. F. and Clayton, J. O. *J. Am. chem. Soc.* 55 (1933) 4875; Armstrong, G. T. *J. Res. natn. Bur. Stand.* 53 (1954) 263

[84] Friedman, A. S. and White, D. *J. Am. chem. Soc.* 72 (1950) 3931; Michels, A., Wassenaar, T., de Graaff, W. and Prins, C. *Physica* 19 (1953) 26

[85] Clusius, K. *Z. phys. Chem.* B3 (1929) 41

[86] Wiebe, R. and Brevoort, M. J. *J. Am. chem. Soc.* 52 (1930) 622

[87] Hoge, H. J. *J. Res. natn. Bur. Stand.* 44 (1950) 321

[88] Mullins, J. C., Ziegler, W. T. and Kirk, B. S. *Adv. cryogen. Engng* 8 (1963) 126

[89] Mathias, E. and Onnes, H. K. *Communs phys. Lab. Univ. Leiden* No. 117 (1911)

[90] van Itterbeek, A. and Verbeke, O. *Cryogenics* 1 (1960–61) 77

[91] Stewart, R. B. *Thesis*, Univ. Iowa, 1966

[92] Giauque, W. F. and Johnston, H. L. *J. Am. chem. Soc.* 51 (1929) 2300

[93] Timrot, D. L. and Borisoglebskii, V. P. *Inzh.-fiz. Zh.* 4 (1961) 3

[94] Armstrong, G. T., Brickwedde, F. G. and Scott, R. B. *J. Res. natn. Bur. Stand.* 55 (1955) 39

[95] Cutler, A. J. B. and Morrison, J. A. *Trans. Faraday Soc.* 61 (1965) 429

[96] Hestermans, P. and White, D. *J. phys. Chem.* 65 (1961) 362

[97] Clusius, K., Endtinger, F. and Schleich, K. *Helv. chim. Acta* 43 (1960) 1267

[98] Mathot, V., Staveley, L. A. K., Young, J. A. and Parsonage, N. G. *Trans. Faraday Soc.* 52 (1956) 1488; Fuks, S., Legros, J.-C. and Bellemans, A. *Physica* 31 (1965) 606

[99] Davenport, A. J., Rowlinson, J. S. and Saville, G. *Trans. Faraday Soc.* 62 (1966) 322; Grigor, A. F. and Steele, W. A. *J. chem. Phys.* 48 (1968) 1032, 1038

[100] Clusius, K. and Weigand, K. *Z. phys. Chem.* B46 (1940) 1

[101] van Itterbeek, A. and Verhaegen, L. *Proc. phys. Soc. Lond.* B62 (1949) 800; *Physica* 31 (1965) 1643; 35 (1967) 162

[102] Sackmann, H. and Boczek, A. *Z. phys. Chem. Frankf. Ausg.* 29 (1961) 329

[103] Pellam, J. R. and Galt, J. K. *J. chem. Phys.* 14 (1946) 608

[104] van Itterbeek, A. and de Bock, A. *Physica* 14 (1948) 609

[105] Lagemann, R. T., McMillan, D. R. and Woolf, W. E. *J. chem. Phys.* 17 (1949) 369

[106] Nozdrev, V. *Dokl. Akad. Nauk SSSR for. Lang. Edn* 53 (1946) 119

[107] Hicks, J. F. G., Hooley, J. G. and Stephenson, C. C. *J. Am. chem. Soc.* 66 (1944) 1064

[108] National Engineering Laboratory, *Steam Tables, 1964* (ed. Bain, R. W.), Edinburgh (H.M.S.O.) 1964

[109] Gibson, M. R. and Bruges, E. A. *J. mech. Engng Sci.* 9 (1967) 24

[110] de Haas, J. *Comité international des Poids et Mésures, Annexe I, Procès Verbaux des Séances*, Ser. 2, Vol. 12 (1950)

[111] Ginnings, D. C. and Furukawa, G. T. *J. Am. chem. Soc.* 75 (1953) 522

[112] Diaz Peña, M. and McGlashan, M. L. *Trans. Faraday Soc.* 55 (1959) 2018

[113] Greenspan, M. and Tschiegg, C. E. *J. Res. natn. Bur. Stand.* 59 (1957) 249; *J. acoust. Soc. Am.* 31 (1959) 75

[114] Wilson, W. D. *J. acoust. Soc. Am.* 31 (1959) 1067

[115] Burlew, J. S. *J. Am. chem. Soc.* 62 (1940) 681, 690, 696

[116] Richards, W. T. and Wallace, J. H. *J. Am. chem. Soc.* 54 (1932) 2705

[117] Damköhler, G. *Z. phys. Chem.* B31 (1936) 439

[118] Michels, A., Geldermans, M. and de Groot, S. R. *Physica* 12 (1946) 105

[119] Rowlinson, J. S. *Handbuch der Physik* (ed. Flügge, S.), Vol. 12, Berlin (Springer) 1958

[120] Herzberg, G. *Infra-red and Raman Spectra of Polyatomic Molecules*, New York (Van Nostrand) 1945

[121] Hilsenrath, J. and Ziegler, G. G. *Tables of Einstein Functions, Natn. Bur. Stand. Monogr.* 49, 1962

[122] Frank, A. and Clusius, K. *Z. phys. Chem.* B42 (1939) 395

[123] Clusius, K. and Konnertz, F. *Z. Naturf.* 4a (1949) 117

[124] Egan, C. J. and Kemp, J. D. *J. Am. chem. Soc.* 59 (1937) 1264

REFERENCES

[125] Rowlinson, J. S. *The Perfect Gas*, p. 59–61, Oxford (Pergamon) 1963
[126] Witt, R. K. and Kemp, J. D. *J. Am. chem. Soc.* 59 (1937) 273
[127] Heuse, W. *Annln Phys.* 59 (1919) 86; Eucken, A., with Parts, A. *Z. phys. Chem.* B20 (1933) 184; with Weigert, K. B23 (1933) 265
[128] Brown, O. L. I. and Manov, G. G. *J. Am. chem. Soc.* 59 (1937) 500
[129] Albright, L. F., Galegar, W. C. and Innes, K. K. *J. Am. chem. Soc.* 76 (1954) 6017
[130] Gelles, E. and Pitzer, K. S. *J. Am. chem. Soc.* 75 (1953) 5259
[131] Eucken, A. *Z. Elektrochem.* 52 (1948) 255
[132] van der Waals, J. D. *Die Kontinuität des gasförmigen und flüssigen Zustandes* (2nd Ed.), Vol. 1 (Single Component Systems), Leipzig (Barth) 1899–1900; Engl. transl. of 1st Ed. of Vol. 1 by Threlfall, R. and Adair, J. F. in *Physical Memoirs*, Vol. 1, Part 3, London (Phys. Soc.) 1890
[133] Wilson, E. B. in *Commentary on the Scientific Writings of J. Willard Gibbs* (ed. Donnan, F. G. and Haas, A.), Vol. 1, p. 41, New Haven (Yale) 1936
[134] Hildebrand, J. H. and Scott, R. L. *The Solubility of Non-electrolytes*, p. 96–101, New York (Reinhold) 1951; *Regular Solutions*, p. 77–79, New Jersey (Prentice-Hall) 1962
[135] Redlich, O., with Kwong, J. N. S. *Chem. Rev.* 44 (1949) 233; with Dunlop, A. K. *Chem. Engng Prog. Symp. Series* 59 (1963) No. 44, p. 95

THE CRITICAL STATE

3.1 Thermodynamics of the Critical Point

The critical state of a fluid is represented by the point on the (p, V, T) surface where the volumes of the gas and liquid phases become identical. It is found that the mechanical stability of this state is of a lower order than that required by the inequalities of Section 2.1. Such a point may be said to lie on the border separating the stable and unstable parts of a continuous (p, V, T) surface. A discussion of the behaviour of thermodynamic functions at and near this point may therefore be based on either of the two surfaces (U, S, V) or (A, V, T). It is shown below that there is no advantage in using the former as long as the condition of thermal stability is satisfied at the point. The development of this Section is therefore made initially by using the (A, V, T) surface. It is impossible to use the (G, p, T) surface, since the condition of mechanical stability cannot be derived from this surface.

Liquid and gas can exist together at equilibrium if the temperatures, pressures and chemical potentials of the two phases are equal. These equalities may be written in terms of the molar Helmholtz free energy of a one-component system

$$T^l = T^g \tag{3.1}$$

$$(\partial a/\partial v)^l_T = (\partial a/\partial v)^g_T \tag{3.2}$$

$$a^l - v^l(\partial a/\partial v)^l_T = a^g - v^g(\partial a/\partial v)^g_T \tag{3.3}$$

Thus a graph of a as a function of v at constant temperature is represented by the full line in *Figure 3.1*. The volumes of the co-existent phases, A and D, are connected by a straight tie-line of slope $(-p)$ which, by (3.2) and (3.3), must be the common tangent to both branches of the curve. Thus the experimental free energy is not a continuous differentiable function of volume at the dew and bubble points. It is, however, convenient to treat it as such a function of the form shown by the dashed curve $ABCD$. This lies above the full curve and is therefore a less stable state.

The instability of the curve $ABCD$ is of two kinds; between B and C the derivative $(\partial^2 a/\partial v^2)_T$ is negative, or $(\partial p/\partial v)_T$ is positive. Such

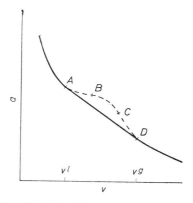

Figure 3.1. The Helmholtz free energy as a function of volume

a system is mechanically unstable; the parts of the curve between A and B and between C and D are mechanically stable but are metastable with respect to the two-phase system. Although the true equilibrium curve is the discontinuous one and although there is reason to believe that an exact statistical treatment of the molar free energy of an infinitely large assembly would lead to this curve, it is useful to suppose that a may be represented by the continuous curve for the following reasons:

(1) The results obtained from this hypothesis and from the rules for constructing the tie-line, (3.2) and (3.3), agree qualitatively with the experimental results.

(2) All approximate statistical theories and all empirical equations of state lead to the continuous curve.

(3) The metastable regions of compressed vapour and expanded liquid are observable experimentally, although their theoretical status is not yet entirely clear[1].

The curve on the (p, V, T) surface which corresponds to the dashed curve in *Figure 3.1* is shown in *Figure 3.2*. The equality of the chemical potential of the two phases requires that (cf. 2.4)

$$\int_{ABCD} v \, dp = 0 \qquad (3.4)$$

Thus the straight line AD cuts the continuous curve to form two equal areas above and below the transition pressure.

77

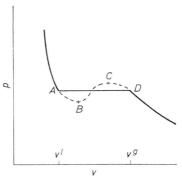

Figure 3.2. The pressure as a function of volume

A critical point occurs on a free-energy surface if the tangent AD becomes vanishingly small, so that the four points A, B, C and D coincide. At such a point

$$\left(\frac{\partial a}{\partial v}\right)_T < 0, \qquad \left(\frac{\partial^2 a}{\partial v^2}\right)_T = 0, \qquad \left(\frac{\partial^3 a}{\partial v^3}\right)_T = 0, \qquad \left(\frac{\partial^4 a}{\partial v^4}\right)_T > 0 \quad (3.5)$$

that is

$$p > 0, \qquad \left(\frac{\partial p}{\partial v}\right)_T = 0, \qquad \left(\frac{\partial^2 p}{\partial v^2}\right)_T = 0, \qquad \left(\frac{\partial^3 p}{\partial v^3}\right)_T < 0 \quad (3.6)$$

The second and third of these conditions are necessary if B and C are to coincide, and the fourth is the condition that the fluid should be stable at volumes immediately above and below the critical point. It is so at this point, since the pressure falls with increasing volume, but the stability is of a lower order than that of other states of the fluid.

A fluid whose critical point is characterized by these conditions is often called a van der Waals fluid, since the conditions are satisfied by his equation of state. Their consequences were first explored in his classic work[2], *Die Kontinuität des gasförmigen und flüssigen Zustandes.* Experiment shows that the first three derivatives of a satisfy (3.5), but there is doubt about the behaviour of the fourth and higher derivatives. These doubts can be brought into the open most clearly by discussing first, and in some detail, the consequences of these equations.

The Helmholtz free energy may be written as a double Taylor expansion in $(v - v^c)$ and $(T - T^c)$ about its value at the critical point

$$a = a^c + \sum_{n=1}^{\infty} \sum_{m=0}^{n} \frac{(v - v^c)^m (T - T^c)^{n-m}}{m!(n-m)!} \left(\frac{\partial^n a}{\partial v^m \partial T^{n-m}}\right)^c \quad (3.7)$$

The assumption of this form of curve is that A is an analytic function of V and T at and near the critical point. Upon this assumption is founded the elementary but ultimately erroneous treatment set out in this Section. In the next, the extent will be discussed to which classical thermodynamics can be usefully applied if this condition of analyticity is waived.

A similar expansion is obtained for the pressure by differentiation with respect to volume. The leading terms of this expansion may be written

$$\delta p = p_T^c(\delta T) + p_{vT}^c(\delta v)(\delta T) + \tfrac{1}{6}p_{3v}^c(\delta v)^3 + \ldots \quad (3.8)$$

where δp, etc. is $(p - p^c)$, etc. and p_{vT}^c, etc. denotes $(\partial^2 p/\partial v \partial T)^c$, etc. The terms in p_v^c and p_{2v}^c are zero, and higher powers of (δT) may be neglected near the critical point. This equation is that of the continuous (p, v, T) surface of which the dashed line $ABCD$ of *Figure 3.2* is a section. At the orthobaric liquid and gas volumes, A and D,

$$\delta p = p_T^c(\delta T) + p_{vT}^c(\delta v^l)(\delta T) + \tfrac{1}{6}p_{3v}^c(\delta v^l)^3 \quad (3.9)$$

$$\delta p = p_T^c(\delta T) + p_{vT}^c(\delta v^g)(\delta T) + \tfrac{1}{6}p_{3v}^c(\delta v^g)^3 \quad (3.10)$$

Addition and subtraction of these equations gives

$$\delta p = p_T^c(\delta T) + \left\{\frac{\delta v^l + \delta v^g}{2}\right\} \{p_{vT}^c(\delta T)$$

$$+ \tfrac{1}{6}p_{3v}^c[(\delta v^l)^2 - (\delta v^l)(\delta v^g) + (\delta v^g)^2]\} \quad (3.11)$$

$$0 = p_{vT}^c(\delta T) + \tfrac{1}{6}p_{3v}^c[(\delta v^l)^2 + (\delta v^l)(\delta v^g) + (\delta v^g)^2] \quad (3.12)$$

These equations are derived from (3.1) and (3.2). A third follows from (3.3), the condition of the equality of the chemical potentials

$$\int_{ABCD} v \, dp = \int_{\delta v^g}^{\delta v^l} (\delta v)\left(\frac{\partial(\delta p)}{\partial(\delta v)}\right)_T d(\delta v) = 0 \quad (3.13)$$

Differentiating (3.8) and integrating (3.13) gives

$$\{(\delta v^l)^2 - (\delta v^g)^2\}\{p_{vT}^c(\delta T) + \tfrac{1}{4}p_{3v}^c[(\delta v^l)^2 + (\delta v^g)^2]\} = 0 \quad (3.14)$$

Substituting for (δT) from (3.12) gives

$$p_{3v}^c[(\delta v^l) + (\delta v^g)][(\delta v^l) - (\delta v^g)]^3 = 0 \quad (3.15)$$

or, since v^g and v^l are not equal,

$$\delta v^g + \delta v^l = 0 \quad (3.16)$$

Thus the critical volume is the mean of the co-existing liquid and gas volumes. The three equations (3.11), (3.12) and (3.16) give δp, δv^l and δv^g in terms of an arbitrary temperature change from the critical point, (δT). From (3.11) and (3.16)

$$(\delta p/\delta T) = p_T^c \qquad \text{or} \qquad \gamma_\sigma^c = \gamma_V^c \qquad (3.17)$$

that is, the vapour-pressure curve is continuous with the critical isochore beyond the critical point. This equality was used extensively in the last Chapter for interpolating values of γ_V. From (3.12) and (3.16)

$$\delta v^g = -\delta v^l = [-6p_{vT}^c(\delta T)/p_{3v}^c]^{1/2} \qquad (3.18)$$

The temperature difference δT is negative, p_{3v}^c must be negative for mechanical stability, and p_{vT}^c is negative since p_v vanishes at the critical point and is negative in the one-phase system at temperatures above T^c. The differences (δv^g) and (δv^l) are obtained by taking the positive root of the right-hand side of (3.18). These results are shown schematically in *Figure 3.3*. By differentiation of (3.8) and

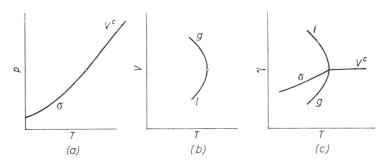

Figure 3.3. Sketches of the variation with temperature of (a) the pressure, (b) the orthobaric volumes, and (c) the derivatives $(\partial p/\partial T)$, according to eqn. (3.17)–(3.19). Curves marked V^c are critical isochores, those marked σ are saturation curves, and g and l denote gas and liquid. The critical point is marked by a circle

substitution from (3.18)

$$\gamma_V = \gamma_\sigma^c \pm [-6(p_{vT}^c)^3(\delta T)/p_{3v}^c]^{1/2} + O(\delta T) \qquad (3.19)$$

where, with a positive root, the positive sign gives γ_V for the liquid and the negative for the gas.

Thus the physical consequence of the assumption that a is a continuous differentiable function of v and T is that the co-existence curve has a rounded top which is quadratic in the volume. The order of the curve depends on that of the first non-vanishing derivative of a with respect to volume. If the fourth derivative is assumed to vanish, then the fifth must do likewise and presumably the sixth would be non-zero and positive.

Mechanical stability requires that the first non-vanishing derivative shall be even but does not indicate its order. If this derivative is of the order $2n$, then an analysis similar to that above shows that (δv) is proportional to $(\delta T)^{1/(2n-2)}$. It is shown below that such proportionality is not in agreement with experiment, which suggests that (δv) is proportional to $(\delta T)^{1/3}$. Such an exponent is inconsistent with an integral value of n. However, the following qualitative consequences of this treatment have been amply confirmed by experiment:

(*1*) The orthobaric curves meet at T^c as a continuous curve, as in *Figure 3.3*, and not at a sharp intersection.

(*2*) The critical volume is the mean of the orthobaric volumes near the critical point.

(*3*) The vapour-pressure curve is co-linear with the critical isochore.

It follows from (3.5)–(3.18) that α_σ, c_σ and $(\partial h/\partial T)_\sigma$ are all proportional to $(\delta T)^{-1/2}$ near T^c for a van der Waals fluid, and so are an order of magnitude smaller than α_p, β_T and c_p which are proportional to $(\delta T)^{-1}$. Again this conclusion is confirmed qualitatively by experiment.

All liquids pass through a Joule–Thomson inversion point some way below the critical point, at the temperature at which α_p is equal to $(1/T)$. The first of the inequalities (2.44) is reversed at this point, and c_p is greater than $(\partial h/\partial T)_\sigma$ from here to the critical point. The isothermal Joule–Thomson coefficient becomes infinite at the critical point but the adiabatic coefficient remains finite and is equal to $(1/\gamma_V^c)$.

It is shown below that there is good experimental evidence that C_V of the one-phase system has a strong maximum as the critical point is approached from temperatures above T^c. It is probable that the heat capacity becomes infinite. Such an infinity would denote incipient thermal instability as was shown in (2.61). In order to show that such instability plays no essential part in determining the gas–liquid critical point, it is necessary to use the less familiar (U, S, V) surface*, since A is not a differentiable function of V and T if

---

* Photographs of a model of the $(-U, S, V)$ surface made by Maxwell are shown by Wilson[3a]. A second model was made by Onnes and Happel[3b]; the (U, V, T) surface is discussed by Wood[3c].

(T/C_V) is anywhere zero. The three equations (3.1)–(3.3) become on this surface

$$(\partial U/\partial S)^l_V = (\partial U/\partial S)^g_V \qquad (3.20)$$

$$(\partial U/\partial V)^l_S = (\partial U/\partial V)^g_S \qquad (3.21)$$

$$U^l - S^l(\partial U/\partial S)^l_V - V^l(\partial U/\partial V)^l_S$$
$$= U^g - S^g(\partial U/\partial S)^g_V - V^g(\partial U/\partial V)^g_S \qquad (3.22)$$

They are more symmetrical on this surface, where all the variables are extensive, than on the (A, V, T) surface. They are the conditions that the tangent planes to the (U, S, V) surface at the gas and liquid points should coincide. As the common tangent plane rolls over the surface, its two points of contact trace out the orthobaric curves which eventually meet at the critical point. These curves form a line along which U, S and V all increase monotonically on passing from liquid, through the critical point, to the gas*. The isotherms and isobars on this surface are the loci of the points of equal slope parallel to the principal axes, (3.20) and (3.21). The region of stability is given by (2.59) as

$$D > 0, \text{ where } D \text{ is the determinant } \begin{vmatrix} U_{2S} & U_{SV} \\ U_{SV} & U_{2V} \end{vmatrix} \qquad (3.23)$$

The determinant is zero on the boundary curve between the regions of stability and instability which passes through the critical point. Hence

$$D^c = 0 \qquad \text{or} \qquad \left(\frac{T}{C_V}\right)^c \left(-\frac{\partial p}{\partial V}\right)^c_T = 0 \qquad (3.24)$$

This equation could be satisfied either by $(\partial p/\partial V)_T$ becoming zero (incipient mechanical instability) or by (T/C_V) becoming zero (incipient thermal instability). However, it will be shown that the second condition without the first does not give a critical point as found experimentally.

By expansion about the critical point, and differentiation, the following expressions are obtained for (δT) and (δp)

$$\delta T = U^c_{2S}(\delta S) + U^c_{SV}(\delta V) + \ldots \qquad (3.25)$$

$$-\delta p = U^c_{VS}(\delta S) + U^c_{2V}(\delta V) + \ldots \qquad (3.26)$$

By equating the temperature and pressure of the two phases,

$$U^c_{2S}(S^g - S^l) + U^c_{SV}(V^g - V^l) = 0 \qquad (3.27)$$

$$U^c_{SV}(S^g - S^l) + U^c_{2V}(V^g - V^l) = 0 \qquad (3.28)$$

---

* If C_σ for the gas becomes positive at low temperatures, there is a maximum in S on this branch. It is everywhere negative for most simple substances.

These equations define the slopes of the projected tie-line on the (S, V) plane. This line becomes tangential to the co-existence curve at the critical point, where it is given by either of the equations

$$U_{2S}^c \, dS + U_{SV}^c \, dV = 0 \qquad (3.29)$$

$$U_{SV}^c \, dS + U_{2V}^c \, dV = 0 \qquad (3.30)$$

The tangent must also be identical with the limiting curve of stability $(D = 0)$ at this point, and so a third equation for this tangent is

$$D_S^c \, dS + D_V^c \, dV = 0 \qquad (3.31)$$

The last three equations may be expressed in more familiar variables

$$\left(\frac{T}{C_V}\right)^c dS + \left[-\left(\frac{T}{C_V}\right)\left(\frac{\partial p}{\partial T}\right)_V\right]^c dV = 0 \qquad (3.32)$$

$$\left[-\left(\frac{T}{C_V}\right)\left(\frac{\partial p}{\partial T}\right)_V\right]^c dS + \left[-\left(\frac{\partial p}{\partial V}\right)_T + \left(\frac{T}{C_V}\right)\left(\frac{\partial p}{\partial T}\right)_V^2\right]^c dV = 0 \qquad (3.33)$$

$$\left[-\left(\frac{T}{C_V}\right)^2\left(\frac{\partial^2 p}{\partial V \, \partial T}\right)\right]^c dS$$

$$+ \left[-\left(\frac{T}{C_V}\right)\left(\frac{\partial^2 p}{\partial V^2}\right)_T + \left(\frac{T}{C_V}\right)^2\left(\frac{\partial p}{\partial T}\right)_V\left(\frac{\partial^2 p}{\partial V \, \partial T}\right)\right]^c dV = 0 \qquad (3.34)$$

A comparison of (3.32) and (3.33) shows that, if these equations are to represent the same line, then $(\partial p/\partial V)_T^c$ must be zero, whether or not $(T/C_V)^c$ is zero. Or, more exactly, the ratio $[(\partial p/\partial V)_T/ (T/C_V)(\partial p/\partial T)_V^2]^c$ must be zero, so that any infinity in C_V must be of a lower order than that of $(\partial V/\partial p)_T^c$. A comparison of (3.34) with the other two equations shows, similarly, that $(\partial^2 p/\partial V^2)_T^c$ is zero. Either of the two conditions of stability in the one-phase region,

$$D_V^c < 0 \qquad \text{or} \qquad D_S^c > 0 \qquad (3.35)$$

shows that $(\partial^2 p/\partial V \, \partial T)^c$ is negative. These conclusions, which are confirmed by experiment, may be expressed concisely by saying that the following inequalities hold near the critical point

$$(\partial p/\partial V)_S > (\partial p/\partial V)_T \geqslant 0 \qquad (3.36)$$

$$(T/C_V) > (T/C_p) \geqslant 0 \qquad (3.37)$$

The shape of the co-existence curve on the (p, V, T) surface is most readily obtained from the (U, S, V) surface by eliminating (δS), by successive approximation, between the two expansions for (δT) and (δp), (3.25) and (3.26). This gives (δp) as a function of (δT) and

(δV) and, after some lengthy algebra, the expansion (3.8) is obtained. Thus any results which can be derived from the (a, v, T) surface can be derived also from the (U, S, V) surface, although often less readily. The latter surface, however, has the advantage that it allows of the discussion of thermal instability, as an infinity in C_V does not produce a singularity on this surface. Such a discussion shows that any such infinity must be of a lower order than that in $(\partial V/\partial p)_T$ and so can play no essential part in determining the properties of the critical point. If it is present, then (3.25) and (3.26) must be taken to higher terms to obtain the equations of the tie-line.

3.2 Inequalities at the Critical Point

The assumption that A is an analytic function of V and T at and near the critical point led in the last Section to a full description of the ways in which $(V^g - V^l)$, $(\partial p/\partial V)_T$, (T/C_p), etc. become zero as the critical point is approached; but it is, of course, irreconcilable with the requirement that the compressibility is everywhere positive. This is clear from *Figure 3.1*. The difficulty is overcome by the device of the common tangent (*Figure 3.1*) or Maxwell's rule (*Figure 3.2*) or by equating potentials, as in eqn. (3.2) and (3.3). However, the description remains conceptually unsatisfactory and, as is shown below, is also quantitatively inaccurate.

The requirements of thermodynamic stability, and in particular that (T/C_v) be positive, lead to some powerful inequalities between the rates at which different functions become zero as the critical point is approached along various paths. These inequalities do not depend upon A being everywhere an analytic function, but do require that A, U, S and p are continuous functions of V and T. They are valuable both for the insight they give into the possible algebraic forms of A and for the means they provide for checking experimental results. In fact, the margins by which real fluids satisfy them are so small that the inequalities may, in reality, be equations, as they are for a van der Waals fluid.

These results can be obtained in two ways. The requirement that C_v is positive means that A is a function of T which is everywhere convex—upwards. Griffiths[4a] used such conditions of convexity to obtain many inequalities, some of which are of great practical value, others less so. However, many, and possibly all, of these inequalities can be derived from exact equations from which one or more terms have been discarded. The omitted terms are functions of heat capacities and so are of known sign. This method of derivation is due to Rushbrooke[4b] who first obtained one of these inequalities for the Curie point of a ferromagnet. His derivation was extended to the critical point of a fluid by Fisher[5]. A variant of this method is followed here, in preference to that of Griffiths, since it is potentially more useful to know in each case which are the omitted terms that turn the equation into an inequality. The variant used has been chosen because it leads, in one operation, to the three most useful inequalities.

The inequalities are between the rates of approach to zero of different functions as $(T - T^c)$ and $(V - V^c)$ tend to zero. Consider some function $X(V, T)$ and define an index χ by

$$\chi^{\pm} = \lim_{T \to T_{\pm}^c} \{\ln X(V, T)/\ln [\pm(T - T^c)]\} \qquad (3.38)$$

This index defines the rate of approach of X to zero, or to infinity if χ is negative. The path to be followed in taking the limit must be specified and is often $V = V^c$. The indices χ^+ and χ^- can be different, and χ^- can sometimes be divided further into χ_1^- and χ_2^- according as the approach to the critical point is made along a path in the one-phase or two-phase fluid. The superscripts and subscripts are omitted when no confusion can arise.

The indices used here are defined in *Table 3.1*, in which the

Table 3.1

Property	Index	Comments
C_v	$-\alpha^+$	along critical isochore, $T > T^c$
	$-\alpha_1^-$	through orthobaric states of homogeneous fluid
	$-\alpha_2^-$	along critical isochore, $T < T^c$
$(V^g - V^c), (V^c - V^l)$	β	through orthobaric states
$-(\partial p/\partial V)_T$	γ^+	along critical isochore, $T > T^c$
	γ_1^-	through orthobaric states of homogeneous fluid
$|p - p^c|$ as function of $|V - V^c|$	δ	along critical isotherm
$(\partial^2 p/\partial T^2)_\sigma$	$-\theta$	curvature of vapour-pressure line

symbols are those now commonly used in this field but which must not be confused with α, the coefficient of thermal expansion, β, the compressibility, etc. introduced in Chapter 2. It is possible to subdivide further the indices α_1^-, β, γ_1^- and δ if the coexistence curve and the critical isotherm are of different degree for $V > V^c$ and $V < V^c$. Rushbrooke[4b] and Griffiths[4a] consider such possibilities, but there is no experimental evidence for such differences and so they are ignored here for simplicity.

An index of zero is ambiguous. It can mean that the function has no zero or infinity (but may have a discontinuity), or else that there is a logarithmic infinity.

We now express the results of the last Section for the generalized van der Waals fluid in terms of these indices. If the first non-vanishing derivative of A with respect of V at the critical point is of order $2n$, where n is necessarily integral, then

$$\alpha^+ = \alpha_1^- = 0 \qquad \alpha_2^- = (n-2)/(n-1) \tag{3.39}$$

$$\beta = 1/2(n-1) \qquad \gamma^+ = \gamma_1^- = 1 \tag{3.40}$$

$$\delta = 2n - 1 \qquad \theta = 0 \tag{3.41}$$

The classical van der Waals fluid $(n = 2)$ has a simple discontinuity in C_v, that is $\alpha_2^- = 0$.

The required inequalities between these indices can now be obtained by considering the function $Y(V, T)$, defined by

$$Y = U - T^c S \tag{3.42}$$

whose derivatives are

$$\left(\frac{\partial Y}{\partial T}\right)_V = -\frac{T^c - T}{T} C_v \qquad \left(\frac{\partial Y}{\partial V}\right)_T = -(T^c - T)\left(\frac{\partial p}{\partial T}\right)_V - p \tag{3.43}$$

The difference

$$\Delta Y = Y(V^c, T) - Y(V^c, T^c) \qquad (T < T^c) \tag{3.44}$$

can now be obtained in three different ways. Equating these results, two at a time, gives three equations, from each of which, by omission of suitable terms, we obtain a different inequality. The difference is found by adding the changes in Y along each of the three paths shown in *Figure 3.4*. These are: (a) from C to D, (b) from C to A^l, A^g to B^l, B^g, and (c) from C to B^l, B^g through the orthobaric states. Each mole of fluid at D corresponds to x^l moles in state B^l and x^g moles in B^g where

$$x^l = \frac{V^g - V^c}{V^g - V^l} \qquad x^g = \frac{V^c - V^l}{V^g - V^l} \tag{3.45}$$

Here V^g and V^l are the volumes at B^g and B^l, and in what follows these are taken to be fixed at those appropriate to the final temperature T; they do not change as the fluid is taken along paths such as A^g to B^g, C to B^g, etc. Quantities that change along the path C to B^g are denoted by the subscript σ; $V = V_\sigma^g$.

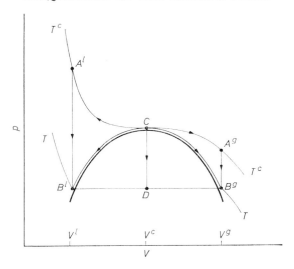

Figure 3.4. The change ΔY of (3.44) is that from point C to point D and may be found in three ways by considering changes of Y along the three paths shown.

The changes in Y are
(*a*) from C to D

$$\Delta Y = \int_{T}^{T^c} \frac{T^c - T}{T} (C_v)_{V=V^c} \, \mathrm{d}T \qquad (3.46)$$

(*b*) from C to A^l, A^g to B^l, B^g.

Here each mole of the fluid at C is split into two samples of x^l and x^g moles each, where these are the mole fractions appropriate to the final temperature T. The first sample is taken along the path CA^lB^l and the second along CA^gB^g

$$\Delta Y = \sum_{l,g} x^{l,g} \left\{ \int_{V^{l,g}}^{V^c} p_{T=T^c} \, \mathrm{d}V + \int_{T}^{T^c} \frac{T^c - T}{T} (C_v)_{V=V^{l,g}} \, \mathrm{d}T \right\} \qquad (3.47)$$

$$= \sum_{l,g} x^{l,g} \left\{ \int_{V^{l,g}}^{V^c} (p - p^c)_{T=T^c} \, \mathrm{d}V + \int_{T}^{T^c} \frac{T^c - T}{T} (C_v)_{V=V^{l,g}} \, \mathrm{d}T \right\} \quad (3.48)$$

where the summation is over the two samples with superscript l and g.

87

(c) from C to $B^l B^g$

$$\Delta Y = -\sum_{l,g} x^{l,g} \int_T^{T^c} \left(\frac{\partial Y}{\partial T}\right)_{V=V_\sigma^{l,g}} \mathrm{d} T \tag{3.49}$$

$$= -\sum_{l,g} x^{l,g} \int_T^{T^c} \left[\left(\frac{\partial Y}{\partial T}\right)_V + \left(\frac{\partial Y}{\partial V}\right)_T \left(\frac{\partial V}{\partial T}\right)_\sigma\right]_{V=V_\sigma^{l,g}} \mathrm{d} T \tag{3.50}$$

$$= \sum_{l,g} x^{l,g} \left\{ \int_T^{T^c} \frac{T^c - T}{T} (C_v)_{V=V_\sigma^{l,g}} \mathrm{d} T \right.$$

$$+ \int_T^{T^c} \left[\left(\frac{\partial V}{\partial T}\right)_\sigma \left[p_\sigma + (T^c - T)\left(\frac{\partial p}{\partial T}\right)_\sigma\right]\right.$$

$$\left. - (T^c - T)\left[\left(\frac{\partial p}{\partial V}\right)_T\right]_\sigma \left(\frac{\partial V}{\partial T}\right)_\sigma^2\right]_{V=V_\sigma^{l,g}} \mathrm{d} T \right\} \tag{3.51}$$

Now, if β is the same on both sides of the critical point[4b]

$$\sum_{l,g} x^{l,g} \int_T^{T^c} \left[\left(\frac{\partial V}{\partial T}\right)_\sigma\right]_{V=V_\sigma^{l,g}} \left[p_\sigma + (T^c - T)\left(\frac{\partial p}{\partial T}\right)_\sigma\right] \mathrm{d} T = 0 \tag{3.52}$$

since $(\partial V/\partial T)_\sigma$ is positive on the liquid branch and negative on the gas branch, and since $[p_\sigma + (T^c - T)(\partial p/\partial T)_\sigma]$ is the same on both branches. Hence (3.51) becomes

$$\Delta Y = \sum_{l,g} x^{l,g} \left\{ \int_T^{T^c} \frac{T^c - T}{T} (C_v)_{V=V_\sigma^{l,g}} \mathrm{d} T \right.$$

$$\left. - \int_T^{T^c} (T^c - T)\left[\left(\frac{\partial p}{\partial V}\right)_T \left(\frac{\partial V}{\partial T}\right)_\sigma^2\right]_{V=V_\sigma^{l,g}} \mathrm{d} T \right\} \tag{3.53}$$

We have three equations for ΔY, (3.46), (3.48) and (3.53). Each term in these is positive and, in particular, the two pairs of integrals (l and g)

$$\int_T^{T^c} \frac{T^c - T}{T} (C_v)_{V=V^{l,g}} \mathrm{d} T > 0 \quad \text{and}$$

$$\int_T^{T^c} \frac{T^c - T}{T} (C_v)_{V=V_\sigma^{l,g}} \mathrm{d} T > 0 \tag{3.54}$$

First, equate (3.46) and (3.48) and omit the first pair of integrals in (3.54). The resulting inequality can be turned into one in the indices of *Table 3.1* by substituting for $(C_v)_{V=V^c}$, etc. the expression $(T^c - T)^{-\alpha_2^-}$, etc. The larger quantity has an index equal to or lower than that of the smaller, and so we obtain

$$\alpha_2^- + \beta(\delta + 1) \geqslant 2 \tag{3.55}$$

Similarly, by equating (3.46) and (3.53) and omitting the second pair of integrals in (3.54), we have

$$\alpha_2^- + 2\beta + \gamma_1^- \geqslant 2 \tag{3.56}$$

A third inequality is obtained by equating (3.48) and (3.53). The equation so formed contains terms that are differences of the integrals in (3.54), that is, of the form

$$\int_T^{T^c} \frac{T^c - T}{T} \left[(C_v)_{V=V_\sigma^{l,g}} - (C_v)_{V=V^{l,g}} \right] \, dT \tag{3.57}$$

Now there is good experimental evidence that C_v increases on approaching the orthobaric boundary from either side along isotherms just below the critical point. This behaviour is also required by the presence of an infinity in C_v for the one-phase fluid (see below). Hence (3.57) is necessarily positive, and its neglect leads to a third inequality, if again β is the same on each side of the critical point,

$$\gamma_1^- - \beta(\delta - 1) \geqslant 0 \tag{3.58}$$

This result was first put forward by Griffiths for the Curie point of a ferromagnet. Liberman[6] derived it first for a fluid.

The only other inequality discussed below is a much weaker one, obtained by both Griffiths and Rushbrooke, namely

$$\alpha_2^- + \beta - \theta \geqslant 0 \tag{3.59}$$

There are analogous inequalities, as has been mentioned, for other 'critical points', such as the Curie point of a ferromagnet, the Néel point of an anti-ferromagnet, and for the corresponding points on many lattice models of these phenomena—the lattice gas, the Ising model and the Heisenberg model. These inequalities are sometimes easier to derive than those for fluids, since there is often an essential symmetry in the ordering parameter with respect to the sign of the field which is not present in a fluid between $(V^g - V^c)$ and $(V^c - V^l)$. This book is not the place to explore the analogies between critical points of different kinds, or between these and the transitions to super-fluid or superconducting states, but it may be said that, despite the diverse physical nature of these phenomena, the underlying singularities in the appropriate thermodynamic functions are remarkably similar[7–10]. The dimensionality of the system and the range of the interactions are probably of greater importance in determining the nature of the singularities than the details of interactions between the elements of the systems. Critical points in fluid mixtures are perhaps the closest to the gas–liquid points of this Chapter, and these are discussed in Chapters 5 and 6.

The inequalities of this Section become equations if A is an analytic function. This follows at once from (3.39)–(3.41). A more realistic representation of A as a function of V and T is to require it to be analytic only in the homogeneous region but not on the phase boundary. This is the minimal assumption needed to justify the 'common tangent' (or Maxwell's) rule, as may be seen by equating chemical potentials in two orthobaric states along a path lying wholly within the homogeneous fluid. A more formal proof has been given by Griffiths[11]. He and Widom, amongst others[10–12], have devised algebraic functions of $(V - V^c)$ and $(T - T^c)$ which make (3.55) and (3.56) equations yet satisfy the experimental results discussed below. However, these 'scaling laws', although plausible, are not yet confirmed rigorously by theory or experiment, and no discussion of them is attempted here.

3.3 THE MEASUREMENT OF CRITICAL CONSTANTS

The classical view of the critical point is that it is the state at which the densities of the co-existing phases are equal, and is also the highest temperature and pressure at which $(\partial p/\partial V)_T$ is zero. It has not been easy to establish experimentally that these two conditions define the same state of the fluid. The difficulties arise from the highly unusual mechanical, thermal and optical properties of the fluid in this region: the compressibility is infinite, and so the earth's gravitational field is large enough to produce large gradients of density in a vessel a few centimetres high; the infinity in C_p and, probably, in C_V make it hard to reach thermal equilibrium. Even slow changes of pressure are more nearly adiabatic than isothermal, and cyclic changes lead to hysteresis.

As the densities of the two phases approach each other, the dividing meniscus becomes first faint and then very hazy, and the measurement of the exact temperature of its disappearance needs great care. Observation of the system is made harder by a strong scattering of light—*the critical opalescence*—which can lead to complete opacity at the critical point.

All these effects make precise equilibrium measurements unusually difficult, and good agreement between critical constants measured in different ways is hard to achieve.

The critical temperature is the easiest of the three constants to measure. Kobe and Lynn, in an extensive review of critical constants in 1953, reported that this had been done for 220 substances. Most of these measurements were made by observing the temperature at which the meniscus vanished in a system maintained at an overall density approximately equal to the critical. If a sealed tube containing a liquid and its vapour is heated uniformly, then one of three things may happen. If the overall density is less than the critical, the meniscus falls as the liquid evaporates. The equation for the rate of change with temperature of the volume of either phase in a closed system follows directly from (2.91)

$$\frac{\mathrm{d}V^l}{\mathrm{d}T} = -\frac{\mathrm{d}V^g}{\mathrm{d}T} = \frac{m^l\alpha_\sigma^l + m^g\alpha_\sigma^g}{(1/v^l) - (1/v^g)} \qquad (3.60)$$

The coefficients of thermal expansion, α_σ^l and α_σ^g, are positive and negative, respectively, and so the right-hand side of this equation is negative if the overall density is low (m^l small). The volume of the liquid decreases until it has all evaporated, after which further heating produces a less rapid rise of pressure than that along the saturation curve.

The second possibility is that the density exceeds the critical (m^l large) when the meniscus rises on heating until no vapour remains. Further heating produces a rapid rise in pressure along a liquid isochore.

If, however, the density is close to the critical, then the meniscus will rise slowly until it is near the centre of the tube where it will become flat and faint and will eventually vanish at the critical temperature.

No great care is needed to load the tube exactly to the critical density for measurements of moderate precision (say, 0·05–0·1 K), for a slight error only causes the meniscus to vanish a little above or below the centre of the tube, at a height at which the local density is equal to the critical. However, for the best work (measurements to 0·01 K or better) the density must be within 1 per cent of the critical, the tube must be short and well-stirred, and the final heating must be carried out very slowly in an accurately controlled thermostat. Conversely, the lack of sensitivity to the loading density means that this method cannot be used for any but the roughest measurements of the critical volume.

If the tube is not sealed but open at its lower end to a reservoir of mercury, then the density may be altered at will and the pressure measured at the same time. The critical pressure may be measured with little more trouble than the temperature, as it is equally insensitive to small changes of density at this point. This was the apparatus used in the original work of Andrews[13] and later by Young[14]. It has not been changed significantly since.

The critical volume is the most difficult of the three constants to measure accurately. The method which is probably the best, and certainly the most commonly used, is to extrapolate the mean of the

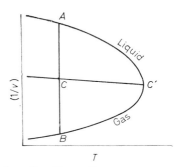

Figure 3.5. The law of rectilinear diameters. The line *CC'* is the locus of the mid-points of diameters such as *AB*

orthobaric liquid and gas densities up to the critical temperature. It was shown above, (3.16), that the classical description of the critical region requires that the critical density should be equal to the mean of the orthobaric densities at temperatures just below the critical.

This was shown to be so experimentally by Cailletet and Mathias[15] in 1886, and the statement is now incorporated in what is called the *law of rectilinear diameters*. They found that if they drew diameters (*AB, Figure 3.5*) across the graph of orthobaric densities as functions of the temperature, then the mid-points of these diameters, *C*, etc., lay on a straight line* which passed through the critical density, *C'*. They thought at first that this line was parallel to the temperature axis, but it is now known that it has a slight slope and a very small but usually negligible curvature. The fact that the law appears to hold even close to the critical point is evidence that the index β of the last Section is the same on both branches of the orthobaric curve.

* The term *rectilinear diameter* is now usually given to this locus of the mid-points and not to the lines *AB*, etc.

This empirical rule holds over the whole liquid range but is most commonly used to fit measurements of v^l and v^g from about 50 to 3 K below T^c, so as to obtain v^c by extrapolation. It reduces to (3.16) as T approaches T^c. *Figure 3.6* shows some accurate measurements[16] of the density of nitrous oxide which conform well to this law and from which a value of v^c may be determined that is probably correct to 1 per cent.

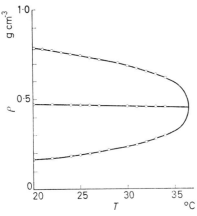

Figure 3.6. The orthobaric densities of nitrous oxide[16]. The straight line through the mean densities has the equation

$$(\rho^l + \rho^g)/2 = [0\cdot452 + 0\cdot00132(T^c - T)]\ \mathrm{g\ cm^{-3}}$$

The measurement of the critical constants by finding the point of zero slope and of inflection on the critical isotherm is much more difficult, and such attempts have in the past led to some notable disagreements. It is now very doubtful if any of the observations that led to different critical points, according to the criteria used to determine the position of the point, are correct descriptions of the true equilibrium behaviour of a real fluid in a negligible gravitational field. Schneider and his colleagues[17] have shown by measurements which are more accurate than most that true equilibrium can be achieved only by keeping the temperature constant to within $0\cdot001$ K and by continuously stirring the fluid for many hours. Under these conditions, the co-existence curves of xenon and sulphur hexafluoride have rounded tops. The effect of gravity was eliminated by studying the curve with the tube in both vertical and horizontal positions. The co-existence curves found in the former position are flatter than those in the latter and lie outside them. The latter are undoubtedly the more 'correct' curves, that is, they represent the behaviour of the fluids in a negligible gravitational field, since no density gradient can be set up in a tube of zero height.

Schneider was further able to show, by using [127]Xe as a tracer, that the density gradient in a vertical tube of xenon was no greater than that to be expected for the earth's gravitational field when a correct allowance was made for the very great compressibility in this region. This conclusion is confirmed by the optical measurements of density by Palmer[18] and by Lorentzen[19].

Habgood and Schneider[17] found also that the meniscus appeared and disappeared at the same temperature, and that above it the compressibility was always finite. The density at which it became infinite on the critical isotherm coincided, within experimental error, with the critical density determined from the law of rectilinear diameters.

The only particulars in which they did not verify the classical description were in the precise shapes of the co-existence curve and of the critical isotherm. They found that $(\partial^3 p/\partial V^3)_T$ and $(\partial^4 p/\partial V^4)_T$ probably vanished.

The heat capacity at constant volume of a fluid near its critical point has been measured in two ways. First, the residual heat capacity may be found from an accurate knowledge of the pressure as a function of volume and temperature. From (2.16) and (2.99)

$$c_v^* = -T \int_v^\infty (\partial^2 p/\partial T^2)_V \, dv \qquad (3.61)$$

The integrand is the curvature of the isochore, or the rate of change of γ_V with temperature. It is negative both in the gas phase and in the saturated liquid at low temperatures. It is always very small and never easy to measure.

Secondly, it is possible to measure the heat capacity directly for a fluid in a sealed metal container near the critical point, where γ_V is never more than about 2 bar K^{-1}. However, the heat capacity of the container is much greater than that of the fluid if it is strong enough to withstand the critical pressure.

A further difficulty with this second method is the maintenance of equilibrium. Very slow changes of temperature are apparently necessary if accurate results are to be obtained at the critical point. This is always feasible in a mechanical measurement but rarely in a thermal one.

Young[20] first showed that $(\partial^2 p/\partial T^2)_V$ changes sign at or near the critical point by some careful measurements of the isotherms of isopentane. *Figure 3.7* shows schematically the variation of p and of

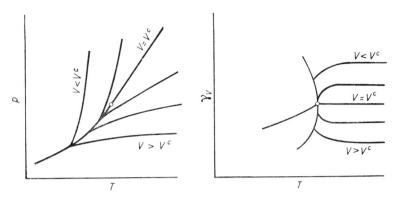

Figure 3.7. Sketches of the observed changes of p and γ_V with temperature very close to the critical point. The curvatures are exaggerated

γ_V with temperature near the critical point. Such a change of sign from negative to positive with increasing density denotes a maximum in C_V.

More recently, Michels, Bijl and Michels[21] have shown that carbon dioxide behaves similarly. At high densities there is a second change of sign for this gas where C_V passes through a minimum. The maximum in C_V decreases with increasing temperature but is still detectable in carbon dioxide 100 K above the critical temperature.

This method of observing the maximum in C_V is, however, not sufficiently precise for determining the coefficient α^+ of *Table 3.1*. The differentiation and subsequent integration needed in (3.61) appear inevitably to smooth out any true infinity into a high but smooth maximum.

The calorimetric measurement of C_V is made by heating the two-phase system through the critical boundary curve and into the homogeneous state beyond it. Below the critical point, the heat capacity is given by (2.92) which may be rewritten in terms of C_V by substitution from (2.28), (2.29) and (2.39)

$$C = m^l c_v^l + m^g c_v^g + m^l T v^l \beta_T^l (\gamma_V^l - \gamma_\sigma)^2 + m^g T v^g \beta_T^g (\gamma_V^g - \gamma_\sigma)^2 \tag{3.62}$$

$$= m^l c_v^l + m^g c_v^g + m^l T v^l (\alpha_\sigma^l)^2 / \beta_T^l + m^g T v^g (\alpha_\sigma^g)^2 / \beta_T^g \tag{3.63}$$

On proceeding to the limit of the critical point for a van der Waals fluid

$$(C_2 - C_1)_V^c = -3 T (p_{VT}^c)^2 / p_{3V}^c \tag{3.64}$$

where $(C_2 - C_1)_V$ denotes the excess heat capacity at constant volume of the two-phase system over the one-phase system. This excess must be positive as p_{3V}^c is negative. By neglecting the terms with c_v on the right-hand side of (3.63) and taking the limit for a fluid in which the zeros and infinities of the different functions are governed by the indices of *Table 3.1*, the inequality (3.56) is recovered.

Early measurements of C_V along the critical isochore confirmed that there was a sharp rise as the critical point was approached from above or below, and also showed that the heat capacity below the critical temperature exceeded that above for a given difference $|T - T^c|$. Michels and Strijland[22] showed that there was almost certainly an infinity below T^c, but their results, together with the study of the curvature of the isochores in the same laboratory[21], do not prove the existence of an infinity on the high-temperature side. It is the more recent work of Voronel' and his colleagues[23] on argon and oxygen and of Buckingham[23] on xenon which suggests most strongly that there are infinities in C_V both above and below T^c. They appear to be logarithmic or perhaps a little sharper.

If the heat capacity of the one-phase system is finite at the critical point, then it may be shown that the equilibrium speed of sound is non-zero. Eqn. (2.50) becomes indeterminate at the critical point, but by substituting for β_S in (2.46) from (2.52) the following expression is obtained

$$W^2 = \frac{v}{\mathcal{M}}\left[\frac{1}{\beta_T} + \frac{Tv\gamma_V^2}{c_v}\right] \tag{3.65}$$

where $\mathcal{M}$ is the molar mass. At the critical point this reduces to

$$W^2 = Tv^2(\gamma_\sigma^c)^2/\mathcal{M}c_v \tag{3.66}$$

where γ_σ^c is the limiting slope of the vapour-pressure curve. Similarly, the adiabatic compressibility is given by

$$\beta_S = c_v/Tv(\gamma_\sigma^c)^2 \tag{3.67}$$

Thus a maximum (or infinity) in the heat capacity will lead to a maximum (or infinity) in β_S and a minimum (or zero) in W at the critical point.

The experimental speeds of sound have all been measured at high frequencies (generally about 0·5 MHz) so that the wavelength can be kept small compared with the dimensions of the sample of fluid. Unfortunately the speed at such frequencies is not the equilibrium speed.

The evidence for this statement is of three kinds. First, the coefficient of absorption always shows a strong maximum in the critical region. Thus Schneider[24], working at 0·6 MHz, found a maximum at the critical point ten times that of the coefficient a few Kelvins above or below the critical temperature in either liquid or gas. Chynoweth and Schneider[25] similarly found a maximum in xenon near the critical point over the frequency range 0·25–1·25 MHz.

Secondly, there is some evidence of the dispersion of the speed, as is to be expected where there is heavy absorption. Thus Chynoweth and Schneider observed a 5 per cent increase in speed in xenon for a five-fold increase in frequency. However, Parbrook and Richardson[26] found no dispersion in ethylene or carbon dioxide for a four-fold increase from 0·5 to 2·0 MHz.

Thirdly, the observed minimum speeds are not zero, as is required by (3.65) if C_v has a true infinity at the critical point. Moreover, there is evidence that for carbon dioxide, the best studied fluid[26,27], the minimum speed on the critical isotherm is not at the critical density. This is understandable if, because of dispersion, the effective value of $(C_v)^{-1}$ is not zero. Differentiation of (3.65) with respect to v shows that the minimum is then near but not exactly at the critical point. However, this displacement is presumably a consequence of the dispersion and not an equilibrium property.

3.4 EXPERIMENTAL VALUES OF THE CRITICAL INDICES

The difficulties of measuring thermodynamic functions in the critical region were set out in the last Section. They make it hard to arrive at precise values of the critical indices of Section 3.2, and several recent reviews[10,28-32] have been devoted to assessing the experimental evidence. These are readily available, some are of great length, and their conclusions are virtually unanimous. There is, therefore, no need to repeat the assessment here, but instead it is sufficient to summarize their conclusions and to indicate the principal experimental sources on which they have relied.

The substances on which most of the best experimental work has been done are argon, xenon, oxygen and carbon dioxide, but there is, apparently, no need to distinguish between them since the evidence is that all substances have the same critical indices. Quantal fluids are possible exceptions[33], but the evidence is ambiguous[10].

We consider the indices in turn.

α^+ The measurements of Voronel' and his colleagues[23] on argon and oxygen and Buckingham[23] on xenon show that there is an infinity in C_v which is a little sharper than logarithmic, say $\alpha^+ = 0 \cdot 2 \pm 0 \cdot 1$.

α_1^- No information.

α_2^- The infinity on the critical isochore below T^c appears to be closer to logarithmic than that above[23], say, $\alpha_2^- = 0 \cdot 1 \pm 0 \cdot 1$.

β This is the easiest index to measure and was, for many years, taken to be $\frac{1}{3}$. The best work on argon[34], xenon[17] and carbon dioxide[21] suggests that is probably a little larger, say, $0 \cdot 35 \pm 0 \cdot 01$.

γ^+ This is significantly larger than unity for both xenon[17] and carbon dioxide[21]; say, $\gamma^+ = 1 \cdot 3 \pm 0 \cdot 2$.

γ_1^- This is very hard to measure and can be written only as $1 \cdot 0 \pm 0 \cdot 3$.

δ This index is certainly larger than its classical value of 3 and appears to be $4 \cdot 8 \pm 0 \cdot 4$. However, there is some doubt about this value, and the true accuracy may be less than the apparent precision. This is a consequence of the fact that the index is so large that the measurements on which it is based are necessarily well removed from the critical point.

θ This is hard to measure but is close to zero. If experimental vapour pressures are fitted to an empirical analytic equation, then it is commonly found that the deviation graph shows a sudden sweep upwards near the critical point. Recent accurate measurements of $\ln p_\sigma$ for benzene[35] were found to be best fitted with an expression containing the term $\ln (T^* - T)$ where T^* was only 8K above T^c. The need for such a term suggests that $\ln p_\sigma$ may not be an analytic function of $(T^c - T)$ at T^c, and that θ is small but positive.

Consider now the first inequality, (3.55). The left-hand side lies between $1 \cdot 9$ and $2 \cdot 3$, with the values and errors suggested above. That of the second, (3.56), lies between $1 \cdot 7$ and $2 \cdot 2$ and of the third, (3.58), between $-0 \cdot 4$ and $+0 \cdot 1$. The fourth, (3.59), is easily satisfied, since θ is of the order of α_2^- whilst β is much larger.

It is clear that the first three are probably satisfied by the best experimental results. It is possible that all three are equations not inequalities and, in particular, if (3.58) is an equation, then (3.55) and (3.56) are the same inequality or equation. This was proposed by Widom[12] and is supported by calculations on several models[10]. However, no rigorous proof for real systems has yet been found.

3.5 FLUCTUATIONS

It is tacitly assumed in the description of any system by classical thermodynamics that it is permissible to ascribe, simultaneously, exact values to all the intensive and extensive variables. This is an assumption which can be justified only by the methods of statistical mechanics, and no detailed examination of it is undertaken here. However, such examinations[36] have shown that for fluids of one phase, it is legitimate to assume that

(1) the pressure and temperature are sensibly constant in an assembly of fixed energy, volume and number of molecules (the micro-canonical ensemble)

(2) the pressure and energy are sensibly constant in an assembly of fixed volume, temperature and number of molecules (the canonical ensemble)

(3) the volume and heat content are sensibly constant in an assembly of fixed pressure, temperature and number of molecules (the constant-pressure ensemble).

In each case, the phrase 'sensibly constant' means that the property takes on a mean value and that the fluctuations about that mean are of the order of $(1/N)$, N being the number of molecules in the assembly.

These conclusions must be modified for a two-phase assembly of one component. The third no longer holds, as pressure and temperature do not define the state of the assembly. Both volume and heat content can vary, within limits, without changing the pressure or the temperature. The statistical expressions for the fluctuations are

$$\overline{(V - \bar{V})^2} = -kT(\partial V/\partial p)_T \qquad (3.68)$$

$$\overline{(H - \bar{H})^2} = kT^2 C_p \qquad (3.69)$$

where a bar denotes a time average for the assembly. The right-hand sides of these equations are of the order of $(1/N)$ for a one-phase assembly but are infinite if two phases are present and at the critical point. The fluctuations in energy in an assembly of constant volume and temperature are given by

$$\overline{(U - \bar{U})^2} = kT^2 C_V \qquad (3.70)$$

This is generally of the order of $(1/N)$ even in an assembly of two phases, but it is clear that the rapid rise in C_V near the critical point is related to increased fluctuations in the energy. C_V becomes infinite in the two-phase assembly just below the critical point, and the energy is here no longer sharply defined by fixing the volume and temperature.

Fluctuations in local density are equivalent to those in volume deduced from the properties of the constant-pressure ensemble. Let m be the fraction of a mole in a sub-volume v_S of an assembly

99

of 1 mole and of total volume v. The average value of m is (v_S/v). The relative fluctuation of m may be obtained from an expansion of the Helmholtz free energy of the sub-volume, at constant v_S and T, about $A(\bar{m})$ as a function of $(m - \bar{m})$. If all terms beyond the second are neglected, then

$$\frac{\overline{(m - \bar{m})^2}}{(\bar{m})^2} = \frac{-kT}{v_S^2(\partial p/\partial v_S)_T} = \frac{1}{\bar{m}N}\left(\frac{-RT}{v^2(\partial p/\partial v)_T}\right) \qquad (3.71)$$

The right-hand side is of the order of $(1/\bar{m}N)$ for an assembly of one phase, and so the fluctuations are of the order of $(1/N)$ if the sub-volume is macroscopic. At the critical point the expansion must be taken beyond the second and third terms (whose coefficients are proportional to $(\partial p/\partial v_S)_T$ and $(\partial^2 p/\partial v_S^2)_T$, respectively) to the fourth term, to give for a van der Waals fluid

$$\frac{\overline{(m - \bar{m})^2}}{(\bar{m})^2} = \frac{2\sqrt{6}\ \Gamma(\tfrac{3}{4})}{\Gamma(\tfrac{1}{4})}\left[\frac{-RT}{v^4(\partial^3 p/\partial v^3)_T}\right]\left(\frac{1}{\bar{m}N}\right)^{1/2} \qquad (3.72)$$

This expression is finite at the critical point, as it has been assumed that $(\partial^3 p/\partial v^3)_T$ is the first non-vanishing derivative. These fluctuations are of the order of $N^{1/2}$ greater than those of (3.71). If the first non-vanishing derivative of the pressure is of a higher order than three, then the fluctuations are even greater. It is this factor of $N^{1/2}$ (or greater) that is responsible for the strong opalescence of a fluid near its critical point, for the fluctuations in density over a distance comparable with the wavelength of visible light cause strong scattering of the light.

The theory of this scattering was first developed by Ornstein and Zernike[37]. They found that the intensity of the scattered light should change from the usual fourth-power dependence on the frequency found by Rayleigh for a dilute gas, to a second-power dependence at the critical point. However, their theory predicted that the total scattering, integrated over all angles, becomes infinite at the critical point. This infinity is a consequence of the fact that correlations of the density fluctuations between one sub-volume and another, which normally fall off very rapidly with their separation, now extend over the whole assembly. One cannot, under these conditions, deal with an infinitely large assembly but must carry integrations only to the boundary of a finite volume of fluid. Placzek[38] showed that the total scattering then remains finite but becomes a function of the total volume. Moreover, the theory is based closely on the concept of a van der Waals fluid in its need for analytic behaviour at the critical point. The same difficulties that beset thermodynamic theory at this point are, therefore, present also in scattering theory[5].

Precise experimental confirmation of this theory has never been obtained. The work of Drickamer and his colleagues[39] has shown that the scattering from a sample of ethane or ethylene maintained at the critical density follows the fourth-power law when several kelvins above the critical point, and that the dependence on frequency becomes less as the critical temperature is approached. However, near the critical point they found that the intensity of the scattered light decreased although the opacity increased. This is undoubtedly due to multiple scattering. More recent work[31,40,41] has confirmed the classical theory for fluids quite near to their critical points, and the advent of lasers allows a greater precision than heretofore which will probably be exploited more fully in the years to come.

3.6 Conclusions

The following are the principal conclusions that have been drawn in this Chapter from the experimental results and thermodynamic theory:

(*1*) The critical point is correctly described either as the state in which the orthobaric liquid and gas become identical, and therefore in which the visible meniscus between them vanishes, or as the homogeneous state in which the compressibility is infinite. There is no good experimental evidence that the compressibility is infinite in any homogeneous state of the system other than the point of coincidence of liquid and gaseous states.

(*2*) The experimental values of the critical indices of *Table 3.1* are irreconcilable with the Helmholtz free energy being an analytic function of V and T at the critical point.

(*3*) The inequalities between these indices are satisfied by the experimental results and it is possible, or even probable, that they are really equations.

(*4*) The experimental speed of sound shows a sharp minimum near the critical point which is associated with the infinity in C_v. This speed is, however, not related directly to the static adiabatic compressibility because of strong dispersion and absorption.

(*5*) The infinity in C_v and the strong opalescence are in qualitative agreement with the theory of fluctuations, but quantitative tests of the agreement are difficult. The use of lasers should greatly increase the precision of work on the scattering of light.

THE CRITICAL STATE

REFERENCES

[1] Temperley, H. N. V. *Changes of State*, p. 41 *et seq.*, London (Cleaver-Hume) 1956; Fisher, M. E. *Proceedings of Centennial Conference on Phase Transformations* (Univ. of Kentucky, 1965); *Physics* 3 (1967) 255; Langer, J. S. *Annls Phys.* 41 (1967) 1

[2] van der Waals, J. D. *Die Kontinuität des gasförmigen und flüssigen Zustandes* (2nd Ed.) Vol. 1 (Single-Component Systems) 1899; Vol. 2 (Binary Mixtures) 1900, Leipzig (Barth); Engl. trans. of 1st Ed. of Vol. 1 by Threlfall, R. and Adair, J. F. in *Physical Memoirs*, Vol. 1, Part 3, London (Phys. Soc.) 1890

[3(a)] Wilson, E. B. in *Commentary on the Scientific Writings of J. Willard Gibbs* (ed. Donnan, F. G. and Haas, A.), Vol. 1, p. 51, New Haven (Yale) 1936; [b] Onnes, H. K. and Happel, H. *Communs phys. Lab. Univ. Leiden* No. 86 (1903); [c] Wood, S. E. *J. phys. Chem.* 66 (1962) 600

[4(a)] Griffiths, R. B. *J. chem. Phys.* 43 (1965) 1958; [b] Rushbrooke, G. S. 39 (1963) 842; 43 (1965) 3439; Rushbrooke, G. S. and Muse, R. A., private communication

[5] Fisher, M. E. *J. math. Phys.* 5 (1964) 944

[6] Liberman, D. A. *J. chem. Phys.* 44 (1966) 419

[7] Fisher, M. E. *Lectures on Theoretical Physics*, Vol. VII C (University of Colorado, 1965)

[8] Tisza, L. *Generalized Thermodynamics.* Cambridge, Mass. (M.I.T. Press) 1966

[9] Green, M. S. and Sengers, J. V. (ed.) *Critical Phenomena, Misc. Publs Bur. Stand.* No. 273 (1966)

[10] Kadanoff, L. P., Götze, W., Hamblen, D., Hecht, R., Lewis, E. A. S., Palciauskas, V. V., Rayl, M. and Swift, J. *Rev. mod. Phys.* 39 (1967) 395

[11] Griffiths, R. B. *Phys. Rev.* 158 (1967) 176; Green, M. S., Vicentini-Missoni, M. and Levelt Sengers, J. M. H. *Phys. Rev. Lett.* 18 (1967) 1113; Levelt Sengers, J. M. H. and Vicentini-Missoni, M. *Symposium on Thermophysical Properties.* p. 79, New York (Am. Soc. mech. Engrs) 1968

[12] Widom, B. *J. chem. Phys.* 43 (1965) 3898

[13] Andrews, T. *Phil. Trans.* 159 (1869) 575

[14] Young, S. *Proc. R. Ir. Acad.* 12 (1909–10) 374

[15] Cailletet, L. and Mathias, E. *C. r. hebd. Séanc. Acad. Sci.*, Paris 102 (1886) 1202; 104 (1887) 1563

[16] Cook, D. *Trans. Faraday Soc.* 49 (1953) 716

[17] Schneider, W. G. *Changements de Phases*, p. 69, Paris (Soc. chim. Phys.) 1952; Atack, D. and Schneider, W. G. *J. phys. Chem.* 54 (1950) 1323; 55 (1951) 532; MacCormack, K. E. and Schneider, W. G. *Can. J. Chem.* 29 (1951) 699; Weinberger, M. A. and Schneider, W. G. 30 (1952) 422, 847; Habgood, H. W. and Schneider, W. G. 32 (1954) 98, 164; Schneider, W. G. and Habgood, H. W. *J. chem. Phys.* 21 (1953) 2080

[18] Palmer, H. B. *J. chem. Phys.* 22 (1954) 625

[19] Lorentzen, H. L. *Acta chem. scand.* 7 (1953) 1335; 9 (1955) 1724

REFERENCES

[20] Young, S. *Proc. phys. Soc. Lond.* 13 (1895) 602
[21] Michels, A., with Bijl, A. and Michels, C. *Proc. R. Soc.* A160 (1937) 376; with Blaisse, B. and Michels, C. *ibid.* 358; with DE Groot, S. R. *Appl. scient. Res.* A1 (1949) 94
[22] Michels, A. and Strijland, J. *Physica* 18 (1952) 613
[23] Bagatskii, M. I., Voronel', A. V. and Gusak, V. G. *Soviet Phys. JETP* 16 (1963) 517; Voronel', A. V., Chashkin, Y. R., Popov, V. A. and Simkin. V. G. 18 (1964) 568; Voronel', A. V., Chashkin, Y. R. and Snigirev, V. G. 21 (1965) 653; Chashkin, Y. R., Gorbunova, V. G. and Voronel', A. V. 22 (1966) 304; Voronel', A. V. and Chashkin, Y. R. 24 (1967) 263; Edwards, C., Lipa, J. A. and Buckingham, M. J. *Phys. Rev. Lett.* 20 (1968) 496
[24] Schneider, W. G. *Can. J. Chem.* 29 (1951) 243 (see Chynoweth, A. G. and Schneider, W. G. *J. chem. Phys.* 19 (1951) 1566 for corrections)
[25] Chynoweth, A. G. and Schneider, W. G. *J. chem. Phys.* 20 (1952) 1777
[26] Parbrook, H. D. and Richardson, E. G. *Proc. phys. Soc. Lond.* B65 (1952) 437
[27] Herget, C. M. *J. chem. Phys.* 8 (1940) 537; Anderson, N. S. and Delsasso, L. P. *J. acoust. Soc. Am.* 23 (1951) 423; Teilsch, H. and Tanneberger, H. Z. *Phys.* 137 (1954) 256
[28] Widom, B. and Rice, O. K. *J. chem. Phys.* 23 (1955) 1250
[29] Fisher, M. E. *Phys. Rev.* 136 (1964) A1599
[30] Rowlinson, J. S., ref. 9, p. 9
[31] Egelstaff, P. A. and Ring, J. W. in *Physics of Simple Liquids* (ed. Temperley, H. N. V., Rowlinson, J. S. and Rushbrooke, G. S.), Amsterdam (North-Holland) 1968
[32] Fisher, M. E. *Rep. Prog. Phys.* 30 (1967) 615; Heller, P. *ibid.* 731
[33] Fisher, M. E. *Phys. Rev. Lett.* 16 (1966) 11
[34] Michels, A., Levelt, J. M., with DE Graaff, W. *Physica* 24 (1958) 659; with Wolkers, G. J. *ibid.* 769
[35] Ambrose, D., Broderick, B. E. and Townsend, R. *J. chem. Soc.* A (1967) 633
[36] Tolman, R. C. *Principles of Statistical Mechanics*, p. 629–649, Oxford University Press, 1938; Hill, T. L., *Statistical Mechanics*, Ch. 4, New York (McGraw-Hill) 1956; Fisher, I. Z., *Statistical Theory of Liquids* (trans. Switz, T. M.), pp. 51–54, 77–93, Chicago Univ. Press, 1964
[37] Ornstein, L. F. and Zernike, F. *Sect. Sci. K. ned. Akad. Wet.* 17 (1914–15) 793; *Phys. Z.* 19 (1918) 134; 27 (1926) 671
[38] Placzek, G. *Phys. Z.* 31 (1930) 1052
[39] Cataldi, H. A. and Drickamer, H. G. *J. chem. Phys.* 18 (1950) 650; Babb, A. L. and Drickamer, H. G. *ibid.* 655; Blosser, L. G. and Drickamer, H. G. 19 (1951) 1244
[40] Ford, N. C. and Benedek, G. B. *Phys. Rev. Lett.* 15 (1965) 649; ref. 9, p. 150
[41] McIntyre, D. and Sengers, J. V. in ref. 31

4

MIXTURES OF SIMPLE LIQUIDS

4.1 INTRODUCTION

There are two principal reasons for the great amount of experimental and theoretical work which has been done on the properties of liquid mixtures. The first is that they provide one way of studying the physical forces acting between two molecules of different species. Liquid mixtures are not, however, the most direct source of such information, owing to the difficulties of the interpretation of the properties of liquids in terms of the intermolecular forces. The equilibrium and, in some cases, the transport properties of dilute gases are our principal source of this information, but the use of liquid mixtures for this purpose is now becoming more important with the advance of their theoretical study. The use of liquid mixtures for the study of strong specific forces between different molecules is of much longer standing.

There is now less emphasis than hitherto on attempts to explain the properties of mixtures solely from a knowledge of those of the pure components[1]. Such attempts rest upon the fallacy that the forces $(\alpha-\beta)$ between two molecules of species α and β are always determinable from the strengths of the forces $(\alpha-\alpha)$ and $(\beta-\beta)$. If it were true that the $(\alpha-\beta)$ forces were always some 'average' of the $(\alpha-\alpha)$ and $(\beta-\beta)$ forces, then the properties of a binary mixture would be predictable, in principle, solely from a knowledge of those of the two pure components.

However, such averaging is not universally valid. It is true that for very simple substances and for the prediction of relatively crude properties there are suitable averages of the intermolecular forces. These are considered further in Chapter 7, on intermolecular forces, and in Chapter 9, on the statistical theory of mixtures. However, such averaging is unsatisfactory for many classes of substances and inadequate for the detailed interpretation even of the simplest mixtures. One should rather take the observed properties of a binary mixture as an experimental source of information about the $(\alpha-\beta)$ forces.

The possibilities of *a priori* prediction are greater in a multicomponent system. The energy of an array of, say, three molecules α, β and γ is approximately given by the sum of the energies of the three pairs $(\alpha-\beta)$, $(\beta-\gamma)$ and $(\gamma-\alpha)$ considered separately. Any small departure of the total energy from this sum (see Chapter 7) can probably be represented adequately by an average of the corresponding departures in the pure components. It should be possible, therefore, to predict the properties of a multi-component mixture from a knowledge of those of the pure substances and of all the binary mixtures. However, even these predictions can be made only by appealing to our knowledge of the intermolecular forces and so are outside the scope of classical thermodynamics. They are discussed briefly in Section 9.7.

The second reason for the study of mixtures is the appearance of new phenomena which are not present in pure substances. The most interesting of these are new types of phase equilibrium which arise from the extra degrees of freedom introduced by the possibility of varying the proportions of the components. The number of degrees of freedom may be calculated from the phase rule of Gibbs. A system of one component and one phase has two degrees of freedom. That is, the two intensive properties, pressure and temperature, may both be changed (within limits) without causing any new phase to appear. A two-component system of one phase has three degrees of freedom, for the composition may also be freely varied. A one-component system of two phases has one degree of freedom. If the temperature is fixed arbitrarily, then there is only one value of the pressure for which the two phases can exist together in equilibrium.

A graph of the co-existing pressures and temperatures defines a vapour-pressure or other similar phase-boundary curve. There is, in general, no such unique curve for a mixture, since the pressure is a function of composition as well as of temperature. Azeotropes are exceptions to this statement and are discussed in Chapter 6.

Three co-existing fluid phases are not found in one-component systems, except for the unusual behaviour of liquid helium at its λ-point, and of those substances that form liquid crystals. They are common in binary fluid mixtures of unlike substances, and it is the co-existence and the critical points of such systems that have been responsible for much of the interest in mixtures. These three-phase systems are described in Chapters 5 and 6.

The mixtures of simple substances discussed in this Chapter form one homogeneous liquid phase that can co-exist with a homogeneous gas phase. The substances come from the first three of the five classes set out in Chapter 1.

4.2 PARTIAL MOLAR QUANTITIES

The composition of a mixture may be expressed in several ways, some of which are symmetrical in the components and some of which are not. The only system used here is a symmetrical one in which the number of moles of each component is denoted m_1, m_2, etc., and in which the relative amount of each component is described by its mole fraction*, x_1, x_2, etc., where

$$x_1 = m_1 / \sum_\alpha m_\alpha \qquad (\alpha = 1, 2, 3, \ldots) \qquad (4.1)$$

If V is the volume of a binary mixture of m_1 moles of component 1 and m_2 of component 2, it is interesting to enquire how much of this volume is to be ascribed to the first and how much to the second component. For, in general, V is not equal to the sum of the volumes occupied by the separate components at the same pressure and temperature before mixing. It is, however, possible in principle to measure the increase in volume (δV) on adding an infinitesimal amount (δm_1) at constant pressure and temperature to a large amount of mixture of known composition. The ratio of (δV) to (δm_1) is the *partial molar volume* of species 1 in this mixture, here denoted v_1. More formally

$$v_1 = (\partial V / \partial m_1)_{m_2, p, T} \qquad (4.2)$$

Partial molar quantities are intensive properties which depend only on the pressure, temperature and composition of the mixture. Thus if $(m_1 + m_2)$ moles of liquid are formed by repeatedly adding small quantities (δm_1) and (δm_2) of the two substances, with the ratio $(\delta m_1 / \delta m_2)$ a constant, then the total volume is given by

$$V = m_1 v_1 + m_2 v_2 \qquad (4.3)$$

This follows at once from the fact that v_1 and v_1 are functions only of the relative composition of the mixture and not of its total amount. It is seen, therefore, that the partial molar properties of a system provide an answer to the question of how much of an extensive property, in this case the volume, is to be ascribed to each component.

General differentiation of (4.3) for a small change of V at constant pressure and temperature gives

$$dV = m_1 \, dv_1 + m_2 \, dv_2 + v_1 \, dm_1 + v_2 \, dm_2 \qquad (4.4)$$

whence, from (4.2),

$$m_1 \, dv_1 + m_2 \, dv_2 = 0 \qquad \text{(const. } p, \ T) \qquad (4.5)$$

This is an important restriction on the simultaneous change of v_1 and v_2 in a mixture and is an example of a *Gibbs–Duhem equation*.

* See Notation, p. xiv.

These equations may be generalized for any extensive property R, and for any number of components

$$r_1 = (\partial R/\partial m_1)_{m',p,T} \tag{4.6}$$

$$R = \sum_\alpha m_\alpha r_\alpha \tag{4.7}$$

$$0 = \sum_\alpha m_\alpha \, dr_\alpha \qquad \text{(Gibbs–Duhem equation)} \tag{4.8}$$

where the prime indicates all components but the one with respect to which the differentiation is performed. $(\partial G/\partial m_1)_{m',p,T}$ is the chemical potential of component 1 in the mixture, and the potentials satisfy the most important form of the Gibbs–Duhem equation

$$\sum_\alpha m_\alpha \, d\mu_\alpha = 0 \qquad \text{(const. } p, \, T) \tag{4.9}$$

It is usual to measure partial molar quantities not by means of the hypothetical experiment described at the beginning of this Section but from a knowledge of the molar quantity r as a function of mole fraction x, where

$$r = R/m = \sum_\alpha x_\alpha r_\alpha \tag{4.10}$$

In order to do this for a binary mixture, it is necessary to consider the relation between the quantities, $(\partial R/\partial m_1)_{m_2,p,T}$ and $(\partial r/\partial x_1)_{p,T}$. The first is the rate of change of the extensive quantity R with m_1 at constant m_2, that is, it is the partial molar quantity. The second is the change of the mean molar quantity r with the mole fraction x_1. This differentiation is not performed at constant m_2 or at constant x_2, since it is clear that the sum of dx_1 and dx_2 must be zero in a binary mixture. By differentiation of (4.10)

$$\left(\frac{\partial r}{\partial x_1}\right) = \frac{\partial}{\partial x_1}[x_1 r_1 + (1 - x_1)r_2] \tag{4.11}$$

$$= r_1 - r_2 + x_1\left(\frac{\partial r_1}{\partial x_1}\right) + x_2\left(\frac{\partial r_2}{\partial x_1}\right) \tag{4.12}$$

The sum of the last two terms of (4.12) is zero, as is seen by multiplying by m, the total number of moles, to obtain the usual form of the Gibbs–Duhem equation, (4.8). Therefore

$$(\partial r/\partial x_1) = -(\partial r/\partial x_2) = r_1 - r_2 \tag{4.13}$$

and, from (4.10)

$$r_1 = r - x_2(\partial r/\partial x_2) \tag{4.14}$$

$$r_2 = r - x_1(\partial r/\partial x_1) \tag{4.15}$$

These are the required relations between the partial molar quantities and the derivatives $(\partial r/\partial x)$.

Byers Brown[2] has extended these equations to multi-component mixtures. From (4.10)

$$\left(\frac{\partial r}{\partial m_\alpha}\right)_{m'} = \frac{r_\alpha}{m} - \frac{R}{m^2} = \frac{r_\alpha - r}{m} \tag{4.16}$$

or

$$r_\alpha = r + m(\partial r/\partial m_\alpha)_{m'} \tag{4.17}$$

where the subscript m' indicates that all numbers of moles except m_α are to be kept constant. In a mixture of q components, r is a function of the mole fractions $x_1, x_2, \ldots x_q$, but only $(q-1)$ of these are independent. Let these be $x_2, \ldots x_q$, and let r be a function of these independent variables

$$\left(\frac{\partial r}{\partial m_1}\right)_{m'} = \sum_{\beta=2}^{q}\left(\frac{\partial r}{\partial x_\beta}\right)\left(\frac{\partial x_\beta}{\partial m_1}\right)_{m'} = -\frac{1}{m}\sum_{\beta=2}^{q} x_\beta\left(\frac{\partial r}{\partial x_\beta}\right) \tag{4.18}$$

and, for α equal to $2, 3 \ldots q$,

$$\left(\frac{\partial r}{\partial m_\alpha}\right)_{m'} = \left(\frac{\partial r}{\partial x_\alpha}\right)\left(\frac{\partial x_\alpha}{\partial m_\alpha}\right)_{m'} + \sum_{\beta=2}^{q}{}'\left(\frac{\partial r}{\partial x_\beta}\right)\left(\frac{\partial x_\beta}{\partial m_\alpha}\right) \tag{4.19}$$

$$= \left(\frac{1-x_\alpha}{m}\right)\left(\frac{\partial r}{\partial x_\alpha}\right) - \frac{1}{m}\sum_{\beta=2}^{q}{}' x_\beta\left(\frac{\partial r}{\partial x_\beta}\right) \tag{4.20}$$

$$= \frac{1}{m}\left[\left(\frac{\partial r}{\partial x_\alpha}\right) - \sum_{\beta=2}^{q} x_\beta\left(\frac{\partial r}{\partial x_\beta}\right)\right] \tag{4.21}$$

where the prime on a summation sign shows that the term with β equal to α is to be omitted. Hence, from (4.17)

$$r_1 = r - \sum_{\beta=2}^{q} x_\beta\left(\frac{\partial r}{\partial x_\beta}\right) \tag{4.22}$$

$$r_\alpha = r + \left(\frac{\partial r}{\partial x_\alpha}\right) - \sum_{\beta=2}^{q} x_\beta\left(\frac{\partial r}{\partial x_\beta}\right) \qquad (\alpha = 2, \ldots q) \tag{4.23}$$

In differentiation with respect to any mole fraction, say x_α, all the others except x_1 and x_α are to be kept constant, as they are all independent variables. These equations are, therefore, the extension of (4.14) and (4.15) to multi-component mixtures. However, they are not the neatest form of the equations, as it is necessary to treat separately the dependent mole fraction, which was chosen here to be x_1. It is more convenient to use a differential operator (D/Dx_α) to denote differentiation with respect to x_α in which all other mole fractions are treated as independent variables and so are held constant. With this convention

$$\left(\frac{\partial r}{\partial x_\alpha}\right) = \left(\frac{Dr}{Dx_\alpha}\right) + \left(\frac{Dr}{Dx_1}\right)\left(\frac{Dx_1}{Dx_\alpha}\right)$$

$$= \left(\frac{Dr}{Dx_\alpha}\right) - \left(\frac{Dr}{Dx_1}\right) \qquad (\alpha = 2, \ldots q) \qquad (4.24)$$

since

$$\left(\frac{Dx_1}{Dx_\alpha}\right) = \frac{D}{Dx_\alpha}\left(1 - \sum_{\beta=2}^{q} x_\beta\right) = -1 \qquad (4.25)$$

Substitution in (4.22) and (4.23) gives

$$r_1 = r - \sum_{\beta=2}^{q} x_\beta\left(\frac{Dr}{Dx_\beta}\right) + (1 - x_1)\left(\frac{Dr}{Dx_1}\right) \qquad (4.26)$$

$$r_\alpha = r + \left(\frac{Dr}{Dx_\alpha}\right) - \sum_{\beta=2}^{q} x_\beta\left(\frac{Dr}{Dx_\beta}\right) - x_1\left(\frac{Dr}{Dx_1}\right)$$

$$(\alpha = 2, \ldots q) \qquad (4.27)$$

These equations may be written in a common and more simple form

$$r_\alpha = r + \left(\frac{Dr}{Dx_\alpha}\right) - \sum_{\beta=1}^{q} x_\beta\left(\frac{Dr}{Dx_\beta}\right) \qquad (\alpha = 1, \ldots q) \qquad (4.28)$$

This equation satisfies (4.7) and is the most convenient way of finding r_α in a multi-component system where r is known as a function of the mole fractions. It is so used in Chapter 9. The differentiation is most simply performed if r is written as a symmetrical function of the mole fractions, but the equation is equally valid for any of the many alternative ways of expressing r as a function of either q or $(q - 1)$ variables.

Eqn. (4.14) and (4.15) are the basis of the commonly used *method of intercepts* for calculating partial molar quantities in binary mixtures. *Figure 4.1* shows a typical graph of a mean molar quantity (say, v, h or c_p) as a function of composition. It is clear from these equations that the intercepts of the tangent to the curve at any point, x_1, give the values of r_1 and r_2 for that composition. However, it is difficult to draw accurately the tangent to an experimental curve, and so this is not a recommended way of obtaining r_1 and r_2. It is usually better to start by defining an apparent molar quantity by

$$r_1^{app} = (r - x_2 r_2^0)/x_1 \qquad (4.29)$$

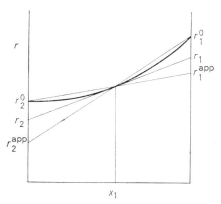

Figure 4.1. A mean molar quantity, r, as a function of the mole fraction, x_1. The curve from r_1^0 to r_2^0 is the value of r. A tangent to this curve at $r(x_1)$ has intercepts of $r_1(x_1)$ and $r_2(x_1)$ (4.14 and 4.15), and the chords from $r(x_1)$ to r_1^0 and r_2^0 have intercepts of r_2^{app} and r_1^{app}, respectively (4.29–4.31)

where r_2^0 is the value in pure component 2. By differentiation of this equation

$$r_1 = r_1^0 - x_2^2(\partial r_2^{app}/\partial x_2) \qquad (4.30)$$

$$r_2 = r_2^0 - x_1^2(\partial r_1^{app}/\partial x_1) \qquad (4.31)$$

If r is close to a linear function of x, then the second terms in this equation are much smaller than the first, and even if r is not linear, it often happens that $(\partial r_1^{app}/\partial x_1)$ is almost independent of x_1. Errors in determining slopes are therefore less serious in this method than in the method of intercepts. For example, *Figure 4.2* shows the

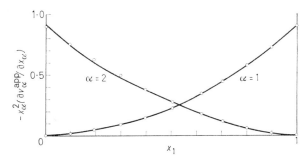

Figure 4.2. The function $[-x_\alpha^2 (\partial v_\alpha^{app}/\partial x_\alpha)_{p,T}]$ in $cm^3\ mol^{-1}$ for benzene + ethylene dichloride at $20°C$, with $\alpha = 1$, benzene; $\alpha = 2$, ethylene dichloride (calculated from Coulson, Hales and Herington[3])

110

values of the second terms in (4.30) and (4.31) for the molar volume of the system benzene + ethylene dichloride at 20°C. They have been calculated from the density measurements of Coulson, Hales and Herington[3]. These terms may be combined with v_1^0 and v_2^0 to give values of v_1 and v_2 that are probably correct to 0·05 cm³ mol⁻¹ (1 part in 2000) even at infinite dilution.

Young and Vogel[4] give a useful summary of other ways of manipulating eqn. (4.14) and (4.15) in order to obtain accurate values of r_1 and r_2 from experimental results.

The relations between different partial molar quantities are the same as those between molar quantities of a pure substance. Thus

$$\left(\frac{\partial \mu_\alpha}{\partial p}\right)_{T,x} = v_\alpha, \quad \left(\frac{\partial \mu_\alpha}{\partial T}\right)_{p,x} = -s_\alpha, \quad \left(\frac{\partial h_\alpha}{\partial T}\right)_{p,x} = (c_p)_\alpha, \quad \text{etc.} \quad (4.32)$$

4.3 THE IDEAL MIXTURE*

The ideal mixture is a hypothetical one whose properties are introduced into the thermodynamic description of real mixtures as convenient standards of normal behaviour. The term is not restricted to mixtures of two (or more) liquids but may be used, for example, for solutions of both solids and gases in liquids. In almost every case there is a certain lack of precision about the definition of an ideal mixture, since it necessarily makes use of the properties of phases, solid, liquid or gas, extrapolated across phase boundaries into regions of pressure and temperature where they do not exist. Fortunately this imprecision is least serious for purely liquid mixtures with which this book is concerned†, and becomes negligible at low vapour pressures.

There are several definitions of an ideal liquid mixture; one of the most convenient is that it is a mixture in which the chemical potentials of all components are given by the equations

$$\mu_\alpha(p, T, x) = \mu_\alpha^0(p, T) + RT \ln x_\alpha \qquad (\alpha = 1, \ldots q) \quad (4.33)$$

where $\mu_\alpha^0(p, T)$ is the potential of pure component α at the same pressure and temperature as the mixture being studied. These equations are to be understood to hold over non-zero ranges of pressure and temperature about (p, T).

---

* The term *perfect mixture* is sometimes used for what is here called an *ideal mixture*. The word *perfect* is used in this book only to describe a gas which has the equation of state, $pv = RT$.

† For the definition and discussion of ideal solutions of solids and gases in liquids, see ref. 5.

This definition is unexceptionable for a gas mixture and, indeed, a mixture of perfect gases is the simplest example of an ideal mixture[6]. However, it is not entirely satisfactory for a liquid mixture on its saturation curve. The vapour pressure of a mixture is usually lower than that of one or more of its components at the same temperature. Some of the $\mu_\alpha^0(p, T)$ must therefore refer to liquid states extrapolated to pressures below their vapour pressures, and so have no precise physical meaning. Fortunately the change of μ^0 with pressure is small for liquids near their triple points, since their molar volumes are much smaller than those of a perfect gas at the same pressure and temperature. The change is given by

$$\frac{1}{RT}\left(\frac{\partial \mu_\alpha^0}{\partial \ln p}\right) = \frac{pv_\alpha^0}{RT} \tag{4.34}$$

Thus at low vapour pressures the extrapolations needed to obtain μ_α^0 are either negligible or at least small enough to be calculated with confidence. The use of the ideal mixture as a standard is therefore restricted to low vapour pressures, that is, below about 3 bar. Most precise work has been carried out at and below the normal boiling points and so may be compared with the ideal mixture, but it is unfortunate that there is no simple standard of normal behaviour at higher vapour pressures, and particularly for mixtures near the gas–liquid critical point.

The consequences of (4.33) are readily set out. In an ideal mixture

$$G = \sum_\alpha m_\alpha \mu_\alpha^0 + RT \sum_\alpha m_\alpha \ln x_\alpha \tag{4.35}$$

$$H = \sum_\alpha m_\alpha h_\alpha^0 \tag{4.36}$$

$$S = \sum_\alpha m_\alpha s_\alpha^0 - R \sum_\alpha m_\alpha \ln x_\alpha \tag{4.37}$$

$$V = \sum_\alpha m_\alpha v_\alpha^0 \tag{4.38}$$

$$C_p = \sum_\alpha m_\alpha (c_p)_\alpha^0 \tag{4.39}$$

where μ_α^0, h_α^0, s_α^0, v_α^0 and $(c_p)_\alpha^0$ are the molar properties of the pure components at the same pressure and temperature as those of the mixture.

It is seen that G and S are not linear functions of the composition. The sums of the logarithmic terms in (4.35) and (4.37) are, respectively, the ideal free energy and entropy of mixing. A thermodynamic function of mixing is the difference between the value of any function in the mixture and the sum of those for the same amount of unmixed components at the same pressure and temperature. Such functions are denoted here G^m, H^m, etc. The ideal free energy of mixing is always negative and the ideal entropy of mixing is always positive. Thus the formation of an ideal mixture from its components is a spontaneous irreversible process, whether carried out isothermally or adiabatically.

It is sometimes useful to discuss a mixture formed from its components at constant temperature and total volume. Functions of mixing in such circumstances are distinguished from those above,

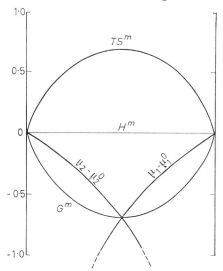

Figure 4.3. The ideal mixture. The free energy, heat and entropy of mixing and the chemical potentials, as functions of x_1. All are in units of RT

at constant pressure, by using V and p as subscripts[7]. V_p^m is zero in an ideal mixture and so it follows that

$$G_p^m = G_V^m = A_p^m = A_V^m; \qquad S_p^m = S_V^m \qquad (4.40)$$

$$H_p^m = H_V^m = U_p^m = U_V^m = 0 \qquad \text{etc.} \qquad (4.41)$$

Figure 4.3 shows graphs of G^m, H^m and S^m for a binary ideal mixture.

An excess thermodynamic function is defined as the difference between the value of a function in a given mixture and that in an ideal mixture of the same composition. It is denoted here by G^E, etc., but is not related to any observable process as is G^m, etc.

The most interesting property of an ideal mixture is the isothermal change with composition of its vapour pressure. An expression for this change may be derived by equating the chemical potentials of each component in gas and liquid phases. Consider a binary mixture:

Liquid

$$\mu_1(\text{liq}, p, x_1) = \mu_1^0(\text{liq}, p^*) + RT \ln x_1 + (p - p^*)v_1^0 \quad (4.42)$$

$$\mu_2(\text{liq}, p, x_2) = \mu_2^0(\text{liq}, p^*) + RT \ln x_2 + (p - p^*)v_2^0 \quad (4.43)$$

where p^* is a small but arbitrary pressure.

Gas[6]

$$\mu_1(\text{gas}, p, y_1) = \mu_1^0(\text{gas}, p^*) + RT \ln (py_1/p^*) \\ + (p - p^*)B_{11} + 2p(\delta B)_{12}\, y_2^2 \quad (4.44)$$

$$\mu_2(\text{gas}, p, y_2) = \mu_2^0(\text{gas}, p^*) + RT \ln (py_2/p^*) \\ + (p - p^*)B_{22} + 2p(\delta B)_{12}\, y_1^2 \quad (4.45)$$

where y denotes a mole fraction in the gas phase, and where B_{11}, B_{12} and B_{22} are the second virial coefficients for the interactions of pairs of molecules in collisions 1–1, 1–2, and 2–2, respectively. The difference $(\delta B)_{12}$ is given by

$$(\delta B)_{12} = B_{12} - \tfrac{1}{2}B_{11} - \tfrac{1}{2}B_{22} \quad (4.46)$$

Higher terms in the virial expansions for the potentials in the gas phase may be neglected at all pressures at which the concept of an ideal mixture is useful. The arbitrary pressure p^* is now set equal to p_1^0, the vapour pressure of pure 1, in (4.42) and (4.44), and equal to p_2^0 in (4.43) and (4.45). Equating μ_1 and μ_2 in each phase gives

$$\mu_1^0(\text{liq}, p_1^0) + RT \ln x_1 + (p - p_1^0)v_1^0 = \mu_1^0(\text{gas}, p_1^0) \\ + RT \ln (py_1/p_1^0) + (p - p_1^0)B_{11} + 2p(\delta B)_{12}\, y_2^2 \quad (4.47)$$

$$\mu_2^0(\text{liq}, p_2^0) + RT \ln x_2 + (p - p_2^0)v_2^0 = \mu_2^0(\text{gas}, p_2^0) \\ + RT \ln (py_2/p_2^0) + (p - p_2^0)B_{22} + 2p(\delta B)_{12}\, y_1^2 \quad (4.48)$$

Now

$$\mu_1^0(\text{liq}, p_1^0) = \mu_1^0(\text{gas}, p_1^0); \quad \mu_2^0(\text{liq}, p_2^0) = \mu_2^0(\text{gas}, p_2^0) \quad (4.49)$$

since p_1^0 and p_2^0 are the vapour pressures of the pure components. Hence

$$RT \ln p =$$

$$RT \ln (x_1 p_1^0/y_1) + (p - p_1^0)(v_1^0 - B_{11}) - 2p(\delta B)_{12}\, y_2^2 \quad (4.50)$$

$$= RT \ln (x_2 p_2^0/y_2) + (p - p_2^0)(v_2^0 - B_{22}) - 2p(\delta B)_{12}\, y_1^2 \quad (4.51)$$

By combining these equations and substituting $(1 - y_1)$ for y_2 in the logarithmic term of (4.51)

$$p = x_1 p_1^0 \exp \left[\frac{(p - p_1^0)(v_1^0 - B_{11}) - 2p(\delta B)_{12} y_2^2}{RT} \right]$$

$$+ x_2 p_2^0 \exp \left[\frac{(p - p_2^0)(v_2^0 - B_{22}) - 2p(\delta B)_{12} y_1^2}{RT} \right] \quad (4.52)$$

This equation is greatly simplified if it is legitimate to put the exponential terms equal to unity; that is, if the vapour is a perfect gas and the molar volumes of the liquids are negligibly small. This gives

$$p = x_1 p_1^0 + x_2 p_2^0 \quad (4.53)$$

That is, the vapour pressure of an ideal liquid mixture of negligible volume in equilibrium with a perfect gas mixture is a linear function of the mole fractions. This is a statement of *Raoult's law* and may be generalized to ideal multi-component mixtures.

This law is sometimes made the definition of an ideal mixture, in place of (4.33), but such a starting point is not so satisfactory as that chosen here, since Raoult's law follows from (4.33) only after making the assumptions which led from (4.52) to (4.53). These assumptions become more correct the lower the temperature, and are the same as those that were necessary for the derivation of the Clapeyron–Clausius equation (2.78) from Clapeyron's equation (2.76).

A more realistic approximation is the assumption that the vapour is not a perfect gas mixture but an ideal mixture of imperfect gases[6]. This assumption requires that $(\delta B)_{12}$ is zero, and is generally more nearly correct than that B_{11}, B_{12} and B_{22} are all zero. It gives the following expression for the vapour pressure after expanding the exponential terms in (4.52) and neglecting all powers of p beyond the first

$$p = x_1 p_1^0 + x_2 p_2^0 - x_1 x_2 (p_1^0 - p_2^0) \left[\frac{p_1^0(v_1^0 - B_{11}) - p_2^0(v_2^0 - B_{22})}{RT} \right]$$

$$(4.54)$$

The second virial coefficient is always negative for a saturated vapour, and so $(v^0 - B)$ is positive. An ideal mixture in equilibrium with an ideal but imperfect gas mixture therefore shows negative deviations from Raoult's law unless B_{11} and B_{22} are very different in size. Conversely, a system which is observed to obey Raoult's law is generally not an ideal mixture as defined by (4.33), but has a small positive excess free energy. The system benzene + ethylene dichloride is an example of this behaviour (see Section 4.9).

The partial pressure of a component in a vapour mixture is defined as the product of the mole fraction and the total pressure. It is not a partial molar quantity in the sense of Section 4.2. The partial pressures of a system which obeys Raoult's law are given by

$$p_\alpha = y_\alpha p = x_\alpha p_\alpha^0 \tag{4.55}$$

The bubble-point line on a pressure–composition graph (*Figure 4.4*) shows p as a function of x, and is here a straight line. The dew-point

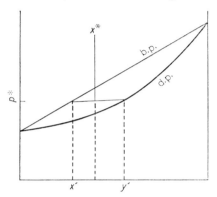

Figure 4.4. The bubble-point and dew-point lines of an ideal mixture at constant temperature

line is p as a function of y and is concave upwards. The equation of this curve in a binary mixture is

$$p = p_1^0 p_2^0 / [p_1^0 - y_1(p_1^0 - p_2^0)] \tag{4.56}$$

and so the curve is part of a rectangular hyperbola.

If a liquid mixture of composition x^* (*Figure 4.4*) is slowly decompressed, then gas first appears where the vertical line through x^* cuts the bubble-point curve. At a pressure p^* the system consists of gas and liquid in equilibrium. The compositions of the phases are, respectively, y', x', and the ratio of the number of moles of liquid to the number of gas is $(y' - x^*)/(x^* - x')$. The (T, x) graph, or boiling-point diagram at constant pressure, may be calculated from the (p, x) diagram if the variation of the vapour pressures with temperature is known. Neither dew- nor bubble-point line is linear for a mixture that obeys Raoult's law, as pressure is not a linear function of temperature[8].

116

Two liquids may be readily separated by distillation if their *volatility ratio* is large. This ratio, α_{21}, is defined as that of (y_2/y_1) to (x_2/x_1). It is a measure of the relative difference of composition of the gas and liquid phases in equilibrium. For an ideal mixture

$$\alpha_{12}(\neq \alpha_{21}) \equiv K_1/K_2 = p_1^0/p_2^0 \quad \text{where} \quad K_1 = y_1/x_1 \qquad (4.57)$$

thus showing, as is well known, that two liquids are the more readily separable by distillation the greater the difference in vapour pressure or, at constant total pressure, the greater their difference in boiling point.

4.4 THERMODYNAMICS OF NON-IDEAL MIXTURES

Few real mixtures are ideal. In this Section, the formal thermo-dynamical treatment of non-ideal mixtures is developed as a necessary preliminary to the description of the behaviour of actual systems in the following Sections.

The equations defining an ideal mixture may be modified so that they are formally valid for any real mixture at low pressure by writing

$$\mu_\alpha(p, T, x) - \mu_\alpha^0(p, T) = RT \ln (x_\alpha \gamma_\alpha) \qquad (4.58)$$

This equation defines the *activity coefficients*, γ_α. They are all unity in ideal mixtures, and in non-ideal mixtures, functions of pressure, temperature and composition. The partial molar quantities are given by

$$h_\alpha = h_\alpha^0 - RT^2(\partial \ln \gamma_\alpha/\partial T)_p \qquad (4.59)$$

$$s_\alpha = s_\alpha^0 - R \ln (x_\alpha \gamma_\alpha) - RT(\partial \ln \gamma_\alpha/\partial T)_p \qquad (4.60)$$

$$v_\alpha = v_\alpha^0 + RT(\partial \ln \gamma_\alpha/\partial p)_T \qquad (4.61)$$

The excess thermodynamic functions are obtained by subtracting from these the ideal quantities to give

$$\mu_\alpha^E = RT \ln \gamma_\alpha, \qquad G^E = RT \sum_\alpha m_\alpha \ln \gamma_\alpha \qquad (4.62)$$

$$h_\alpha^E = -RT^2(\partial \ln \gamma_\alpha/\partial T)_p, \qquad H^E = -RT^2 \sum_\alpha m_\alpha(\partial \ln \gamma_\alpha/\partial T)_p$$
$$\text{etc.} \quad (4.63)$$

Excess functions are related by equations of the usual type

$$G^E = H^E - TS^E = H^E + T(\partial G^E/\partial T)_p \qquad (4.64)$$

$$(C_p)^E = T(\partial S^E/\partial T)_p = (\partial H^E/\partial T)_p, \quad \text{etc.} \qquad (4.65)$$

117

The relation of V^E to the other excess functions is purely formal, for in practice there is no convenient method of measuring the pressure derivative of γ_α or of G^E other than that of measuring the excess volume.

The excess Helmholtz free energy and the excess energy at constant pressure are given by

$$G_p^E - A_p^E = H_p^E - U_p^E = pV_p^E \simeq 0 \qquad (4.66)$$

They are little used. The excess functions and functions of mixing at constant total volume are more interesting. They may be related to the constant pressure functions as follows[7].

Consider a binary mixture of mole fraction x formed from its components at constant, and essentially zero, pressure and at constant temperature

$$G_p^m = G(x, 0) - (1 - x)G(0, 0) - xG(1, 0) \qquad (4.67)$$

where the two variables are x and p. If the mixing is carried out at constant total volume, then the pressure will change to p_V^m. This will be large and positive if V_p^m is positive, and negative if V_p^m is negative. Hence

$$G_V^m = G(x, p_V^m) - (1 - x)G(0, 0) - xG(1, 0) \qquad (4.68)$$

or

$$G_V^m - G_p^m = G(x, p_V^m) - G(x, 0) \qquad (4.69)$$

$$= \int_0^{p_V^m} \left(\frac{\partial G(x)}{\partial p}\right)_{T,x} dp = \int_0^{p_V^m} V(x)\, dp \qquad (4.70)$$

Similarly

$$V_p^m = V(x, 0) - V(x, p_V^m) = -\int_0^{p_V^m} \left(\frac{\partial V(x)}{\partial p}\right)_{T,x} dp \qquad (4.71)$$

$V(x, p)$ may be expressed as a Taylor series in p

$$V(x, p) = V(x, 0) + \left(\frac{\partial V(x)}{\partial p}\right)_{p=0} p + \ldots \qquad (4.72)$$

and, to a first approximation, all terms beyond the second may be neglected—an approximation which is similar to assuming that β_T is independent of pressure. Substitution from this equation into

118

(4.70) and (4.71) gives

$$V_p^m = -(\partial V(x)/\partial p)_{p=0} \, p_V^m + \ldots \tag{4.73}$$

$$G_V^m - G_p^m = - \left[\frac{V(x)}{\partial V(x)/\partial p} \right]_{p=0} V_p^m$$

$$+ \tfrac{1}{2} \left[\frac{1}{\partial V(x)/\partial p} \right]_{p=0} (V_p^m)^2 + \ldots \tag{4.74}$$

and

$$G_V^m - A_V^m = V(x, p_V^m) p_V^m \tag{4.75}$$

$$= - \left[\frac{V(x)}{\partial V(x)/\partial p} \right]_{p=0} V_p^m + \left[\frac{1}{\partial V(x)/\partial p} \right]_{p=0} (V_p^m)^2 + \ldots \tag{4.76}$$

Whence

$$G_p^m - A_V^m = G_p^E - A_V^E = \tfrac{1}{2} \left[\frac{1}{\partial V(x)/\partial p} \right]_{p=0} (V_p^m)^2 \tag{4.77}$$

$$= \tfrac{1}{2} \left(\frac{1}{V\beta_T} \right) (V_p^m)^2 \tag{4.78}$$

The inclusion of higher terms in the Taylor expansion for the volume shows that the next non-vanishing term in (4.77) is of the order of $(V_p^m)^3$. Similarly

$$S_p^m - S_V^m = S(x, 0) - S(x, p_V^m) \tag{4.79}$$

$$= \int_0^{p_V^m} \left(\frac{\partial V(x)}{\partial T} \right)_p \mathrm{d}p \tag{4.80}$$

which gives

$$TS_p^m - TS_V^m = T \left(\frac{\partial V(x)}{\partial T} \right)_p p_V^m = \left[T \left(\frac{\partial p}{\partial T} \right)_V \right]_{p=0} V_p^m + O(V_p^m)^2 \tag{4.81}$$

By addition to (4.77)

$$H_p^m - U_V^m = \left[T \left(\frac{\partial p}{\partial T} \right)_V \right]_{p=0} V_p^m + O(V_p^m)^2 \tag{4.82}$$

Thus the differences in energy and entropy are of the order of V_p^m and that in the free energy of $(V_p^m)^2$. The latter difference is negligible compared to G_p^m and small compared to G_p^E, but the former is comparable with H_p^m and TS_p^m. Typical values for an equimolar mixture at room temperature are

$$g_p^m = -1500 \text{ J mol}^{-1}, \quad g_p^E = 200 \text{ J mol}^{-1}, \quad h_p^E = 300 \text{ J mol}^{-1},$$

$$v_p^E = 1 \text{ cm}^3 \text{ mol}^{-1}, \quad v = 100 \text{ cm}^3 \text{ mol}^{-1}, \quad \beta_T = 10^{-4} \text{ bar}^{-1}$$

$$T\gamma_V = 3000 \text{ bar}$$

These figures give

$$g_p^m - a_V^m = 5 \text{ J mol}^{-1}$$

$$h_p^m - u_V^m \approx Ts_p^m - Ts_V^m = 300 \text{ J mol}^{-1}$$

Thus the excess heat and entropy of a solution have very different values at constant total volume and at constant pressure. Only the latter are measured directly, and the former are calculated from them by using the equations above. TS_V^E is sometimes much smaller than TS_p^E, but it is doubtful if excess functions at constant volume are more closely related to intermolecular forces than those at constant pressure.

The variation of the vapour pressure with composition at constant temperature is closely related to G_p^E. The condition of equilibrium between liquid and vapour in a binary mixture is, as before, the equality of the chemical potentials of both species in each phase. The potentials of the gas are given by (4.44) and (4.45) and of the liquid by (4.58). Hence

$$\mu_1^E(p) = RT \ln \left(y_1 p/x_1 p_1^0\right) - (p - p_1^0)(v_1^0 - B_{11}) + 2p(\delta B)_{12} y_2^2 \tag{4.83}$$

and similarly for component 2. The molar excess free energy is given by

$$g_p^E(p^*) = x_1 \mu_1^E(p) + x_2 \mu_2^E(p) + (p^* - p)v_p^E \tag{4.84}$$

where p^* is a small arbitrary pressure. The last term is negligible if p^* is of the order of atmospheric pressure, and so g_p^E is almost independent of p^*.

It is seen that the activity coefficients are found most directly by measuring the vapour pressure and composition (p, y_1, y_2) in equilibrium with a liquid mixture of known composition (x_1, x_2) at a fixed temperature, T. Subsidiary measurements are needed to obtain the molar volumes of the liquids (v_1^0, v_2^0) and the second virial coefficients of the vapour (B_{11}, B_{12}, B_{22}).

The apparatus in which vapour pressure and composition are usually measured is an *equilibrium still*, the principle of which is illustrated in *Figure 4.5*. Vapour from the boiling mixture in A is condensed into a small trap B and returns to the boiler through a capillary C. The apparatus is connected, through the condenser, to a manostat at D. The tube leading from the boiler is heated to prevent any partial condensation of the vapour occurring before it reaches B. After the mixture has passed round the still for a few hours, to reach equilibrium, small samples of liquid are withdrawn from A and B and analysed, usually by measurement of their

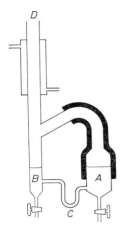

Figure 4.5. An equilibrium still. *A* is the boiler, whose outlet is heated and lagged, *B* is the trap in which the condensed vapour is collected, *C* is the capillary through which it is returned to the boiler, and *D* leads to a manostat (schematic only)

densities or refractive indices. These two samples will have the compositions of the equilibrium liquid and vapour, respectively.

The principle is simple but the practice is difficult, as is shown, for example, by the very large number of designs of still which have been put forward*. It is difficult both to avoid some condensation of the vapour as it leaves the boiler and to ensure that the vapour carries over no drops of the liquid. The condensed vapour that is returned to the boiler must be rapidly and uniformly mixed with the liquid, if the sample taken for analysis is to be representative of the bulk. Sometimes the condensed vapour is re-evaporated in a separate flash boiler and returned as vapour.

Many of these practical difficulties can be overcome by measuring only p and x and deducing y from them by using the Gibbs–Duhem equation. That is, it is sufficient to measure the total static vapour pressure as a function of liquid composition in order to obtain a complete knowledge of p, x, y and G^E at a given temperature. This may be done by measuring either the absolute pressure of the system or the difference between the vapour pressure of the mixture and that of the pure components†. In both cases it is desirable to keep the vapour space as small as possible, so that the whole system

* The classical work on the measurement of p, x and y is that of J. v. Zawidzki[9]. His still did not re-cycle the vapour, and subsequent improvements are described by other authors[9].

† For accurate absolute measurements of total vapour pressure see [10] and for typical differential methods[11].

may be kept at a uniform temperature and that the volume and composition of the liquid are not changed appreciably by evaporation as the temperature is raised.

A second possible choice of the three variables p, x and y is to measure p and y; that is, to study the dew-point curve and to determine x from the Gibbs–Duhem equation[12]. This is particularly useful for mixed crystals in equilibrium with their vapour, since the observation of y and p at the point of the first precipitation of the solid allows one to avoid the difficulties of bringing large crystals to equilibrium with respect to composition. A further variant is to avoid accurate measurement of either x or y by observing both dew-point and bubble-point pressure in a liquid–gas system[13].

The calculation of y and G^E from isothermal measurements of p and x requires the solution of the Gibbs–Duhem differential equation. Some of the graphical and algebraic methods of solution that have been proposed neglect the departures of the vapour from the perfect-gas laws. A more satisfactory method is the algebraic one of Barker[14] who assumes a particular form of g^E, as a function of x, with one or more adjustable parameters. The parameters are chosen by a least-squares method to minimize the errors in the total pressure. The function to which he fits g^E has been widely used, before and since,

$$g^E = x_1 x_2 [\xi_1 + \xi_2(x_1 - x_2) + \xi_3(x_1 - x_2)^2 + \ldots] \quad (4.85)$$

Such an equation satisfies the obvious requirement that g^E should be zero for both pure substances, and can be made to fit any experimental results by choosing sufficient terms. Differentiation of (4.85) gives

$$\mu_1^E = x_2^2[\xi_1 + \xi_2(3 - 4x_2) + \xi_3(5 - 16x_2 + 12x_2^2) + \ldots] \quad (4.86)$$

and similarly for component 2 but with a negative coefficient of ξ_2. It is seen that the lowest power of x_2 in the expansion for μ_1^E is the second. The absence of the first power is necessary in any expressions for μ_1^E and μ_2^E which satisfy the Gibbs–Duhem equation. Thus the simplest class of non-ideal mixtures is that for which ξ_2, and all higher coefficients in (4.85) and (4.86), vanish over a non-zero range of p and T. Such a system is often called a *regular mixture*, although many other meanings have been given to that over-worked adjective. They are called here *quadratic mixtures*, and for these we have

$$g^E = x_1 x_2 \xi_1, \qquad \mu_1^E = x_2^2 \xi_1, \qquad \mu_2^E = x_1^2 \xi_1 \quad (4.87)$$

$$h^E = x_1 x_2 [\xi_1 - T(\partial \xi_1 / \partial T)_p] \quad (4.88)$$

$$s^E = x_1 x_2 [-(\partial \xi_1 / \partial T)_p] \quad (4.89)$$

$$v^E = x_1 x_2 [(\partial \xi_1 / \partial p)_T] \quad (4.90)$$

If ξ_1 is assumed to be independent of temperature, then s^E is zero—a restriction which would bring the definition close to that of a regular mixture of Hildebrand[5]. There are many mixtures for which (4.87)–(4.89) are an adequate approximation, but in few of these is TS_p^E (or TS_V^E) small compared to H_p^E. Calculations of G^E from the total or partial pressures of many real mixtures show that the first term of (4.85) is usually much the most important at low vapour pressures. However, the first anti-symmetric term $(x_1^2 x_2 - x_1 x_2^2)$ is often dominant in H^E and S^E.

Equations other than the expansion (4.85) have been widely used to represent g^E and γ as functions of composition. That of van Laar has been used for many years[1,5], but a recent proposal by Wilson[15] has aroused much interest because of its apparent flexibility and power[16]. This has the form

$$g^E = -RT[x_1 \ln (1 - A_{21}x_2) + x_2 \ln (1 - A_{12}x_1)] \quad (4.91)$$

where $A_{12} \neq A_{21}$.

Its convenience, accuracy and the ease with which it can be extended to multi-component systems are discussed in a recent book by Prausnitz and his colleagues[17].

The development of gas–liquid chromatography has given us a new method of measuring the activity coefficients of volatile components at high dilution in a solute of low volatility. Briefly, in an ideal column the activity coefficient is inversely proportional to the product of the vapour pressure and retention volume of the volatile component. This has been known for many years, but only recently have columns been built which are sufficiently flexible in their operating conditions to allow all the minor corrections to be measured precisely[18]. A by-product of this work is the measurement of the cross second virial coefficient, B_{12}, for the interaction of the volatile component and the carrier gas. The method is restricted in the kinds of solution to which it is applicable, but it is one of great potential sensitivity—it has been used, for example, to measure the difference in activity coefficients of isotopically substituted species[19]. Brown[20] has reviewed the field.

The heat of mixing, H^m (or H^E), is related to G^E by the Gibbs–Helmholtz equation but, in practice, this does not provide a satisfactory method of determining it. Measurements of vapour pressure, and so of G^E, rarely extend over a temperature range of more than 15 per cent of the absolute temperature. This limit is imposed partly by practical difficulties, for a given apparatus is rarely designed to measure pressure accurately over a range of greater than a factor of ten, and partly by the difficulty that has already been discussed of defining G^E at vapour pressures greater than 2–3 bar. If G^E is known to, say, 2 per cent over a temperature range of $1\cdot0$ T to $1\cdot1$ T and if TS^E is about as large as G^E, then the probable errors in derived values of H^E and TS^E, at $1\cdot05$ T, are 15 per cent and 30 per cent, respectively. The accuracy of H^E and TS^E obtained from the temperature derivative of G^E must always be an order of magnitude less than that of G^E, and some very bad estimates of H^E have been made by this method in the past.

The only satisfactory method of obtaining H^E is the direct one, using either an adiabatic or an isothermal calorimeter. In an adiabatic experiment, the two liquids are mixed in a vessel which is, as far as possible, in thermal isolation. If H^E is positive, there will be a lowering of temperature on adiabatic mixing. This drop in temperature may be nullified by the simultaneous or subsequent supply of heat. If this is supplied simultaneously, then the mixing is done under conditions that are more nearly isothermal than adiabatic, and the correction for the exchange of heat with the surroundings is made very small. If H^E is negative, then the mixture warms on adiabatic mixing. The temperature rise is measured and, after cooling, a second experiment is made to find the amount of heat needed to produce such a rise.

The difficulties are the usual ones of adiabatic calorimetry— exchange of heat with the surroundings, satisfactory stirring, rapid and sensitive measurement of temperature and, in the case of volatile liquids, ensuring the absence of any appreciable volume of vapour. If there is vapour in equilibrium with the mixture, then any change of temperature will lead to evaporation or condensation, and would vitiate measurement of H^E which is always small compared to the molar heat of evaporation. It appears that, in practice, H^E can be measured to about 1 per cent at room temperature and with rather less accuracy at higher temperatures. The best work in this field is that of McGlashan[21] who has paid great attention to the removal of errors, in particular those arising from volatility and from imperfect mixing.

The excess heat capacity, $(C_p)^E$, was little studied until the last twenty years, although its measurement is the logical way of finding out how H^E varies with temperature. This neglect was probably due to the fact that even the best theories of solutions are not accurate enough to predict reliably the size of the second derivative of the excess free energy with respect to temperature.

The excess volume, V^E, is obtained directly or from measurements of the orthobaric liquid densities, and is now included in almost all systematic studies of the excess functions of binary mixtures.

4.5 Tests for Consistency

The Gibbs–Duhem equation (4.8) is a necessary relation between the partial molar properties of components in a mixture and so may be used to test experimental measurements for thermodynamic consistency. The tests are of two kinds. First, the equation, as it stands, may be used to test the experimental observations and calculations which have led to the partial molar quantities. Such tests are most commonly applied to the chemical potentials and

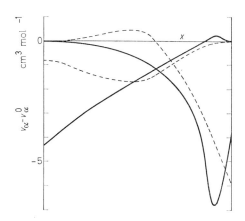

Figure 4.6. Maxima and minima in partial molar volumes[22]. Full lines, ethanol + water at 0°C; dashed lines, dioxan + water at 25°C. The mole fraction, x, is that of water

partial molar volumes. A second form of the test is to examine the consistency of simultaneous measurements of p, x and y (at constant T) over the whole range of composition of a binary mixture by calculating the volatility ratio. Such a test is, of course, one of the consistency of the chemical potentials, although these quantities are not usually calculated explicitly.

The first type of test is most simply made by writing the Gibbs–Duhem equation in the form

$$x_1(\partial r_1/\partial x_1)_T = x_2(\partial r_2/\partial x_2)_T \qquad (4.92)$$

The most obvious consequence of this equation is that if $(\partial r_1/\partial x_1)$ is zero at a maximum of r_1, then $(\partial r_2/\partial x_2)$ is zero at a minimum of r_2. Such behaviour is shown, for example, by the partial molar volumes in aqueous solutions of ethanol and of dioxan[22] (*Figure 4.6*). However, Griffiths[23] has reported partial molar volumes for the latter system in which a cusp in one curve is opposed to a minimum in the other and which therefore do not satisfy (4.92). The partial molar volumes of Schott[23] have improbable extrema.

The corresponding equation for the activity coefficients is obtained by substituting $(\mu_1 - \mu_1^0)$ for r_1 in (4.92)

$$\frac{(\partial x_1\gamma_1/\partial x_1)}{\gamma_1} = \frac{(\partial x_2\gamma_2/\partial x_2)}{\gamma_2} \qquad (4.93)$$

If the vapour is a perfect gas mixture, then γ_1 is equal to $(y_1 p/x_1 p_1^0)$. Hence

$$\frac{(\partial p_1/\partial x_1)}{p_1/x_1} = \frac{(\partial p_2/\partial x_2)}{p_2/x_2} \qquad (4.94)$$

This form of the Gibbs–Duhem equation is usually called the *Duhem–Margules equation*, but its practical value in tests for consistency is not great, since it holds only for a system in which the vapour is a perfect gas mixture. However, gross violations of (4.94) are always evidence of inconsistency. A bad example is the partial pressure measurements of Smyth and Engel[24] on the system ethanol + n-heptane. Here the partial pressure of ethanol at 50°C is reported to show a maximum whilst that of heptane behaves normally. Such a maximum not only violates (4.94) but would lead to material instability and so to the separation of the mixture into two phases (see next Chapter).

Beatty and Calingaert[25] have formulated neatly the consequences of (4.94). They observe that each side of the equation is the ratio of the slope of the partial pressure curve to that of the line joining the partial pressure to the origin (*Figure 4.7*). The equation requires that these ratios be the same for both components at all compositions. In particular, if the line through the origin becomes a tangent to the partial pressure curve for one component, then the same relationship must hold for the second. Reported violations of these conditions are quite common. The results of von Zawidzki[9] for aqueous solutions of pyridine and of Bredig and Bayer[26] for those of methanol both show tangents which pass through the origin for one component only at a given composition. Lee's results on the system methanol + benzene do not violate this condition but are quantitatively[25] in disagreement with (4.94). In these cases it is charitable to assume that part at least of the discrepancies would disappear if proper account were taken of the imperfection of the vapours, that is, if the exact test (4.93) were used and not the inexact test (4.94). An example which fails to satisfy (4.94) but which probably satisfies (4.93) is the system benzene + bromobenzene[27] at 80°C.

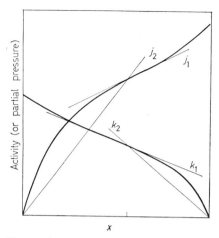

Figure 4.7. The test for consistency of Beatty and Calingaert[25]. The ratio of the slope of the tangent j_1 to the chord j_2 must be the same as the ratio of k_1 to k_2

The test for the consistency of simultaneous measurements of p, x and y uses the volatility ratio, α. This is defined by the first part of (4.57) in a binary mixture. By subtraction of (4.83) from the corresponding equation for component 2 and substitution from (4.13)

$$\mu_2^E - \mu_1^E = RT \ln (\gamma_2/\gamma_1) = (\partial g^E/\partial x_2)_T \qquad (4.95)$$

$$= RT \ln \left(\frac{\alpha p_1^0}{p_2^0}\right) + (p - p_1^0)(v_1^0 - B_{11})$$

$$- (p - p_2^0)(v_2^0 - B_{22}) + 2p(\delta B)_{12}(y_1^2 - y_2^2) \qquad (4.96)$$

This equation may be integrated over x_2 from 0 to 1 to give

$$\int_0^1 \ln \left(\frac{\alpha p_1^0}{p_2^0}\right) dx_2 = \frac{1}{RT} \int_0^1 [(p - p_2^0)(v_2^0 - B_{22})$$

$$- (p - p_1^0)(v_1^0 - B_{11}) - 2p(\delta B)_{12}(y_1^2 - y_2^2)] \, dx_2 \qquad (4.97)$$

since g^E is zero both at $x_2 = 0$ and at $x_2 = 1$. The following statements follow directly from these equations:

(1) The integrands on both sides of (4.97) are zero for an ideal liquid mixture in equilibrium with a perfect gas mixture.
(2) The volatility ratio is equal to (p_2^0/p_1^0) at the composition at which g^E has a maximum or a minimum in a non-ideal mixture

in equilibrium with a perfect gas. In such a system the integrand on the left-hand side of (4.97) takes on both positive and negative values and the integral vanishes.

(3) The function $\ln (\alpha p_1^0/p_2^0)$ is a linear function of x in a quadratic liquid mixture in equilibrium with a perfect gas mixture.

The second of these conclusions is the test for consistency proposed[28] independently by Coulson and Herington and by Redlich and Kister. They plotted $\ln (\alpha p_1^0/p_2^0)$ against x_2 and, by graphical integration, found whether or not the areas above and below the x axis were equal.

This simple form of the test is adequate only if the vapour pressures of the components are close, since it neglects imperfections of the vapour. They and others[28] have considered the modifications necessary to account for these imperfections.

One simple form of (4.97) which takes adequate account of gas imperfection, except in the most extreme cases, can be obtained as follows. First, it is found that the integrand on the right-hand side of (4.97) is a well-behaved function of x to which the last term contributes very little if $(\delta B)_{12}$ is much smaller than either B_{11} or B_{22}. The first approximation is, therefore, the neglect of this term. The second is the replacement of p by the value required by Raoult's law, namely $(x_1 p_1^0 + x_2 p_2^0)$. This allows the integration to be performed analytically to give

$$\int_0^1 \ln \left(\frac{\alpha p_1^0}{p_2^0}\right) dx_2 = \frac{(p_1^0 - p_2^0)(v_1^0 + v_2^0 - B_{11} - B_{22})}{2RT} \qquad (4.98)$$

This equation is a convenient and generally accurate test of the consistency of measurements of p, x and y for binary mixtures of non-polar or but weakly polar substances. As an example, consider the measurements by McGlashan, Prue and Sainsbury[29] of the pressure and composition of the vapour of mixtures of chloroform and carbon tetrachloride at 55°C. *Figure 4.8* is the graph of $\ln (\alpha p_1^0/p_2^0)$ against x_2, the mole fraction of chloroform. The volatility ratio is calculated from their measurements of p, x and y. The experimental errors at the extremes of composition are magnified on such a graph, but it is clear that, as the authors observe, the mixture is quadratic, since the points lie on a straight line. This cuts the axis at $x_2 = 0.43$, so that the area below it exceeds that above, and the integral in (4.98) is -0.017. The right-hand side is -0.0146 with the values of the virial coefficients that the authors recommend, including their value of $(\delta B)_{12} = 0$. The exact equation (4.97), again with $(\delta B)_{12} = 0$, gives the almost identical figure of -0.0149.

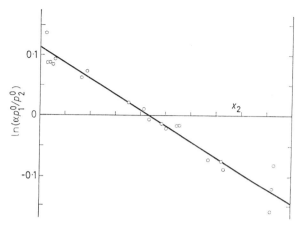

Figure 4.8. The function $\ln\,(\alpha p_1^0/p_2^0)$ for carbon tetrachloride (1) + chloroform (2) at 55°C, as a function of the mole fraction of chloroform (calculated from the results of McGlashan, Prue and Sainsbury[29])

The agreement between -0.017 for the left-hand side and -0.015 for the right-hand side is an adequate test of the consistency of the experimental results. However, the simple area test which would require the integral to be zero, would here falsely indicate an inconsistency.

Tests for consistency at high vapour pressures and above the critical temperature of one of the components raise problems beyond the scope of this Section, and discussion is deferred to Chapter 6.

4.6 MIXTURES OF CONDENSED GASES

The excess thermodynamic properties of mixtures of non-polar liquids have long been the testing ground of statistical theories of solutions. The most favoured have probably been the three binary systems formed from benzene, cyclohexane and carbon tetrachloride, although these are by no means the most suitable for the purpose. The constituent molecules are of different sizes and shapes. None is spherical, and little is known of the variation of the intermolecular forces with orientation. It is better, therefore, to examine first the experimental results for more simple systems, choosing, as far as possible, those containing monatomic and diatomic molecules.

We consider, first, mixtures of the inert gases. Unfortunately, their critical and triple points are so far apart that it is difficult to choose mixtures in which the components have liquid ranges that overlap. Only the pairs argon + krypton and krypton + xenon satisfy this criterion, and even here the vapour pressure of the first component is inconveniently high at the triple point of the second, e.g. 9·5 bar for argon at the triple point of krypton. Measurements of vapour pressure and of heats of dilution can be made usefully even at temperatures below the triple point of one of the components, but the range of composition becomes increasingly restricted as the temperature is lowered. Useful discussion of such results can be made only insofar as the liquid vapour pressure of the second component can be extrapolated below its triple point.

Values of g^E, etc. in this Section are those for the equimolar mixture, unless otherwise defined, and it is implied that this value is also close to the maximum.

Argon + Krypton

This system has been studied by Staveley and his colleagues[30] at and near the triple point of krypton (115·8 K), by several of the group at Göttingen[31-34] at this and lower temperatures, and by Yunker and Halsey[35] at 84 K, the triple point of argon. Unfortunately, the results tabulated below for the lower temperatures are derived from those on dilute solutions only, but this extrapolation cannot be the cause of the great differences shown.

The principal disagreement is between the free energies of Staveley and of the Göttingen group, but there is an equally serious disagreement between the two measurements of g^E at 104 and 116 K, on the one hand, and the calorimetric measurement of h^E on the

T K	g^E J mol^{-1}	h^E	v^E cm^3 mol^{-1}	References
84	(150 ± 30)	—	—	35
87–88	(170)	—	—	31,32
104	83	—	—	30
116	84	—	−0·52	30
117	133	103	—	33

other. Some evidence that the lower free energies are perhaps the more likely to be correct comes from g^E in the solid solution of 84 K which is reported[36] to be 160 J mol^{-1}. It is likely that this value is much larger than that in the liquid, in view of the well-known difficulties of accommodating molecules of different sizes in a common crystal lattice.

Krypton + Xenon

Seemeyer[34] has found $g^E = 145$ J mol^{-1} at 166 K, but there must be some uncertainty in this figure until the discrepancy in the system argon + krypton is resolved.

Argon + Xenon

The activity coefficient of xenon at high dilution in argon at 84–88 K has been measured by Yunker and Halsey[35].

Argon + Nitrogen

The recent work of Staveley[37], of Narinskii[38] and of Sprow and Prausnitz[39] is in accord, and is supported by the older work of Holst and Hamburger[40]. The substances are partially miscible in the solid state[41].

T K	g^E	h^E	v^E	References
	J mol^{-1}		cm^3 mol^{-1}	
83·82	34·4	51	−0·180	37
83·82	33·8	—	—	39

Argon + Oxygen

This is a much studied system. We may now ignore the older Russian work and are left with the more recent work of Narinskii[38], Burn and Din[42] and Staveley[37] on the vapour pressure of the system. The excess heat has been measured by Köhler[33], Staveley[37] and Beenakker and his colleagues[43], with good agreement. Their results are confirmed by the rate of change of g^E with temperature, which can be represented

$$g^E/\text{J mol}^{-1} = 61\cdot6 - 0\cdot292(T/\text{K}) \qquad (4.99)$$

T K	g^E	h^E	v^E	References
	J mol^{-1}		cm^3 mol^{-1}	
77·5	—	54	—	33
83·8	37·1	60	+0·136	37
86	—	57	—	43
89·6	35·3	—	—	37
90	33	—	—	42
90	33	—	—	38
90	—	—	+0·140	37
90	—	—	+0·138	44
95	31	—	—	42
100	30	—	—	42
100	31·3	—	—	38
110	29·5	—	—	38

Wang[45] claims that there is a maximum in the activity coefficient of argon in dilute solution, but this has still to be confirmed.

Argon + Carbon Monoxide

The excess free energy and volume are known.

T K	g^E J mol⁻¹	v^E cm³ mol⁻¹	Reference
83·82	56·7	+0·094	30

Argon + Methane

Free energy, heat and volume have all been measured.

T K	g^E	h^E J mol⁻¹	v^E cm³ mol⁻¹	References
86·7	76·0	—	—	46
90·7	72·4	—	—	39
91	—	103	+0·18	47
91	—	99	+0·16	48

Krypton + Methane

There are two discordant values of the free energy. Scott and Thorp[49] find 60 J mol⁻¹, the Belgian groups[46] 30 J mol⁻¹ at 116 K. Unpublished work of Calado and Staveley confirms the latter figure.

Nitrogen + Oxygen

Again, there is a discrepancy between the free energies (which are internally consistent) and the excess heat measured calorimetrically. The excess free energy of Din[50] is consistent with those listed but less accurate. For good measure, even the volume of mixing is uncertain in this important system.

T K	g^E	h^E J mol⁻¹	v^E cm³ mol⁻¹	References
63·1	45·5	—	—	30
70	44	—	—	51
77	—	46	—	43
77·5	—	46	—	33
77·5	40	—	—	51
78	—	—	−0·21	44
83·8	38·5	—	−0·31	37

Nitrogen + Carbon Monoxide

This system is not as ideal as might be imagined. The excess free energy is substantial and its variation with temperature implies an excess heat of about 40 J mol⁻¹.

132

T K	g^E J mol^{-1}	v^E cm^3 mol^{-1}	References
68·1	26·7	—	30
83·8	23·0	+0·127	37
83·8	22·7	—	39

Nitrogen + Methane

The excess free energy is large[39,46], 140 J mol^{-1} at 90·7 K. The excess volume[46] is −0·21 cm^3 mol^{-1}.

Carbon Monoxide + Methane

A well-studied system in which there is an asymmetry in h^E and hence in s^E. However, the latter is probably negative at all compositions[47], and not weakly positive in solutions rich in methane as was thought at one time[52] The excess volume also has its minimum in solutions poorer in methane.

T K	g^E	h^E J mol^{-1}	v^E cm^3 mol^{-1}	References
90·7	110	105	−0·32	52
90·7	121	—	—	39
91·2	—	106	−0·34	47

Nitric Oxide + Methane

This system is very far from ideal. There is a strong positive azeotrope[53] and both excess heat and free energy appear to be of the order of 400 J mol^{-1} at 111 K.

Argon + Nitrogen + Oxygen

The most complete study of the ternary system is that of Wilson, Silverberg and Zellner[54].

4.7 MIXTURES OF PARAFFIN HYDROCARBONS

Paraffin hydrocarbons are non-polar and their mixtures are the simplest class of solutions that has been studied extensively. Almost all the work has been at room temperature or above, so there is little to report on measurements at low pressure on systems with fewer than six carbon atoms to the molecule.

The greatest amount of work is that on mixtures of the normal alkanes which has inspired, or been inspired by, the recent theoretical interest in this comparatively simple class of mixtures. The theoretical discussion may be said to have started with the empirical 'principle of congruence' put forward by Brønsted and Koefoed[55] in

1946, but it is now more closely integrated with the statistical mechanical theories of simple mixtures, and so is deferred to Chapter 9. The experimental results follow a common pattern whose general features are:

(a) The excess Gibbs free energy and excess volume are negative and approximately quadratic. They increase in magnitude as the temperature increases.

(b) The excess heat is positive and quadratic at low but becomes negative at high temperatures. It crosses the axis $h^E = 0$ as a sigmoid curve which has $h^E < 0$ for mixtures weak, and $h^E > 0$ for those strong in the longer component. The temperature[56] at which $h^E = 0$ at $x = \frac{1}{2}$ is 65°C for n-C_6H_{14} + n-$C_{16}H_{34}$, 80°C for n-C_6H_{14} + n-$C_{24}H_{50}$, and 95°C for n-C_8H_{18} + n-$C_{24}H_{50}$.

(c) The magnitudes of g^E, h^E and v^E increase rapidly with the differences in chain length.

Measurements have been reported for the systems listed below. Here each normal paraffin is denoted simply by the number of carbon atoms in the molecule.

Excess Gibbs free energy[18,55,57,58]

1 + 3, 4 + 18, 5 + 18, 6 + 12, 6 + 16, 6 + 18, 7 + 16, 8 + 18

Excess enthalpy[56,58−63]

1 + 3, 5 + 16, 6 + 7, 6 + 12, 6 + 16, 6 + 24, 6 + 36, 7 + 16, 7 + 36, 8 + 16, 8 + 24, 8 + 32, 9 + 36, 10 + 16, 16 + 36

Excess volume[56,58,63−66]

1 + 2, 1 + 3, 1 + 4, 2 + 3, 2 + 4, 5 + 16, 6 + 12, 6 + 16, 6 + 24, 7 + 12, 7 + 16, 7 + 24, 7 + 36, 8 + 16, 8 + 24, 8 + 32, 8 + 36, 9 + 16, 9 + 24, 9 + 32, 9 + 36, 9 + 62, 10 + 12, 10 + 14, 10 + 16, 12 + 16

This list is representative rather than exhaustive but includes the most accurate measurements—those of McGlashan[57,61] and his colleagues and the more recent work[56,64] from Amsterdam. It is seen that, unusually, the excess heat has been more widely studied than the excess free energy. This interest has arisen from the change of sign with change of temperature which was noted above.

Measurements of density and of liquid–vapour equilibrium have been made for hydrocarbons mixtures below C_6, but most of these are at pressures significantly above 1 bar and so are discussed in Chapter 6.

It is less easy to generalize about mixtures of normal, branched and cyclo-paraffins. In general, all excess functions are more positive if one of the components is branched or is a cyclo-paraffin. Thus h^E for branched hexanes with n-$C_{16}H_{34}$ is approximately twice that of the normal hexane[67]. Similarly, cyclohexane[68] has g^E positive with n-C_6H_{14}, $g^E \sim 0$ with n-C_7H_{16} and g^E negative with n-$C_{12}H_{26}$ and n-$C_{16}H_{34}$ which, however, are less strongly negative than those for mixtures of n-hexane with these long-chain hydrocarbons.

It will be shown in Chapter 9 that theories of mixtures are at their best when the component molecules are of similar size. The system neopentane + cyclohexane conforms to this requirement, and here Mathot and Desmyter[69] have shown that the free energy is positive with a maximum of 184 J mol^{-1}, and the excess volume negative, with a minimum of $-1 \cdot 1$ cm^3 mol^{-1}, both at 0°C.

4.8 MIXTURES OF PARAFFIN AND AROMATIC HYDROCARBONS

Mixtures formed from paraffin hydrocarbons and aromatic hydrocarbons generally have larger positive excess free energies and heats than those formed solely from paraffins.

Thus benzene + neopentane[69] has an equimolar excess free energy of $+570$ J mol^{-1} and an excess volume of $-0 \cdot 5$ cm^3 mol^{-1} at 0°C, values which exceed substantially those quoted above for cyclohexane + neopentane.

The equimolar excess heats rise slowly along the series benzene + n-alkanes. Thus at (or near) 25°C we have

	J mol^{-1}
benzene + n-hexane[59, 70]	$+ 870$
benzene + n-heptane[62, 71, 72]	$+ 950$
benzene + n-hexadecane[62]	$+1210$

The excess volumes rise similarly from $+0 \cdot 5$ cm^3 mol^{-1} for n-hexane[73] and $+0 \cdot 6$ for n-heptane[74, 75] to $+0 \cdot 9$ cm^3 mol^{-1} for n-dodecane[73]. The equimolar excess free energies at 70°C are about $+280$ J mol^{-1} for mixtures with n-hexane and with n-heptane[74]. Callot[76] has shown, by study of dilute solutions of n-alkanes in benzene, that both excess free energy and excess heat remain positive at least to n-$C_{32}H_{66}$ at 5°C, whilst Gainey and Young[18] find that the activity coefficient of benzene at infinite dilution becomes negative at higher temperatures, e.g. at 50°C for n-$C_{16}H_{34}$ and 20°C for n-$C_{20}H_{42}$.

Benzene + cyclohexane is perhaps the most studied hydrocarbon system. There are innumerable measurements of the heat of mixing at 25°C, most of which[62, 72, 77, 78] lie close to an equimolar value of +810 J mol^{-1}. This falls[79, 80] to +750 J mol^{-1} at 50°C and to[81] +590 J mol^{-1} at 90°C. The equimolar excess free energy[82] falls from +300 J mol^{-1} at 40°C to +250 at 70°C, a fall which corresponds to a mean excess heat of 810 J mol^{-1}, in adequate agreement with the more reliable values measured directly. The excess volume[59, 75, 78] is almost independent of temperature from 20° to 70°C at +0·66 cm^3 mol^{-1}.

The equimolar excess heat of benzene with other cyclo-paraffins[78] at 25°C is similar, namely +620 J mol^{-1} with cyclopentane, +750 with cycloheptane and +780 with cyclo-octane. Toluene[72, 78] has rather smaller values with the same four cycloparaffins from C$_5$ to C$_8$, but shows a similar increase along the series of n-alkanes[62], namely from +550 J mol^{-1} at n-heptane to +730 at n-hexadecane.

4.9 MIXTURES CONTAINING HALIDES

Most organic halides and some of the covalent inorganic ones are liquids of low polarity which mix readily with each other and with hydrocarbons. Such systems have been widely studied, and the more important results are collected in this Section.

Carbon tetrachloride has a volume and shape similar to neopentane, and the system[69, 84] is, therefore, of interest for the testing of theories of mixtures. It is quadratic at 0°C, and the equimolar excess free energy, heat and volume are +320 J mol^{-1}, +310 J mol^{-1} and −0·5 cm^3 mol^{-1}, respectively. The magnitude of the excess volume decreases with increasing pressure. These substances are miscible in the solid if the temperature is high enough for both to be in the 'plastic crystal' phases, in which the molecules have considerable rotational freedom. However, even the plastic phase is more rigid than the liquid, and the excess heat[85] at 230 K is four times that in the liquid at 273 K, namely +1170 J mol^{-1}.

Mixtures of carbon tetrachloride with cyclohexane and with benzene are the most thoroughly studied systems of this Section. In the former, the equimolar excess free energy[74, 82] falls from +74 J mol^{-1} at 10°C to +70 at 25°C and to +62 at 55°C. The measurements of the excess heat and volume have been reviewed by Kehlen and Sackmann[86]. Their own equimolar value, confirmed by other recent measurements[77, 80, 87], is +166 J mol^{-1} at 20°C. An earlier figure of +150 J mol^{-1} of Adcock and McGlashan[83] is probably a little low. The excess volume[86-88] is +0·16 cm^3 mol^{-1}, independent of temperature from 10°C to 55°C. Diaz Peña and McGlashan[88] have measured the compressibility of the mixture and so obtained the excess energy for mixing at constant volume from the (slightly low) value of the excess heat mentioned above. There is evidence of miscibility in the solid state[89].

The system carbon tetrachloride + benzene has often been used for testing calorimeters, and so there are many measurements of the heat of mixing at room temperature. The equimolar value[62,77,79,80,83,90] at 25°C is +115 J mol^{-1}. The excess free energy[82] falls from +82 J mol^{-1} at 25°C to +75 at 70°C. It appears to be quadratic at all temperatures, although direct measurements of the excess heat capacity[91] imply that h^E and, therefore, g^E become asymmetric at high temperatures, with the maxima in mixtures rich in benzene. The equimolar excess volume[91,92] is negligible at 25°C and only about +0·10 cm^3 mol^{-1} at 70°C.

The partially chlorinated alkanes, such as chloroform, methylene and ethylene dichloride, are weakly polar. They have, therefore, quite large excess heats and free energies with carbon tetrachloride and with cyclohexane. Thus the system chloroform + carbon tetrachloride[29,83] is quadratic, with maximum excess free energy, heat and volume of +107 J mol^{-1}, +230 J mol^{-1} and +0·17 cm^3 mol^{-1} at 25°C. Methylene dichloride + carbon tetrachloride[93] has an equimolar excess free energy of +290 J mol^{-1}, a heat about twice this size and an excess volume of +0·33 cm^3 mol^{-1}. Benzene, however, can form complexes with these halides (and, to a small degree, with carbon tetrachloride[94]) through its π-electron system, and the behaviour of these mixtures is not so simple. Thus the excess heat is negative[95] with chloroform and with methylene dichloride.

The system ethylene dichloride + benzene is a classical example of a mixture which obeys Raoult's law[96] and is, therefore, ideal by this simple definition. However, obedience to Raoult's law does not imply that the excess free energy is zero, since the vapour is not a perfect gas mixture. The equimolar excess free energy[97] is +33 J mol^{-1} at 20°C. The excess heat[98] is markedly asymmetrical, with its maximum at a mole fraction of benzene of about 0·3 at 20°C. The equimolar excess heat is here about +60 J mol^{-1}, and it increases with increasing temperature. The equimolar excess volume[3,98] is +0·25 cm^3 mol^{-1} at 20°C and changes little with temperature.

Negative heats, which can be taken as evidence of weak complexes in these systems, have been found in mixtures of benzene with chlorobenzene, and of toluene with chloro- or bromobenzene[99].

REFERENCES

[1] Hildebrand, J. H. *Solubility of Nonelectrolytes*, 1st and 2nd edn., New York (Reinhold), 1924 and 1936

[2] Byers Brown, W. *Phil. Trans.* A250 (1957) 175

[3] Coulson, E. A., Hales, J. L. and Herington, E. F. G. *Trans. Faraday Soc.* 44 (1948) 636

[4] Young, T. F. and Vogel, O. G. *J. Am. chem. Soc.* 54 (1932) 3025; Van Ness, H. C. and Mrazek, R. V. *A.I.Ch.E.Jl* 5 (1959) 209

[5] Hildebrand, J. H. and Scott, R. L., *Solubility of Nonelectrolytes* (3rd edn.), p. 25–28, 239–246, 270–299, New York (Reinhold) 1950; *Regular Solutions*, New Jersey (Prentice-Hall) 1962

[6] Rowlinson, J. S. *Handbuch der Physik* (ed. Flügge, S.), Vol. 12, Berlin (Springer) 1958

[7] Scatchard, G. *Trans. Faraday Soc.* 33 (1937) 160; McGlashan, M. L., Morcom, K. W. and Williamson, A. G. 57 (1961) 601; Scott, R. L. *J. phys. Chem.* 64 (1960) 1241

[8] Prigogine, I. and Defay, R. *Chemical Thermodynamics* (trans. Everett, D. H.) p. 350, London (Longmans) 1954

[9] von Zawidzki, J. Z. *phys. Chem.* 35 (1900) 129; Gillespie, D. T. C. *Industr. Engng Chem.* 18 (1946) 575; Kretschmer, C. B., Nowakowska, J. and Wiebe, R. *J. Am. chem. Soc.* 70 (1948) 1785; 71 (1949) 1793; Scatchard, G., Kavanagh, G. M. and Ticknor, L. B. 74 (1952) 3715; Brown, I. and Ewald, A. H. *Aust. J. scient. Res.* A3 (1950) 306; McGlashan, M. L., Prue, J. E. and Sainsbury, I. E. J. *Trans Faraday Soc.* 50 (1954) 1284; Orr, V. and Coates, J. *Industr. Engng Chem.* 52 (1960) 27; Othmer, D. F., Gilmont, R. and Conti, J. J. *ibid.* 625; Hála, E., Pick, J., Fried, V. and Vilím, O. *Vapour–Liquid Equilibrium*, 2nd edn., Oxford (Pergamon) 1967

[10] Baxendale, J. H., Enüstün, B. V. and Stern, J. *Phil. Trans.* A243 (1951) 169; Allen, P. W., Everett, D. H. and Penney, M. F. *Proc. R. Soc.* A212 (1952) 149

[11] Redlich, O. and Kister, A. T. *J. Am. chem. Soc.* 71 (1949) 505; Clark, A. M., Din, F. and Robb, J. *Proc. R. Soc.* A221 (1954) 517; Taylor, J. B. and Rowlinson, J. S. *Trans. Faraday Soc.* 51 (1955) 1183

[12] Walling, J. F. and Halsey, G. D. *J. chem. Phys.* 30 (1959) 1514; Bellemans, A. *Bull. Soc. chim. Belg.* 68 (1959) 355; with Lefebvre, C. and Guisset, J.-L. 69 (1960) 441; Lefebvre, C. and Guisset, J. *Molec. Phys.* 4 (1961) 199; Christian, S. D., Neparko, E., Affsprung, H. E. and Gibbard, F. *J. phys. Chem.* 65 (1961) 1048

[13] Dixon, D. T. and McGlashan, M. L. *Nature, Lond.* 206 (1965) 710

[14] Barker, J. A. *Aust. J. Chem.* 6 (1953) 207

[15] Wilson, G. M. *J. Am. chem. Soc.* 86 (1964) 127

[16] Scatchard, G., with Wilson, G., M. *J. Am. chem. Soc.* 86 (1964) 133; with Satkiewicz, F. G. *ibid.* 130; Orye, R. V. and Prausnitz, J. M. *Industr. Engng Chem.* 57 (1965) No. 5, 18

REFERENCES

17 Prausnitz, J. M., Eckert, C. A., Orye, R. V. and O'Connell, J. P. *Computer Calculations for Multi-component Vapor-liquid Equilibria*, New Jersey (Prentice-Hall) 1967

18 Everett, D. H. and Stoddart, C. T. H. *Trans. Faraday Soc.* 57 (1961) 746; Everett, D. H. 61 (1965) 1637; Cruickshank, A. J. B., Gainey, B. W. and Young, C. L. 64 (1968) 337; Gainey, B. W. and Young, C. L. *ibid.* 349; Conder, J. R. and Purnell, J. H. *ibid.* 1505; Young, C. L. *ibid.* 1537; with Hicks, C. P. *ibid.* 2675; Langer, S. H. and Purnell, J. H. *J. phys. Chem.* 67 (1963) 263; Cruickshank, A. J. B., Windsor, M. L. and Young, C. L. *Proc. R. Soc.* A295 (1966) 259, 271

19 Liberti, A., Cartoni, G. P. and Bruner, F., in *Gas Chromatography 1964* (ed. Goldup, A.), p. 301, London (Inst. Petrol.) 1965

20 Brown, I. A. *Rev. phys. Chem.* 16 (1965) 147

21 Larkin, J. A. and McGlashan, M. L. *J. chem. Soc.* (1961) 3425; McGlashan, M. L., *Heats of Mixing* in *Experimental Thermochemistry* (ed. Skinner, H. A.), Vol. 2, Ch. 15, New York (Interscience) 1962; *Pure appl. Chem.* 8 (1964) 157; see also Mrazek, R. V. and Van Ness, H. C. *A.I.Ch.E.Jl* 7 (1961) 190; Savini, C. G., Winterhalter, D. R., Kovach, L. H. and Van Ness, H. C. *J. chem. Engng Data* 11 (1966) 40; Winterhalter, D. R. and Van Ness, H. C. *ibid.* 189

22 Mitchell, A. G. and Wynne-Jones, W. F. K. *Discuss. Faraday Soc.* 15 (1953) 161; Malcolm, G. N. and Rowlinson, J. S. *Trans. Faraday Soc.* 53 (1957) 921

23 Griffiths, V. S. *J. chem. Soc.* (1954) 860; Schott, H. *J. chem. Engng Data* 6 (1961) 19

24 Smyth, C. P. and Engel, E. W. *J. Am. chem. Soc.* 51 (1929) 2660

25 Beatty, H. A. and Calingaert, G. *Industr. Engng Chem.* 26 (1934) 904

26 Bredig, G. and Bayer, R. *Z. phys. Chem.* 130 (1927) 1

27 McGlashan, M. L. and Wingrove, R. J. *Trans. Faraday Soc.* 52 (1956) 470

28 Coulson, E. A. and Herington, E. F. G. *Trans. Faraday Soc.* 44 (1948) 629; Herington, E. F. G. *J. Inst. Petrol.* 37 (1951) 332; Redlich, O. and Kister, A. T. *Industr. Engng Chem.* 40 (1948) 341; Ibl, N. V. and Dodge, B. F. *Chem. Engng. Sci.* 2 (1953) 120; Stevenson, F. D. and Sater, V. E. *A.I.Ch.E.Jl* 12 (1966) 586

29 McGlashan, M. L., Prue, J. E. and Sainsbury, I. E. J. *Trans. Faraday Soc.* 50 (1954) 1284

30 Duncan, A. G. and Staveley, L. A. K. *Trans. Faraday Soc.* 62 (1966) 548; Davies, R. H.; Duncan, A. G., Saville, G. and Staveley, L. A. K. 63 (1967) 855

31 Schmidt, H. *Z. phys. Chem. Frankf. Ausg.* 20 (1959) 363; 24 (1960) 265

32 Wilhelm, G. and Schneider, G. *Z. phys. Chem. Frankf. Ausg.* 32 (1962) 62

33 Köhler, W. *Dissertation*, Univ. Göttingen, 1964

34 Seemeyer, D. *Dissertation*, Univ. Göttingen, 1965

35 Yunker, W. H. and Halsey, G. D. *J. phys. Chem.* 64 (1960) 484

36 Walling, J. F. and Halsey, G. D. *J. phys. Chem.* 62 (1958) 752

37 Pool, R. A. H., Saville, G., Herington, T. M., Shields, B. D. C. and Staveley, L. A. K. *Trans. Faraday Soc.* 58 (1962) 1692

[38] Narinskii, G. B. *Kislorod* 10 (1957) No. 3 p. 9; *Z. phys. Chem. Frankf. Ausg.* 34 (1960) 1778; *Russ. J. phys. Chem.* 40 (1966) 1093

[39] Sprow, F. B. and Prausnitz, J. M. *A.I.Ch.E.Jl* 12 (1966) 780

[40] Holst, G. and Hamburger, L. *Proc. Sect. Sci. K. ned. Akad. Wet.* 18 (1915–16) 872; *Z. phys. Chem.* 91 (1916) 513

[41] Long, H. M. and DiPaolo, F. S. *Chem. Engng Prog. Symp. Ser.* 59 (1963) No. 44 p. 30; Barrett, C. S. and Meyer, L. *J. chem. Phys.* 42 (1965) 107

[42] Burn, I. and Din, F. *Trans. Faraday Soc.* 58 (1962) 1341

[43] Knobler, C. M., van Heijningen, R. J. J. and Beenakker, J. J. M. *Physica* 27 (1961) 296

[44] Knaap, H. F. P., Knoester, M. and Beenakker, J. J. M. *Physica* 27 (1961) 309

[45] Wang, D. I. J. *Adv. cryogen. Engng* 3 (1960) 294

[46] Mathot, V. *Nuovo Cim.* 9 (1958) Suppl. No. 1 p. 356; Mathot, V. and Lefebvre, C., to be published; Fuks, S. and Bellemans, A. *Bull. Soc. chim. Belg.* 76 (1967) 290

[47] Lambert, M. and Simon, M. *Physica* 28 (1962) 1191

[48] Jeener, J. *Rev. scient. Instrum.* 28 (1957) 263

[49] Thorp, N. and Scott, R. L. *J. phys. Chem.* 60 (1956) 670

[50] Din, F. *Trans. Faraday Soc.* 56 (1960) 668

[51] Armstrong, G. T., Goldstein, J. M. and Roberts, D. E. *J. Res. natn. Bur. Stand.* 55 (1955) 265

[52] Mathot, V., Staveley, L. A. K., Young, J. A. and Parsonage, N. G. *Trans. Faraday Soc.* 52 (1956) 1488; Pool, R. A. H. and Staveley, L. A. K. 53 (1957) 1186

[53] Clusius, K., Piesbergen, U. and Vardi, E. *Helv. chim. Acta* 45 (1962) 1211

[54] Wilson, G. M., Silverberg, P. M. and Zellner, M. G. *International Advances in Cryogenic Engineering* (ed. Timmerhaus, K. D.), p. 192, New York (Plenum Press) 1965; *U.S. Off. tech. Rep. No. APL TDR* 64–64 (1964)

[55] Brønsted, J. N. and Koefoed, J. *K. danske Vidensk. Selsk. (Mat. Fys. Shr.)* 22 (1946) No. 17

[56] Holleman, Th. *Physica* 29 (1963) 585; 31 (1965) 49; *Ph.D. Thesis*, Univ. Amsterdam 1964

[57] McGlashan, M. L. and Williamson, A. G. *Trans. Faraday Soc.* 57 (1961) 588

[58] Cutler, A. J. B. and Morrison, J. A. *Trans. Faraday Soc.* 61 (1965) 429; Shana'a, M. Y. and Canfield, F. B. 64 (1968) 2281

[59] Mathieson, A. R. and Thynne, J. C. J. *J. chem. Soc.* (1956) 3708

[60] van der Waals, J. H. and Hermans, J. J. *Recl Trav. chim. Pays-Bas Belg.* 68 (1949) 181; 69 (1950) 949, 971; van der Waals, J. H. 70 (1951) 101

[61] McGlashan, M. L. and Morcom, K. W. *Trans. Faraday Soc.* 57 (1961) 581; with Williamson, A. G. 57 (1961) 601

[62] Lundberg, G. W. *J. chem. Engng Data* 9 (1964) 193

[63] Fernandez-Garcia, J. G. and Boissonnas, Ch. G. *Helv. chim. Acta* 49 (1966) 854; Stoeckli, H. F., Fernandez-Garcia, J. G. and Boissonnas, Ch. G. *Trans. Faraday Soc.* 62 (1966) 3044

[64] Desmyter, A. and van der Waals, J. H. *Recl Trav. chim. Pays-Bas Belg.* 77 (1958) 53; Hijmans, J. *Molec. Phys.* 1 (1958) 307

REFERENCES

[65] Gomez-Ibanez, J. D. and Liu, C.-T. *J. phys. Chem.* 65 (1962) 2148; 67 (1963) 1388

[66] Harrison, C. and Winnick, J. *J. chem. Engng Data* 12 (1967) 176

[67] Larkin, J. A., Fenby, D. V., Gilman, T. S. and Scott, R. L. *J. phys. Chem.* 70 (1966) 1959

[68] Mathot, V. *Bull. Soc. chim. Belg.* 59 (1950) 111; Crützen, J. L., Haase, R. and Sieg, L. *Z. Naturf.* 5a (1950) 600; Gomez-Ibanez, J. D. and Shieh, J. J. C. *J. phys. Chem.* 69 (1965) 1660; with Thorsteinson, E. M. 70 (1966) 1998

[69] Mathot, V. and Desmyter, A. *J. chem. Phys.* 21 (1953) 782

[70] Jones, H. K. De Q. and Lu, B. C.-Y. *J. chem. Engng Data* 11 (1966) 488

[71] Brown, C. P., Mathieson, A. R. and Thynne, J. C. J. *J. chem. Soc.* (1955) 4141

[72] Schnaible, H. W., Van Ness, H. C. and Smith, J. M. *A.I.Ch.E.Jl* 3 (1957) 147

[73] Schmidt, R. L., Randall, J. C. and Clever, H. L. *J. phys. Chem.* 70 (1966) 3912

[74] Brown, I. and Ewald, A. H. *Aust. J. scient. Res.* A3 (1950) 306; A4 (1951) 198

[75] Danusso, F. *Atti Accad. naz. Lincei Memorie* 13 (1952) 131; 17 (1954) 109; Powell, R. J. and Swinton, F. L. *J. chem. Engng Data* 13 (1968) 260

[76] Callot, P. *Ph.D. Thesis* Univ. Strasbourg, 1967

[77] Scatchard, G., Ticknor, L. B., Goates, J. R. and McCartney, E. R. *J. Am. chem. Soc.* 74 (1952) 3721; Goates, J. R., Sullivan, R. J. and Ott, J. B. *J. phys. Chem.* 63 (1959) 589

[78] Watson, A. E. P., McLure, I. A., Bennett, J. E. and Benson, G. C. *J. phys. Chem.* 69 (1965) 2753, 2759

[79] Mrazek, R. V. and Van Ness, H. C. *A.I.Ch.E.Jl* 7 (1961) 190; Savini, C. G., Winterhalter, D. R., Kovach, L. H. and Van Ness, H. C. *J. chem. Engng Data* 11 (1966) 40

[80] Noordtzij, R. M. A. *Helv. chim. Acta* 39 (1956) 637

[81] Nicholson, D. E. *J. chem. Engng Data* 6 (1961) 5

[82] Scatchard, G., Wood, S. E. and Mochel, J. M. *J. phys. Chem.* 43 (1939) 119; *J. Am. chem. Soc.* 61 (1939) 3206; 62 (1940) 712

[83] Cheesman, G. H. and Whitaker, A. M. B. *Proc. R. Soc.* A212 (1952) 406; Adcock, D. S. and McGlashan, M. L. A226 (1954) 266

[84] Englert-Chwoles, A. *J. chem. Phys.* 23 (1955) 1168; Jeener, J. 25 (1956) 534; Prigogine, I. *The Molecular Theory of Solutions*, p. 211, 213, 214, 223–6, Amsterdam (North-Holland) 1957

[85] Chang, E. T. and Westrum, E. F. *J. phys. Chem.* 69 (1965) 2176

[86] Kehlen, H. and Sackmann, H. *Z. phys. Chem. Frankf. Ausg.* 50 (1966) 144

[87] Wood, S. E. and Gray, J. A. *J. Am. chem. Soc.* 74 (1952) 3729

[88] Diaz Peña, M. and McGlashan, M. L. *Trans. Faraday Soc.* 57 (1961) 1511

[89] Rastogi, R. P. and Nigam, R. K. *Trans. Faraday Soc.* 55 (1959) 2005

[90] Larkin, J. A. and McGlashan, M. L. *J. chem. Soc.* (1961) 3425

[91] Staveley, L. A. K., Tupman, W. I. and Hart, K. R. *Trans. Faraday Soc.* 51 (1955) 323

[92] Wood, S. E. and Brusie, J. P. *J. Am. chem. Soc.* 65 (1943) 1891

[93] Mueller, C. R. and Ignatowski, A. J. *J. chem. Phys.* 32 (1960) 1430
[94] Ott, J. B., Goates, J. R. and Budge, A. H. *J. phys. Chem.* 66 (1962) 1387; Rastogi, R. P., Nath, J. and Misra, J. 71 (1967) 1277; Morcom, K. W. and Travers, D. N. *Trans. Faraday Soc.* 62 (1966) 2063
[95] Barker, J. A. and Smith, F. *J. chem. Phys.* 22 (1954) 375; Otterstedt, J.-E. A. and Missen, R. W. *J. chem. Engng Data* 11 (1966) 360
[96] von Zawidzki, J. *Z. phys. Chem.* 35 (1900) 129
[97] Seig, L., Crützen, J. L. and Jost, W. *Z. phys. Chem.* 198 (1951) 263
[98] Ruiter, L. H. *Recl Trav. chim. Pays-Bas Belg.* 74 (1955) 1131, 1467, 1491
[99] Canning, J. and Cheesman, G. H. *J. chem. Soc.* (1955) 1230

5

MIXTURES OF COMPLEX LIQUIDS

5.1 Introduction

The mixtures discussed in the last Chapter all had excess heats and free energies that were much smaller than RT (2500 J mol⁻¹... at room temperature). All the substances were non-polar or but weakly polar, and all were miscible with their partners at all concentrations. They were simple and similar substances and, in the common phrase, 'like dissolves like'.

However, many liquid pairs are not completely miscible and have excess heats and free energies that are comparable with RT. For want of a better name, such liquids are called here *complex liquids*, although the complexity or abnormality is often attributable to only one of the partners and should more properly be ascribed to the mixture rather than to its components. One or both of the components are generally from the fourth or fifth of the classes set out in Chapter 1. Such mixtures have excess functions which are often not *quadratic* (in the sense of Section 4.4) as well as being large.

This Chapter starts with a discussion of the conditions of stability and equilibrium of a binary mixture of one liquid phase at low pressures. The temperature at which it changes to a heterogeneous mixture of two phases is called a *critical solution temperature* (C.S.T.) or *consolute temperature*. Such a point has many of the characteristics of a gas–liquid critical point in a system of one component. The later Sections contain examples of such behaviour and of the excess functions of some important complex mixtures.

5.2 Thermodynamics of Partially Miscible Liquids

A homogeneous mixture must satisfy not only the two conditions of mechanical and thermal stability (Section 2.1) but also a third, that of material (or diffusional) stability. A statement of this condition may be most simply obtained from the requirement that all spontaneous fluctuations in a system at equilibrium at constant pressure and temperature must lead to an increase in the Gibbs free energy. This can be so in a binary mixture only if the curve representing g as a function of mole fraction at constant p and T is everywhere concave upwards*, that is, if

$$(\partial^2 g/\partial x_1^2)_{p,T} = (\partial^2 g/\partial x_2^2)_{p,T} > 0 \qquad (5.1)$$

This condition can also be derived together with the condition of mechanical stability by considering the (a, v, x) surface. This second derivation is the analogue of that of the conditions of mechanical and thermal stability in a one-component system from the (U, S, V) surface. It is needed in the next Chapter. In principle, all three conditions of stability could be derived by considering the hyper-surface representing U as a function of S, V, m_1 and m_2, but fortunately such a derivation has never yet been found necessary.

The inequality (5.1) is similar to the condition of mechanical stability derived from a graph of a as a function of v (Section 3.1) and may be illustrated by a graph of g as a function of x (*Figure 5.1*).

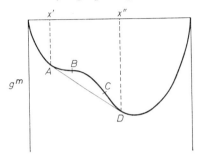

Figure 5.1. The molar free energy of mixing as a function of mole fraction, when g is a continuous function of x

The portion BC is unstable with respect to material fluctuations and is surrounded by the portions AB and CD which are materially stable, but are metastable with respect to the heterogeneous mixture represented by the straight line AD.

The drawing of such a graph requires the assumption that it is meaningful to represent g as a continuous function through stable and unstable phases. Such an assumption is as questionable as the corresponding one in Chapter 3 about the continuity of a, and is as necessary for the simple application of classical thermodynamics to a critical point. It is not necessary for deriving the conditions of equilibrium between the phases at temperatures well removed from a critical point, since the portion of the curve BC is now separated from the equilibrium states by portions which are materially stable.

The two phases in equilibrium have compositions A and D, for it is

* See Prigogine and Defay[1] for a detailed discussion of both binary and ternary mixtures.

simple to show that the common tangent AD satisfies the equilibrium equations

$$\mu_1' = \mu_1'', \qquad \mu_2' = \mu_2'' \tag{5.2}$$

where the prime and double-prime denote the two phases. From (4.14) and (4.15)

$$\mu_1' = g' - x_2'(\partial g/\partial x_2)_{p,T}' = \mu_1'' = g'' - x_2''(\partial g/\partial x_2)_{p,T}'' \tag{5.3}$$

$$\mu_2' = g' + x_1'(\partial g/\partial x_2)_{p,T}' = \mu_2'' = g'' + x_1''(\partial g/\partial x_2)_{p,T}'' \tag{5.4}$$

Subtraction of these equations gives

$$(\partial g/\partial x_2)_{p,T}' = (\partial g/\partial x_2)_{p,T}'' \tag{5.5}$$

and substitution in the first

$$(g' - g'')/(x_2' - x_2'') = (\partial g/\partial x_2)_{p,T} \tag{5.6}$$

These two equations show that AD satisfies (5.2). Any point on this line of overall composition X_2 represents two phases, of m' and m'' moles, where

$$m' = 1 - m'' = (x_2'' - X_2)/(x_2'' - x_2') \tag{5.7}$$

The number of moles of component 1 in *phase'* is $(x_1'm')$.

The condition of material stability may be expressed in terms of the chemical potentials by differentiating with respect to x_2 the equation

$$\mu_1 = g - x_2(\partial g/\partial x_2)_{p,T} \tag{5.8}$$

This differentiation gives

$$(\partial \mu_1/\partial x_2)_{p,T} = -x_2(\partial^2 g/\partial x_2^2)_{p,T} < 0 \tag{5.9}$$

Similarly,

$$(\partial \mu_2/\partial x_1)_{p,T} = -x_1(\partial^2 g/\partial x_1^2)_{p,T} = (x_1/x_2)(\partial \mu_1/\partial x_2)_{p,T} < 0 \tag{5.10}$$

since

$$(\partial^2 g/\partial x_1^2)_{p,T} = (\partial^2 g/\partial x_2^2)_{p,T} \tag{5.11}$$

The compositions of the equilibrium phases A and D of *Figure 5.1* change with pressure and temperature. Consider a pressure p, a temperature T and compositions x_2' and x_2'' at which the system is in equilibrium. The potentials satisfy (5.2). Consider now a neighbouring state of the system $(p + \delta p)$, $(T + \delta T)$, $(x_2' + \delta x_2')$, $(x_2'' + \delta x_2'')$, in which it is also at equilibrium. If the potentials are still to satisfy (5.2), then

$$(\partial \mu_1/\partial p)_{T,x}' \delta p + (\partial \mu_1/\partial T)_{p,x}' \delta T + (\partial \mu_1/\partial x_2)_{p,T}' \delta x_2'$$
$$= (\partial \mu_1/\partial p)_{T,x}'' \delta p + (\partial \mu_1/\partial T)_{p,x}'' \delta T + (\partial \mu_1/\partial x_2)_{p,T}'' \delta x_2'' \tag{5.12}$$

and similarly for component 2. Subtraction of the two sides of these equations gives

$$\Delta v_1 \, \delta p - \Delta s_1 \, \delta T - x_2'(\partial^2 g/\partial x^2)_{p,T}' \, \delta x_2' + x_2''(\partial^2 g/\partial x^2)_{p,T}'' \, \delta x_2'' = 0 \tag{5.13}$$

$$\Delta v_2 \, \delta p - \Delta s_2 \, \delta T + x_1'(\partial^2 g/\partial x^2)_{p,T}' \, \delta x_2' - x_1''(\partial^2 g/\partial x^2)_{p,T}'' \, \delta x_2'' = 0 \tag{5.14}$$

where

$$\Delta v_1 = v_1' - v_1'', \qquad \text{etc.} \tag{5.15}$$

Since

$$\Delta \mu_1 = \Delta h_1 - T\Delta s_1 = 0 \tag{5.16}$$

then

$$\Delta s_1 = \Delta h_1/T \tag{5.17}$$

The study of partially miscible liquids is usually made at constant pressure or at a low saturation pressure which may, without sensible error, be treated as a constant zero pressure. The pair of equations (5.13) and (5.14) may be solved at constant pressure to give

$$\left(\frac{\partial x_2}{\partial T}\right)_p' = - \frac{\Delta h_1 x_2'' + \Delta h_2 x_2''}{T(g_{2x}')\Delta x_2} \tag{5.18}$$

$$\left(\frac{\partial x_2}{\partial T}\right)_p'' = - \frac{\Delta h_1 x_1' + \Delta h_2 x_2'}{T(g_{2x}'')\Delta x_2} \tag{5.19}$$

where g_{2x} is an abbreviation for $(\partial^2 g/\partial x^2)_{p,T}$. The numerator of (5.18) is a molar heat of solution of a drop of *phase″* of composition (x_1'', x_2'') in *phase′* at constant pressure and temperature. It may be written in another form by using (4.14)

$$\Delta h_1 x_1'' + \Delta h_2 x_2'' = \Delta h - \Delta x_2(\partial h/\partial x_2)_{p,T}' \tag{5.20}$$

Hence

$$\left(\frac{\partial x_2}{\partial T}\right)_p' = \frac{1}{Tg_{2x}'}\left[\left(\frac{\partial h}{\partial x_2}\right)_{p,T}' - \frac{\Delta h}{\Delta x_2}\right] \tag{5.21}$$

and similarly for the second phase.

A mixture reaches a critical solution point when A, B, C and D of *Figure 5.1* all coincide. B and C are the limits of material stability, and so it follows that g_{2x} is zero at a critical point. If all points near the critical are to be stable, then

$$g_{2x}^c = 0, \qquad g_{3x}^c = 0, \qquad g_{4x}^c > 0 \tag{5.22}$$

These conditions determine the limiting form of (5.21) near a critical point. Let g be represented by a Taylor expansion in T and x_2, at constant pressure, about its value at the critical point. The leading terms are

$$g = g^c + g^c_x(\delta x) - s^c(\delta T) - s^c_x(\delta x)(\delta T) - \tfrac{1}{2}s^c_{2x}(\delta x)^2(\delta T)$$
$$+ \tfrac{1}{24}g^c_{4x}(\delta x)^4 + \ldots \quad (5.23)$$

where (δx) now denotes $(x_2 - x_2^c)$ and g^c_{2x} and g^c_{3x} have been put equal to zero. Higher powers of (δT) may be neglected. The differential coefficients of g with respect to x and T, that is, g_x, g_{2x}, s and s_x, are easily obtained from (5.23). Equilibrium between two phases require the equality of both g_x and $(g - (\delta x)g_x)$ in each phase, (5.5 and 5.6). This may be expressed in terms of the derivatives of (5.23)

$$-s^c_{2x}(\delta T)(\delta x' - \delta x'') + \tfrac{1}{6}g^c_{4x}[(\delta x')^3 - (\delta x'')^3] = 0 \quad (5.24)$$

$$g^c_{4x}[(\delta x')^2 - (\delta x'')^2][(\delta x') - (\delta x'')]^2 = 0 \quad (5.25)$$

The second equation gives at once

$$\delta x' = -\delta x'' = \tfrac{1}{2}\Delta x \quad (5.26)$$

The first then gives

$$\tfrac{1}{6}g^c_{4x}(\delta x')^2 = \tfrac{1}{6}g^c_{4x}(\delta x'')^2 = s^c_{2x}(\delta T) \quad (5.27)$$

The right-hand side of (5.20) may be expressed in terms of the derivatives of g

$$\frac{1}{T}\left[\left(\frac{\partial h}{\partial x}\right)'_{p,T} - \frac{\Delta h}{\Delta x}\right] = \left(\frac{\partial s}{\partial x}\right)'_{p,T} - \frac{\Delta s}{\Delta x} = \tfrac{1}{2}s^c_{2x}\Delta x \quad (5.28)$$

whence

$$\left(\frac{\partial x_2}{\partial T}\right)' = -\left(\frac{\partial x_2}{\partial T}\right)'' = \frac{6s^c_{2x}}{g^c_{4x}\Delta x_2} \quad (5.29)$$

This equation shows that x is a quadratic function of $(T - T^c)$ near the critical point for a mixture at constant (or negligible) pressure. It is analogous to (3.18) for the gas–liquid critical point. The sign of the right-hand side of (5.29) is determined by that of s^c_{2x}, since g^c_{4x} is necessarily positive. The sign of s^c_{2x} is the same as that of h^c_{2x}, as g^c_{2x} is zero. If $x''_2 > x^c_2 > x'_2$, then $(\partial x_2/\partial T)'_p$ is positive and $(\partial x_2/\partial T)''_p$ is negative, if s^c_{2x} and h^c_{2x} are negative. These signs define an upper critical solution point[2] (*Figure 5.2*). The inequalities at upper and lower points may be expressed concisely by using the excess thermodynamic functions*

$$g^c_{2x} = RT^c/x_1x_2 + (g^E_{2x})^c = 0 \quad (5.30)$$

$$h^c_{2x} = (h^E_{2x})^c < 0 \text{ (U.C.S.T.) or} > 0 \text{ (L.C.S.T.)} \quad (5.31)$$

$$s^c_{2x} = -R/x_1x_2 + (s^E_{2x})^c < 0 \text{ (U.C.S.T.) or} > 0 \text{ (L.C.S.T.)} \quad (5.32)$$

* See, for example, Copp and Everett[3] and the discussion of their paper (ref. 3 p. 267–278).

The signs of the second derivatives of h and s determine those of the functions themselves only if the $h - x$ and $s - x$ graphs have no points of inflection. This is true in a quadratic mixture for which

$$x_1 x_2 g_{2x} = RT - 2g^E \qquad (5.33)$$

$$x_1 x_2 h_{2x} = -2h^E \qquad (5.34)$$

$$x_1 x_2 s_{2x} = -R - 2s^E \qquad (5.35)$$

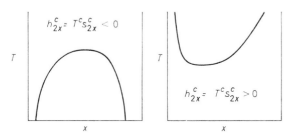

Figure 5.2. Typical sketches of the phase-boundary curves near upper and lower critical solution points (U.C.S.T. and L.C.S.T.)

A quadratic mixture can have a U.C.S.T if h^E is positive, irrespective of the sign of s^E as long as it is greater than $(-R/2)$. It can have a L.C.S.T. only if h^E and s^E are both negative and if the latter is smaller than $(-R/2)$. In both cases the phase-boundary curve is symmetrical in x_1 and x_2 and the critical point is at the equimolar composition.

In practice, it is found that mixtures which are sufficiently nonideal to show a L.C.S.T. are rarely quadratic, but that these inequalities are qualitatively correct. It is seen that a L.C.S.T. occurs only with a large negative value of s^E, whilst a U.C.S.T. can occur with a small s^E of either sign. The former are much the less common and their interpretation in terms of the properties of molecules is less simple. They are discussed in more detail in Section 5.5.

There are no thermodynamic restrictions on the signs or sizes of the excess heat capacity and excess volume at critical solution points, but it is most common for the former to be negative and the latter positive at a U.C.S.T., and vice versa at a L.C.S.T. If the negative excess heat capacity at a L.C.S.T. keeps this sign as the temperature is raised, then h^E and s^E eventually become positive and the conditions for a U.C.S.T. may be satisfied. Such a mixture shows a closed solubility loop, there being a range of temperature bounded above and below in which the components are only partially miscible. It is found that L.C.S.T. are followed by U.C.S.T. if the temperature is raised sufficiently, and if a gas–liquid critical point is not reached first. The sign of the excess volume (or, more strictly, of its second derivative) determines the effect of pressure on a critical temperature. A displacement along a critical line in (p, T, x) space is one for which g_{2x} remains equal to zero. Hence, for a small displacement δp, etc.

$$\delta(g_{2x}) = g^c_{p2x}(\delta p) + g^c_{T2x}(\delta T) + g^c_{3x}(\delta x) = 0 \qquad (5.36)$$

The third term is itself zero, and so

$$(\mathrm{d}T^c/\mathrm{d}p) = -g^c_{p2x}/g^c_{T2x} = v^c_{2x}/s^c_{2x} \qquad (5.37)$$

The sign of v^c_{2x} is the opposite of that of v^E in the absence of a point of inflection on the $v^E - x$ graph. The usual effect of an increase of pressure is, therefore, to raise critical solution temperatures. This is discussed more fully in the next Chapter.

Much of the development of this Section has been based on the assumptions, first, that the Taylor expansion (5.23) is valid near the critical point and, secondly, that g_{4x} is the first non-vanishing derivative at this point. Both assumptions are subject to the same uncertainty as were those of the continuity of a and its derivatives in the discussion of the gas–liquid critical point in Chapter 3. It is interesting to relax the second assumption and to let g_{2nx} be the first non-vanishing derivative, where n is any integer equal to or greater than 2. The derivative g_{2x} is now of the order of $(x - x^c)^{2n-2}$. The left-hand side of (5.28) is still of the order of $(x - x^c)$, and so Δx is a function of order $1/(2n - 2)$ in $(T - T^c)$. That is, the co-existence curve is of even order near the critical point. In practice, it seems that cubic curves are much the best representation of the experimental results at both upper and lower critical points

$$|x' - x''| \propto |T - T^c|^{1/3} \qquad (5.38)$$

This is the exact analogue of the behaviour of the orthobaric densities in a one-component system at a gas–liquid critical point.

This cubic equation has been found to fit best most modern measurements[4-8] in the range of 1–30 K for $|T - T^c|$. A co-existence curve near a U.C.S.T. is usually reasonably symmetrical in the mole fractions of the components and the mean composition $(x' + x'')/2$ follows a rectilinear diameter, as is implied by (5.26). The curve is often even more symmetrical if plotted in terms of volume fractions and not mole fractions[7]. Lower critical solution temperatures are usually far from symmetrical on both mole and volume fraction graphs, and rarely have a rectilinear diameter. However, Cox and Herington[6] have shown that twelve mixtures with U.C.S.T. and four with L.C.S.T. all conform reasonably well to equations of the type

$$\ln \left[\frac{x_1' x_2^c}{x_2' x_1^c}\right] = \ln \left[\frac{x_2'' x_1^c}{x_1'' x_2^c}\right] = B \, |T - T^c|^{1/3} \qquad (5.39)$$

where B is an empirical parameter. These equations are equivalent to (5.38) only in the immediate neighbourhood of the critical point but, as is shown in *Figure 5.3*, they may be obeyed over quite wide ranges of temperature.

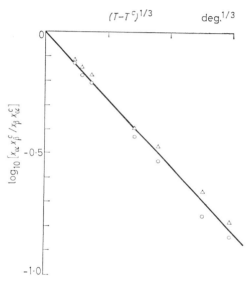

Figure 5.3. A test of equation (5.39) for water + 2,6-dimethyl pyridine near the L.C.S.T. of 34·06°C (from the results of Cox and Herington[6]). The circles represent the phase rich in water (β = water) and the triangles the phase weak in water (α = water). Both sets of points fall near the straight line but could be more accurately represented by two lines, one for each phase[6]. The critical composition is a mole fraction of water of 0·9355

It is useful to have a quantitative criterion of the closeness of a mixture to phase separation. There are many mixtures for which g^E, h^E and s^E have the right signs for exhibiting a U.C.S.T. or a L.C.S.T., but which remain miscible at all temperatures because the excess functions are too small. A rough criterion is, therefore, the size of g^E. If this exceeds $\frac{1}{2}RT$, the critical value for a quadratic mixture, then phase separation is likely[3]. A rigorous but experimentally less accessible criterion is provided by the function[9,10]

$$(x_1 x_2 / RT)(\partial^2 g^E / \partial x^2)_{p,T}$$

which, by (5.30), is equal to -1 at a critical point and lies above this in a homogeneous mixture. The minimum value of this function[10] for an aqueous solution of 3-methyl pyridine is -0.995 at 70°C and a mole fraction of water of 0.905. The mixture does not separate into two phases but shows the characteristic critical opalescence around this point.

The heat capacity at constant volume was shown in Chapter 3 to be sensitive to the order of discontinuity at a gas–liquid critical point. If C_V became infinite in the homogeneous phase, then the (a, v, T) surface was inadequate to discuss the critical point. It was necessary to appeal to the (U, S, V) surface to show that such an infinity must be of lower order than that of the compressibility. In fact, the experimental evidence is that this heat capacity is probably infinite, and that there is also an infinity in the heat capacity of the two-phase system at constant total volume.

The heat capacity at constant pressure plays an analogous role in the discussion of the critical solution temperature of two liquids. The experimental evidence for an infinity is weaker than that for C_V in systems of one component, but if the analogy holds, then the two infinities stand or fall together. However, before discussing this analogy more closely, it is worth analysing the behaviour of C_p of the two-phase system on the assumption that g is an analytic function of x and T.

Consider, as before, one mole of mixture of overall composition X_2, of which *phase'* contains $(x_1'm')$ moles of component 1 and $(x_2'm')$ moles of component 2, and *phase"* similarly $(x_1''m'')$ and $(x_2''m'')$ moles, (5.7). The heat capacity of such a mixture near, say, a U.C.S.T. is composed of two terms. The first is the heat supplied to raise the temperature of the phases at constant pressure and composition. This is given simply by the product of the known amounts of each component in each phase and their partial molar heat capacities. It may be ignored in the present discussion, as it behaves relatively smoothly on passing the critical point. The second term is that related to the changes in amount and composition of each phase and to the difference of the partial molar heat contents in the two phases. This heat-of-transfer term is the characteristic excess heat capacity of the two-phase system over a one-phase system. It may be written

$$(C_2 - C_1)_p = \Delta h_1 \left(\frac{\partial (x_1'm')}{\partial T} \right)_p + \Delta h_2 \left(\frac{\partial (x_2'm')}{\partial T} \right)_p \qquad (5.40)$$

where Δh_1 denotes, as before, $(h_1' - h_1'')$. By substitution for m' from (5.7), and by using (5.18) and (5.19), this equation may be put in the form

$$(C_2 - C_1)_p = Tm'g'_{2x}\left(\frac{\partial x'_2}{\partial T}\right)_p^2 + Tm''g''_{2x}\left(\frac{\partial x''_2}{\partial T}\right)_p^2 \qquad (5.41)$$

This expression is always positive, irrespective of the signs of Δh_1 and Δh_2, since g_{2x} must be positive to maintain material stability. If g_{4x} is the first non-vanishing derivative at the critical point, then g_{2x} is of the order of $(x - x^c)^2$ and $(\partial x_2/\partial T)_p$ is of the order of $(x - x^c)^{-1}$. The difference $(C_2 - C_1)_p$ is then finite at the critical point and is given by

$$(C_2 - C_1)_p^c = \frac{3T^c(s_{2x}^c)^2}{g_{4x}^c} \qquad (5.42)$$

This difference is $(3R/2)$ in a quadratic mixture in which g^E is independent of temperature. If g_{2nx} is the first non-vanishing derivative of the free energy, then g_{2x} is of the order of $(x - x^c)^{2n-2}$, $(\partial x/\partial T)_p$ is of the order of $(x - x^c)^{-2n+3}$ and

$$(C_2 - C_1)_p \propto (x - x^c)^{-2n+4} \propto (T - T^c)^{-\left(\frac{n-2}{n-1}\right)} \qquad (5.43)$$

Thus C_2 shows an infinity at the critical point if $n > 2$.

The difference between the coefficients of thermal expansion of a two-phase mixture and that of the separated homogeneous phases may be found by a similar argument

$$(\alpha_2 - \alpha_1)_p = \frac{\Delta v_1}{v}\left(\frac{\partial(x'_1 m')}{\partial T}\right)_p + \frac{\Delta v_2}{v}\left(\frac{\partial(x'_2 m')}{\partial T}\right)_p \qquad (5.44)$$

If g_{4x} is the first non-vanishing derivative at the critical point, then

$$(\alpha_2 - \alpha_1)_p^c = \frac{3s_{2x}^c v_{2x}^c}{v^c g_{4x}^c} \qquad (5.45)$$

If the first non-vanishing derivative is g_{2nx}, the variation of $(\alpha_2 - \alpha_1)_p$ with temperature is that of the right-hand side of (5.43). The fundamental equations (5.13) and (5.14) are formally symmetrical in δT and δp, and so $(\beta_2 - \beta_1)_T$ is given by an equation analogous to (5.44) and, in the simple case,

$$(\beta_2 - \beta_1)_T = \frac{3(v_{2x}^c)^2}{v^c g_{4x}^c} \qquad (5.46)$$

Thus $(\gamma_2 - \gamma_1)_V$ and so $(C_2 - C_1)_V$ remain finite whatever the order of the first non-vanishing derivative of g, as

$$C_p - C_V = TV\alpha_p\gamma_V = TV\beta_T\gamma_V^2 \qquad (5.47)$$

holds for both 2-phase and 1-phase systems. *Table 5.1* shows the formal similarity between C_p at a liquid–liquid critical point in a two-component system and C_V at a gas–liquid critical point in a one-component system if a and g are analytic. The dashed lines enclose the two parts of the Table that correspond.

Table 5.1. The heat capacities of systems of 2 phases and of 1 phase at a critical point

		$(C_2)_V$	$(C_1)_V$	$(C_2)_p$	$(C_1)_p$
1 component gas–liquid	a_{4v}^c not zero	finite > finite		infinite	infinite
	a_{4v}^c zero	infinite finite		infinite	infinite
2 components liquid–liquid	g_{4x}^c not zero	finite finite		finite > finite	
	g_{4x}^c zero	finite finite		infinite finite	

A comparison of (5.42), (5.45) and (5.46) shows that $(C_2)_p$ and $(\beta_2)_T$ are necessarily positive, as is required by thermal and mechanical stability, but that $(\alpha_2)_p$ can have either sign. It will usually be greater than $(\alpha_1)_p$ as s_{2x}^c and v_{2x}^c generally have the same sign—negative at a U.C.S.T. and positive at a L.C.S.T.

Measurements of C_2 and α_2 appear to conform qualitatively with these equations. The heat capacity has been measured for the systems i-octane + perfluoro-n-heptane[11] (U.C.S.T.), for water + phenol[12] (U.C.S.T.) and for water + triethylamine[11,12] (L.C.S.T.). In all these systems there is a large increase in the heat capacity of the two-phase system as the critical point is approached, followed by a fall as it is passed. The limiting values may even be infinite but, if so, the approach to infinity is more sudden than that required by (5.43) with any integral value of n.

The heat capacity is still large in the one-phase system, thus showing that there is considerable short-range order which extends for several degrees beyond the critical point. Hildebrand and his colleagues[11] have measured the molar volume of the first system as it is heated through the critical point, and their results show that the coefficient of thermal expansion rises very rapidly near it. It does not appear to become infinite at the critical point but there is the required discontinuity in α, which then returns smoothly to a normal value some degrees higher. However, the peak of α in the two-phase region is not proportional to that of C_p, as is required by the treatment above. The heat-capacity peak extends over about 5 K but that in the coefficient of expansion is confined to the last 0·03 K below the critical point.

The system nitrobenzene + n-hexane is unusual in having v_{2x}^c positive at a U.C.S.T., at which s_{2x}^c is necessarily negative. This difference in sign is shown by the fact that $(\mathrm{d}T^c/\mathrm{d}p)$ is negative[13]

(cf. 5.37). If g_{4x}^c vanishes, then $(\alpha_2)_p^c$ would be negative and infinite. It is found experimentally that it probably remains positive[14] but is less than $(\alpha_1)_p^c$.

The agreement between experiment and these predictions based on a Taylor expansion of the free energy about its value at the critical point is similar to that found for a one-component system in Chapter 3. Qualitatively, theory and experiment agree well, but quantitatively the classical theory appears to be inadequate. In both cases the inadequacy is shown first by the variation of the degree of order of the system [that is, $(v^g - v^l)$ or $(x' - x'')$] with $(T - T^c)^{1/3}$ and not with $(T - T^c)^{1/2}$ or $(T - T^c)^{1/4}$, etc. and, secondly, by the sudden infinities in the heat capacities that are quantitatively inconsistent with (5.43) and the corresponding equation for C_V of a one-component system.

The inequalities of Chapter 3 can be extended to binary systems by considering not A as a function of V and T but G as one of x and T in a system maintained at a constant pressure. The function Y of (3.42) is now replaced by $H - T^c S$, and the derivation then takes a parallel development. Alternatively, Rushbrooke's inequality (3.56) follows at once for a binary system from (5.41), since $C_2 > C_1 > 0$.

The analogy between the two situations is best made clear by writing the derivatives in a table in which the entries on each line have, formally, the same singularity. (It must be decided by experiment if the numerical values of α, β, γ, etc. are the same; *Table 5.2* shows only that they satisfy the same inequalities in both situations.)

Since the critical line of a binary system follows a smooth trajectory in p, T, x-space (5.37), a system can be brought to a critical point by changing p at constant T, as well as by changing T at constant p. Hence there are two cases to consider for the binary system, namely $G(x, T)$ at constant p, and $G(x, p)$ at constant T. These have certain features in common[15], as is shown in *Table 5.2*.

Table 5.2. Thermodynamic analogy between a one-component and a two-component system near a critical point

Index	One component $A(V, T)$	Two components $G(x_2, T)$ p constant	$G(x_2, p)$ T constant
δ	p	$(\partial g/\partial x_1)_{p,T} = \mu_1 - \mu_2$	
γ	$-(\partial p/\partial V)_T$	$-(\partial^2 g/\partial x^2)_{p,T}$	
β	V^l, V^g	x', x''	
	S	S	$-V$
α	C_V	C_p	$pV\beta_T$
θ	$(\partial^2 p/\partial T^2)_\sigma$	$-[(\partial^2 S/\partial x_1 \partial T)_p]_2$	$[(\partial^2 V/\partial x_1 \partial p)_T]_2$

154

The experimental evidence for the numerical values of the indices is rather sparse when compared with that for systems of one component. It is too early to say how far this reflects the inherent difficulty of the measurements or how far it is accounted for by the greater interest in the past in one-component systems.

The index α is determined by C_p and, as stated above, these are consistent with a weak infinity but do not support it very strongly. The index β is governed by the shape of the coexistence curve and, in at least one case, carbon tetrachloride + perfluoromethylcyclohexane, there is good evidence that it is close to $\frac{1}{3}$. Thompson and Rice[5] found $0 \cdot 33 \pm 0 \cdot 02$.

The index γ governs the rate at which $(\partial^2 g / \partial x^2)_{p,T}$ becomes zero as the critical point is approached through the homogeneous fluid along a path of constant pressure (or constant temperature). The evidence here is indirect, for if $\gamma^+ > 1$, then $(\partial^2 h^E / \partial x^2)_{p,T}$ and $(\partial^2 v^E / \partial x^2)_{p,T}$ must vanish at the critical point[15]. Dunlap and Furrow[16] have shown that the evidence from n-C_6F_{14} + n-C_6H_{14} (for h^E) and from n-C_7F_{16} + i-C_8H_{18} (for v^E) supports a strong presumption that these derivatives do go to zero at the critical point. Clearly (5.37) breaks down in these circumstances and the appropriate limit must be substituted for the right-hand side. If v^E and h^E are of the same functional form, then it is sufficient to replace the ratio on the right-hand side by v^E/h^E. Scott and his colleagues[17] have shown that this is often an acceptable approximation.

A further consequence of $\gamma^+ > 1$, for which there is some experimental evidence, is that coexistent curves calculated by extrapolation from values of g^E in the homogeneous mixture on the implicit assumption that $\gamma^+ = 1$ must always be too high at an U.C.S.T. and too low at a L.C.S.T. It is common experience that this is so[18,19]. A paper by Scatchard and Wilson[19] shows a closed solubility loop, calculated by such extrapolations, which shows simultaneously too high a U.C.S.T. and too low a L.C.S.T.

In short, the evidence available, although sparse, suggests that all indices are the same for a binary system at a liquid–liquid critical point as for a system of one component at a gas–liquid critical point.

Francis[18] has published a useful bibliography of work on partially miscible liquid systems.

5.3 MIXTURES CONTAINING FLUOROCARBONS

Most of the liquid mixtures that have large excess functions and are but partially miscible at some temperatures contain at least one polar component. A striking exception is the class of mixtures in which one of the components is a completely fluorinated non-polar compound of carbon, silicon or sulphur and the second an aliphatic hydrocarbon or another organic halide of little or no polarity. Such mixtures have large positive excess free energies, heats, entropies and volumes. They usually have upper critical solution points.

Thorp and Scott[19] have studied the simplest system of this type, *carbon tetrafluoride + krypton*. The excess free energy is almost symmetrical with an equimolar value of 315 J mol^{-1} at 117 K. This is as large as that of many hydrocarbon mixtures at room temperature but represents a much larger fraction, almost $\frac{1}{3}$, of the value of RT. It may be compared with 30 J mol^{-1} for methane + krypton at the same temperature. However, large though this free energy is, it is insufficient for partial immiscibility, for which a value of about $\frac{1}{2}RT$ is required. The system *carbon tetrafluoride + methane*[19] has a U.C.S.T. at 94·5 K and an equimolar excess free energy of 360 J mol^{-1} at 110 K. That of *perfluoroethane + ethane*[19] is of similar size relative to RT, namely 660 J mol^{-1} at 176 K.

Immiscibility is found also in mixtures containing fluoroform. This substance differs considerably from carbon tetrafluoride and, in fact, is partially immiscible with it[19] below the U.C.S.T. of 130·5 K. It is similarly immiscible with xenon and with ethane below about 186 K, but is miscible with perfluoroethane and with methylene difluoride[19]. The mixture with perfluoroethane has an equimolar excess free energy of 615 J mol^{-1} at 176 K (that is, 0·42 RT), but that with methylene difluoride is apparently almost ideal. The latter substance is itself only partially miscible with carbon tetrafluoride, perfluorethane and ethane at 150 K.

These results may be contrasted with those for the corresponding chlorides to show that fluoroform and methylene difluoride are strongly polar molecules. Chloroform, and to a lesser extent methylene dichloride, behave towards paraffin hydrocarbons and carbon tetrachloride as if they were almost non-polar. The difference is due no doubt to the great electronegativity of fluorine which both enhances the partial positive charges on the hydrogen atoms and ensures that the outer end of the C—F bonds can attract these.

Scott and his colleagues[19-21] have now studied a large number of mixtures of the aliphatic fluorocarbons with aliphatic hydrocarbons. These systems can be listed conveniently by the following set of figures, in which the first is the number of carbon atoms in the fluorocarbon, the second in the hydrocarbon: 1 + 1, 1 + 2, 2 + 2, 2 + 3, 3 + 1, 3 + 2, 3 + 3, 3 + n-4, 3 + i-4, n-4 + 3, n-4 + n-6, n-4 + n-7, n-4 + n-10, n-6 + n-6, n-7 + i-8. The properties measured are usually g^E, h^E, v^E and the liquid–liquid phase boundary which yields the U.C.S.T. The systems show little individuality. The equimolar excess free energies are about $\frac{1}{2}RT$ at the normal boiling point, the equimolar excess heats lie between $\frac{1}{2}RT$ and RT, and the excess volumes are positive. The following conclusions can be drawn from these and similar measurements on related systems.

(1) The excess heats are generally substantially larger than the excess free energies, so the excess entropies are positive and large. However, the excess entropy for mixing at constant total volume is small and probably negative[22].

(2) Perfluoro-ethers and perfluoro-amines behave indistinguishably from perfluorocarbons[23].

(3) Mixtures of aliphatic fluorocarbons with aromatic hydrocarbons have excess free energies that are little, if any, greater than those of mixtures with aliphatic hydrocarbons[24]. Mixtures with halides such as carbon tetrachloride, chloroform, tin tetrachloride and chlorobenzene have equally large excess free energies[24,25].

(4) Mixtures of two fluorocarbons are almost ideal[26,27] with excess free energies of ca. 50 J mol^{-1}.

(5) Whatever the cause of these large excess functions, it is not the large difference of molar volume between a fluorocarbon and the corresponding hydrocarbon. This is shown most convincingly by the large excess free energies of pairs such as *carbon tetrafluoride + ethane*[19], where the molar volumes are almost equal, and from the fact that the excess free energy[27] is greater for a mixture of perfluorocyclohexane ($v = 170$ cm^3 mol^{-1}) with 1,3,5-trimethylcyclohexane ($v = 170$ cm^3 mol^{-1}) than with cyclohexane ($v = 113$ cm^3 mol^{-1}). Similar examples can be found in the long series of mixtures listed above which have been studied by Scott. The system *sulphur hexafluoride + propane* is clearly as abnormal as any fluorocarbon mixture, although the components have the same critical volumes. Unfortunately, it has been studied only at high vapour pressures and its discussion is therefore deferred to the next Chapter.

(6) If there is a large difference between the molar volumes of the fluorocarbon and the hydrocarbon, then the miscibility curve is more symmetrical if plotted against the volume fractions than if plotted against the mole fractions[7,21,28]. This fact is almost the only evidence that volume fractions are to be preferred to mole fractions in discussing solutions other than those of polymers.

The large positive deviations found in these aliphatic systems are not present in the aromatic systems. When C_6F_6 first became available in quantity, it was soon apparent that, far from 'repelling' aromatic hydrocarbons, it often forms weak complexes with them. This association is shown most strikingly by the precipitation of solid complexes. Thus an equimolar mixture of C_6F_6 (m.p. $+ 5·1°C$) and C_6H_6 (m.p. $+ 5·5°C$) forms a complex which has a melting point above room temperature, at $+24·1°C$. Similar complexes (usually 1:1) have been found in the systems[29,30] C_6F_6 + toluene, +p-xylene, +mesitylene, +2-methyl naphthalene, in $C_{10}F_8$ (perfluoronaphthalene) + benzene, and in C_6HF_5 + benzene. The formation of complexes in the solid state can be an unreliable guide to the presence of unusually strong forces between the unlike molecules; it may, for example, be a mere accident of molecular shape and crystal geometry. However, complexes whose melting points are as high as that of C_6F_6 + C_6H_6 are firm evidence for strong forces.

This evidence is reinforced by direct studies of the excess heats and volumes, the former of which have been measured by Scott and his colleagues[31] and the latter by Swinton[30]. The system C_6F_6 + C_6H_6 has a minimum excess heat of -540 J mol^{-1} at a mole fraction of C_6F_6 of 0·6 at 25°C. The excess volume has a maximum of $+0·85$ cm^3 mol^{-1} at a mole fraction of 0·4 at 40°C. Such asymmetry is common in mixtures in which specific interaction occurs. It is discussed below and, at greater length, in the next Section on mixtures of polar molecules. Negative heats have been found also in C_6HF_5 + C_6H_5F and with mixtures of the three $C_6H_4F_2$ with 1,2,3,4-$C_6H_2F_4$. Other systems in which one or both molecules are of mixed type show either positive or negative heats, and curves that change sign with composition are not uncommon. Mixtures of the perfluoroaromatic compounds with aliphatic systems do not form these strong complexes[32,33]. C_6F_6 shows evidence of weak (incongruent) solid complexes with cyclohexane in which there are 3, 5 or 6 molecules of fluorocarbon to one of hydrocarbon, but this evidence is less convincing than that for complexes with benzene.

Scott[31,34] suggests that there are at least three competing effects in these systems; first, the usual fluorocarbon–hydrocarbon antipathy which is probably proportional to $(n - m)^2$ where n and m are the number of hydrogen atoms in the two molecules; secondly, an interaction (presumably classical electrostatic) between hydrogen and fluorine atoms on adjacent rings arising from the bond dipole moments of C–H and C–F and, thirdly, a charge-transfer complexing between the hydrogen-rich molecule as donor and the fluorine-rich as acceptor. The first of these effects contributes a positive term to h^E and the last two, negative terms. However, the terms do not all have the same dependence upon composition, as is seen for the corresponding effects for polar molecules in the next Section.

The free energies of these systems have not been studied so systematically, but it is known[32,33] that g^E of $C_6F_6 + C_6H_6$ is small and 'cubic' in composition, a fact that gives rise to an unusual kind of azeotropy, discussion of which is deferred to Chapter 6. The excess free energy becomes more negative as the benzene ring is substituted with methyl groups. Thus in the equimolar mixture at 40°C, the values of g^E are -44 J mol^{-1} for $C_6F_6 + C_6H_6$, -184 J mol^{-1} for $C_6F_6 + C_6H_5CH_3$, and -395 J mol^{-1} for $C_6F_6 + p\text{-}C_6H_4(CH_3)_2$. This appears to be strong thermodynamic evidence for donor–acceptor complexes. Some doubt remains, however, as Scott[35] has emphasized, since the non-thermodynamic evidence (spectroscopic, n.m.r., dielectric constant, etc.) is surprisingly weak. Perhaps the strongest is the intense infra-red band in $C_6F_6 + C_6H_6$ which Steele and his colleagues[36] have reported and which they interpret as a vibronic interaction.

5.4 MIXTURES OF POLAR LIQUIDS

A polar substance is usually defined as one whose molecules have permanent dipole moments. However, this simple criterion is not very useful in discussing the effect of polarity on the properties of liquids or mixtures.

It will be shown in Chapter 8 that the effective polarity of a molecule increases with increasing size of the ratio $(\mu^2/\sigma^3 kT)$ where μ is the permanent dipole moment and σ the collision diameter. Even this expression is unable to show the increase in effective polarity that follows from an unsymmetrical disposition of the polar group within the whole molecule, as, for example, occurs with alcohols and primary amines. However, it is adequate to explain why mixtures of, say, benzene with substances of moderate dipole moment and reasonable symmetry, such as toluene ($\mu = 0.4$ D) or even chlorobenzene ($\mu = 1.5$ D), may reasonably be classed as non-polar mixtures. This Section is given to mixtures in which the polarity of one or both of the components plays a decisive part in determining the excess properties. There are many hundred such mixtures and only a representative selection can be discussed here. They are placed in order of increasing complexity. Aqueous mixtures are discussed in the next Section.

Ozone has a small dipole moment of 0·55 D, but in a small molecule (the molar volume of the liquid is 30·5 cm³ at 90 K) this is sufficient to produce appreciably polar behaviour. The paramagnetism is negligible compared with that of liquid oxygen. Systems containing liquid ozone or liquid oxygen are often surprisingly immiscible, but it is not clear to what extent these abnormalities are due to the paramagnetism of oxygen or to the polarity of ozone. However, the facts are as follows:

$O_2 + O_3$ are immiscible[37,38] with a U.C.S.T. of 93·2 K, at which temperature v^E is small and negative, as is often found in systems of similar molar volumes but different boiling points. However, both liquids are miscible[39] with liquid F_2.

O_2 is completely miscible[40] with CH_4 at all temperatures, but is immiscible[41] with C_2H_6(U.C.S.T. = 105 K), C_3H_8(U.C.S.T. = 110 K), and with the olefins C_2H_4(U.C.S.T. = 115 K), C_3H_6 (U.C.S.T. = 105 K).

O_3 is immiscible[42] with CF_4(U.C.S.T. = 103 K) and with[43] N_2, (U.C.S.T. > 93 K) but is miscible[43] with CO.

The more conventional polar organic molecules can be divided into two classes: first, those which cannot act as proton donors in a hydrogen bond, such as acetonitrile, acetone and nitromethane, and, secondly, proton donors such as the primary and secondary amines and the alcohols. We consider them in this order.

Acetonitrile mixes with non-polar liquids such as carbon tetrachloride[44], benzene[44] and toluene[45], with positive excess free energies and heats. The equimolar values at 45°C are (in J mol⁻¹)

	CCl_4	C_6H_6	$C_6H_5CH_3$
g^E	+1190	+670	+780
h^E	+ 920	+490	+500

The heats are not as close to quadratic as are the free energies, but the maxima differ little from these values. It can be seen that s^E is negative in each equimolar mixture (see *Figure 5.4*). The excess volume[46] is small and negative (less than 0·1 cm³ mol⁻¹) with carbon tetrachloride and 'cubic' with benzene.

The corresponding systems containing acetone[45,47] behave similarly:

	CCl_4	C_6H_6	$C_6H_5CH_3$
g^E	+550	+290	+440
h^E	+320	+160	+250

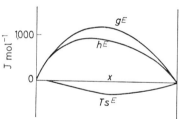

Figure 5.4. The excess functions of the system acetonitrile + carbon tetrachloride at 45°C as a function of the mole fraction of acetonitrile

The excess volumes[46] are again small and negative. Acetone has large excess heats and free energies with paraffin hydrocarbons. Thus with n-heptane, the equimolar excess heat[48] rises from $+1280 \text{ J mol}^{-1}$ at $-30°C$ to $+1570 \text{ J mol}^{-1}$ at $+20°C$. The equimolar excess free energy[48] with iso-octane is $+950 \text{ J mol}^{-1}$ at $35°C$.

Nitromethane[44,46,49] differs from the last two polar liquids in that both s^E and v^E are here positive. We have

	CCl_4	C_6H_6
g^E	$+1340$	$+770$
h^E	$+1420$	$+815$

The excess functions are smaller with benzene than with aliphatic hydrocarbons or even with carbon tetrachloride, and it is probable that some complexing is occurring with the π-electrons. This is apparent also from the critical solution temperatures. For acetonitrile and nitromethane these are, typically, above 0°C with aliphatic and below 0°C with aromatic hydrocarbons[18]. This preferential solubility of aromatic hydrocarbons is shown also in the polar solvents ammonia and sulphur dioxide. The latter is used for the removal of aromatic hydrocarbons from petroleum in the Edeleanu process.

The molecular nature of the complexing cannot be obtained from thermodynamic evidence alone[35], but the n.m.r. shifts suggest that the acetonitrile lies in a plane parallel with that of the benzene ring[50].

The systems[46] acetonitrile + acetone and acetone + nitromethane show much smaller (and irregular) deviations from ideal behaviour than those discussed above. This is to be expected, since each component has the negative end of its dipole at the exterior of the molecule.

Many hydrogen-bonded systems have been studied in the last few years and only a selection can be discussed here. Those chosen are solutions of amines and alcohols in hydrocarbons and similar non-polar solvents.

Aniline is only partially miscible with aliphatic hydrocarbons at room temperature. The U.C.S.T. vary with chain length and branching, and with the number of rings[18]. This temperature is therefore a useful property for characterizing petroleum fractions. The U.C.S.T. with normal paraffins of increasing chain length pass through a minimum of 69·1°C at n-hexane. The temperatures are sensitive to impurities in either component. The activity coefficients[51, 52] and excess partial molar heats[52] are positive on both sides of the miscibility gap in aniline + n-hexane, and in aniline + cyclohexane, as is to be expected. However, the excess volume is positive in mixtures rich in hexane but negative in those rich in aniline[53].

Aniline is miscible with aromatic hydrocarbons and there is evidence of complexing between the —NH_2 group and the π-electrons. Thus the equimolar excess free energies with carbon tetrachloride[54] are about +950 J mol^{-1}, with benzene[51, 55] about +500 J mol^{-1} and with toluene[52, 56] about +650 J mol^{-1}. The heats are larger, +1200 J mol^{-1} in carbon tetrachloride[57], +700 in benzene[57] and +1000 in toluene[56].

Aliphatic amines behave similarly in that their excess heats with aliphatic hydrocarbons are larger than with aromatic. Kehiaian[58] has made extensive comparisons of the behaviour of an amine with that of the hydrocarbon containing —CH_3 in the place of —NH_2, or —CH_2— in the place of —NH—.

The two lowest alcohols, methanol and ethanol, differ in their behaviour towards hydrocarbons. Methanol is the more polar and is not completely miscible with the paraffins at room temperature. The U.C.S.T. rise[59, 60] from 14°C with n-pentane to 34°C with n-hexane and 66°C with n-octane, whilst that with cyclohexane is 46°C. Ethanol is miscible with the paraffins, and so are both alcohols with carbon tetrachloride and the aromatic hydrocarbons. Mixtures of methanol with paraffins have received less attention than the other mixtures discussed below, but positive heats of mixing have been measured[60, 61] above and below the U.C.S.T. in mixtures with n-hexane, n-heptane and cyclohexane. The excess volumes are positive[62].

Methanol + benzene was studied in detail by Scatchard and his colleagues[63], and the many later measurements[64–67] do not change the picture in its essentials (*Figure 5.5*). The excess volume[62, 67] is 'cubic,' being positive at 25°C only if the mole fraction of methanol is less than 0·5.

Methanol + carbon tetrachloride is, perhaps, the simplest

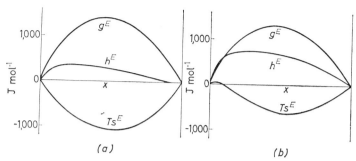

Figure 5.5. The excess functions at 35°C of the systems (*a*) methanol + carbon tetrachloride, and (*b*) methanol + benzene, as functions of the mole fraction of methanol

example of a hydrogen-bonded liquid in an inert diluent. *Figure 5.5* shows the results of Scatchard and his colleagues[63]. Later measurements, mainly by Missen and his colleagues[68], have shown that the excess heat falls with decreasing temperature but retains its asymmetry. It has assumed a 'cubic' form by 0°C. n-Propanol behaves similarly[68].

Ethanol mixes freely with the paraffins. The excess heats are large and positive[60,70] with n-hexane, n-heptane and i-octane. The results for the latter system are shown in *Figure 5.6*. The excess heat rises with increasing temperature in mixtures of each of the alcohols from ethanol to n-octanol with n-hexane[71]. The asymmetry is retained, however, as with similar mixtures containing methanol. The system ethanol + cyclohexane has an equimolar excess free energy[63,72] at 25°C of +1320 J mol^{-1}, an excess heat[64,69] of

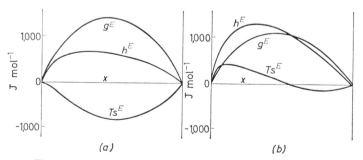

Figure 5.6. The excess functions of (*a*) ethanol + i-octane at 25°C, and (*b*) ethanol + benzene at 45°C, as functions of the mole fraction of ethanol

163

$+650$ J mol^{-1} and an excess volume[62,73] of $+0.55$ cm^3 mol^{-1}. Ethanol $+$ methyl cyclohexane[70,74] behaves similarly.

The system ethanol $+$ benzene has been studied exhaustively[64-67,70,75-77] and some of the results are shown in *Figure 5.6*. The excess heat again rises with increasing temperature. The excess volume[62,63,67] at room temperature is positive in mixtures rich in benzene and negative in those rich in alcohol. The whole curve becomes more positive as the temperature increases.

Ethanol $+$ carbon tetrachloride[70,78] has a symmetrical excess free energy with a maximum of $+1190$ J mol^{-1} at 45°C. That of the excess heat is $+850$ J mol^{-1} at a mole fraction of alcohol of only 0.2. The excess volume is 'cubic.'

These examples show that the typical properties of a mixture of an associated liquid with a non-polar liquid are, first, an excess heat that is positive with a maximum in a mixture weak in the polar component and which increases with increasing temperature; secondly, an excess entropy that is negative with a minimum in a mixture rich in the polar component and, thirdly, in consequence, an excess free energy that is large, positive and nearly symmetrical in composition.

Figures 5.4–5.6 are typical of such mixtures. The positive excess heat is, in the main, a measure of the number of hydrogen bonds, or other local electrostatic interactions, that are broken on forming the mixture. This heat is small in mixtures, say, rich in alcohol, since the addition of a small amount of an inert diluent breaks few bonds. Most of the diluent is probably accommodated interstitially in a matrix of bonded alcohol molecules. The heat is large, however, in mixtures weak in alcohol, as the addition of a small amount of it to a large amount of a non-polar liquid must break all the hydrogen bonds.

The excess entropy is probably positive in mixtures very weak in alcohol, owing to the loss of orientational order that must follow the breaking of all the hydrogen bonds. However, it soon becomes negative with increasing concentration of alcohol, as the mixture now contains a number of hydrogen bonds which impose both a positional and orientational order on the system that is greater than that to be expected in a randomly disposed mixture. The asymmetry of the excess entropy is therefore similar to that of the excess heat.

The opposite signs of the two functions follow from the fact that, roughly, zero excess heat corresponds to no hydrogen bonds broken on forming a mixture, and zero excess entropy to very few hydrogen bonds remaining.

The departures of real systems from these hypothetical states account for the signs and asymmetries of h^E and s^E, and lead naturally to the symmetrical positive g^E and so to the exhibition, in many cases, of upper critical solution points. This explanation has been put into more quantitative form by Münster[79], Tompa[80] and, in great detail, by Barker and his colleagues[78,81], by considering the number of arrangements of molecules on a lattice and the energy of each arrangement, when different relative orientations of a pair of neighbours correspond to different energies. The treatment is difficult and specialized and so will not be considered further. But there is little doubt that it is generally an acceptable model and places the qualitative arguments above on a firm footing.

It is seen from the examples given that alcohol + benzene mixtures have more positive excess heats and entropies and lower excess free energies than those of alcohols with paraffins or carbon tetrachloride. Barker attributes this behaviour to a more favourable energy of interaction between a hydroxy group and the π-electrons of an aromatic molecule than with the less polarizable electrons of a saturated molecule. Such interaction, although not as strong as a conventional hydrogen bond, is less demanding in its geometrical requirements, leads to the breaking of more hydroxy bonds and so, paradoxically, to a slightly larger excess heat and a considerably larger excess entropy. The greater miscibility of all highly polar liquids with aromatic than with aliphatic hydrocarbons has already been noted and is also evidence for such interaction.

Another way of interpreting quantitatively the behaviour of such mixtures is to treat the association of the polar component to dimers, trimers, etc. as the formation of new chemical species whose concentrations are related to those of the monomers by the equilibrium constants of the law of mass action. This model is called an *ideal associated solution* if the equilibrium concentrations of dimers, etc. are supposed to form an ideal mixture with each other, with the monomers and with the second component. Such a solution can never separate into two phases[82], as the chemical potential of each molecular species (monomer, dimer, etc.) is given by (4.33) and at equilibrium the potential of each species must be the same in every phase. It follows that the mole fraction is also the same in every phase, and so the supposed immiscible phases must have the same composition.

However, phase separation can occur readily if the molecular species are not supposed to form an ideal mixture and, in fact, is made much more likely by the association of one component. Prigogine and his colleagues[83] have made a thorough quantitative study of this model, and have made considerable use of the infra-red spectra of these mixtures in its development. The spectrum of an alcoholic solution generally has two bands that can be assigned to the OH stretching frequency. A sharp band is the absorption of the free molecule and a broad band of lower frequency that of hydroxyl groups which are hydrogen-bonded.

Freymann[84] was the first to recognize the effects of association on the OH frequency—in this case, of the overtone bands. He has been followed by Mecke and his colleagues[85], and the fundamental bands have been studied by Errara and his colleagues[86]. Many others have since entered the field[87], but few have succeeded in calculating with any confidence the number of molecules in the different states of monomer, dimer, etc.

Errara and Mollet[86] pointed out in their first papers that the broad association band was probably formed of several overlapping bands, each due to an association group containing a different number of molecules. This is now known to be so. Measurement of the intensity of this band does not, therefore, give directly the concentration of any molecular species.

A further difficulty is that the coefficients of absorption may be functions of temperature, as was shown by Davies and Sutherland[88] for the carboxylic acids, and has since been shown for the alcohols by the careful work of Becker[89]. Thus the spectroscopic results give a useful picture of the association of alcohols in non-polar solvents, but they have not yet been unambiguously correlated with the thermodynamic properties.

There is not so large a body of systematic work on mixtures of two polar components, except for that on aqueous solutions which is discussed in the next Section, and the interpretation of such results as there are is difficult. In a few cases it is clear that there is a strong and specific interaction between the unlike molecules which is not present between those of either of the pure components.

The classical example of this behaviour is the system chloroform + acetone[81,90]. Here the excess free energy, heat and entropy are all negative and also the excess volume except for mixtures weak in chloroform. The specific interaction is here a hydrogen bond between the hydrogen atom of a chloroform molecule and the carbonyl group of an acetone molecule. Hydrogen bonding cannot occur in either of the pure components.

Chloroform can interact similarly with the oxygen atom of ethers[91] and the π-electrons of benzene[50,81,92]. A weak hydrogen bond between chloroform and aromatic and olefinic systems has been detected by the 'chemical shift' of the proton magnetic resonance frequency[92]. Such a bond is of a type between the conventional localized hydrogen bond and the formation of an electron-transfer complex.

166

It is important to know the relative strengths of the hydrogen bonds formed from a hydroxy group in an alcohol or in water towards proton acceptors such as ethers, ketones, nitriles, amines and other alcohols. Gordy and Stanford[93] classified such bonds by studying the perturbation of the OD fundamental frequency in solutions of CH_3OD in a large number of polar solvents. They took the frequency of the band in dilute solution in benzene as that of the unperturbed monomer and found the shifts to lower frequencies to increase in the order: nitriles, ketones, ethers, amines.

Thus the nitrile and carbonyl groups are not good proton acceptors in spite of their high dipole moments. Ethers and amines—primary, secondary, tertiary and aromatic—are better acceptors because the electrons around the oxygen and nitrogen atoms have less s and more p character than those in ketones and nitriles. This order of increasing affinity for protons is found also from a study of the thermodynamic properties. The excess heat of isopropanol in equimolar mixtures of the following liquids at 25°C is[94]: propionitrile ($+1720$ J mol^{-1}), acetone ($+1710$ J mol^{-1}), isopropanol (0 J mol^{-1}), isopropylamine (-2500 J mol^{-1}). This sequence confirms the order chosen by Gordy and Stanford from their spectroscopic results and is of considerable use in interpreting the thermodynamic results for aqueous systems.

Most of the specific interactions discussed in this Section have involved a hydrogen bond, in which a positive proton acts as a link between two (negative) oxygens, but is joined to one of them only by a full covalent bond. Kreglewski and his colleagues[95] have adduced evidence for a direct oxygen–oxygen link, without a proton, in systems containing trifluoracetic anhydride.

5.5 AQUEOUS MIXTURES

No one has yet proposed a quantitative theory of aqueous solutions of non-electrolytes, and such solutions will probably be the last to be understood fully. Nevertheless they may be usefully classified by the strength and number of the proton-accepting groups in a molecule of the second component. The mixtures are in many ways analogous to those of highly polar substances in an inert solvent, as, for example, of methanol in carbon tetrachloride. But in aqueous solutions the organic liquid, although necessarily polar, plays the role of the inert diluent, as water is one of the most strongly and most regularly hydrogen-bonded liquids.

The addition to water of any molecules containing inert groups such as CH_3 reduces the total number of hydrogen bonds, even if the inert group is itself attached to a highly polar group such as OH. Extremely dilute solutions in water are exceptions[99]. Aqueous solutions are, therefore, discussed in this Section in the order of the increasing strength of the second component as a proton acceptor. This order is that established above, namely, nitriles, ketones, alcohols and amines.

The equimolar excess free energy[96] of the system water + acetonitrile is about $+1100$ J mol^{-1} at 35°C. The excess heat[96] at 25°C has a maximum of $+1100$ J mol^{-1} at a mole fraction of water of 0·38 and apparently becomes slightly negative at mole fractions greater than 0·96. The excess entropy is, therefore, everywhere negative. Qualitatively the system resembles methanol + carbon tetrachloride (*Figure 5.5*), with water taking the part of methanol. The system forms a positive azeotrope and is immiscible below -1°C.

Acetone[96,97] behaves very similarly to acetonitrile but forms an azeotrope only above 85°C.

Methyl ethyl ketone, acetyl acetone and propionitrile are immiscible with water and have upper critical solution temperatures[18] above 100°C.

These two classes of proton acceptors, nitriles and ketones, have their excess properties in the following order: $g^E > h^E > 0 > Ts^E$ and have a U.C.S.T. if g^E is sufficiently large. Such substances rarely, if ever, show L.C.S.T in equilibrium with the saturated vapour, but methyl ethyl ketone has one at high pressures and would clearly have one at the vapour pressure if the system did not solidify first (see Chapter 6). Nevertheless the typical phase behaviour of these systems is the formation of U.C.S.T. only.

If the solute is capable of accepting a small number (per molecule) of reasonably strong hydrogen bonds from water, then there is added at room temperature to an excess heat of the type described a negative and symmetrical term. The sign and symmetry follow from the fact that the term arises from a direct interaction between molecules of opposite species. The total excess heat is now generally positive in mixtures rich, and negative in those weak, in solute. The effect on the excess entropy is less spectacular but must be a decrease. Dioxan[98] is a good example of such a solute (*Figure 5.7*). Ethanol[99–101] (above room temperature), n-propanol[99,102] and i-propanol[99–103] behave similarly.

Such systems have negative excess volumes, caused mainly by the solute–water bond, and positive excess heat capacities which arise from the increased orientational freedom of both components as the temperature is raised. The solute–water bond is strong enough with many alcohols and ethers for them to be miscible at all temperatures, although some come close to the formation of a closed solubility loop. Dioxan is one of these, for it has been shown[98] that

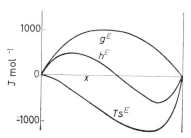

Figure 5.7. The excess functions of water + dioxan[98] at 25°C as a function of the mole fraction of water

g^E is too small by only 10 per cent over a range of at least 125 K for the formation of a closed loop. n-Butanol[104] shows only a U.C.S.T. of 125°C; isobutanol[105] has a U.C.S.T. of 133°C and is tending towards a L.C.S.T. at 0°C; secondary butanol forms a closed loop at high pressures (see Chapter 6), and tertiary butanol is completely miscible at all temperatures. Ethyl ether + water is clearly tending towards a L.C.S.T. as the mutual solubilities decrease with increasing temperatures[104].

A further increase in the strength or number of solute–water bonds gives an excess heat that is everywhere negative at room temperature, but which retains the same asymmetry, and leads to a considerable lowering of the excess entropy. Examples of this behaviour are shown by methanol[99–102,106], by ethanol at room temperature[99–101], by glycol ethers[107], by polyethylene and polypropylene glycols[98,108], by glycerol[108,109], by aliphatic amines[110], and by pyridine bases[111] (*Figure 5.8*). In all these systems h^E is entirely negative and g^E is positive at some temperature in the range

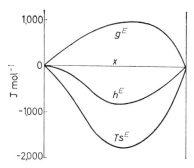

Figure 5.8. The excess functions of water + pyridine[111] at 80°C as a function of the mole fraction of water

studied. This situation can lead to the exhibition of a lower critical solution point; indeed, such points are almost entirely confined to the list above. As $(C_p)^E$ is still positive, the systems often show a U.C.S.T. as well.

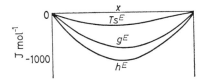

Figure 5.9. The excess functions of water + hydrogen peroxide[112,113] at 25°C as a function of the mole fraction of water

Finally, there are mixtures in which the solute–water bonds are so strong or so numerous that H^E is more negative than TS^E. These mixtures are thermodynamically most stable, as G^E is negative, and never separate into two liquid phases. Substances in this category are generally polyalcohols or polyamines, such as hydrogen peroxide[100,112,113] (*Figure 5.9*), hydrazine[114], diethylamine[3,9,110], ethylene diamine[115], glucose[116], sucrose[116] and agar-agar[117].

Table 5.3. Aqueous solutions of non-electrolytes in order of increasing strength and number of hydrogen bonds

H^E	G^E	TS^E	V^E	$(C_p)^E$	Examples	Typical phase behaviour
$+$	$+$	$-$	$+$	$-$?	nitriles, ketones	U.C.S.T.
$(+, -)$	$+$	$-$	$-$	$+$	ethers, alcohols	U.C.S.T. but tending towards closed loop
$-$	$+$	$-$	$-$	$+$	polyethers, amines	Closed loop
$-$	$-$	$-$	$-$	$+$	polyalcohols, polyamines	Completely miscible

This classification of aqueous solutions of non-electrolytes by the strength of the hydrogen bonds from the hydroxy group in water is not very precise but does bring some order into this confused field. It is summarized in *Table 5.3*.

5.6 MIXTURES OF QUANTUM LIQUIDS

Quantum liquids are outside the scope of this book, but it would be pedantic to omit all discussion of some remarkable phase equilibria and U.C.S.T. which have been found recently in mixtures of these liquids.

At high temperatures, isotopic mixtures of heavy molecules are perhaps the best examples we have of ideal mixtures, and remain so at temperatures down to the melting curves. However, this is not so for the system ^{3}He $+$ ^{4}He which does not solidify at atmospheric pressure. Some years ago, Prigogine and his colleagues[118] predicted that this mixture would have a small positive excess free energy and hence, since neither component is solid at zero temperature, that there must be a U.C.S.T. They estimated this at 0·7 K. Shortly afterwards the critical point was observed by Walters and Fairbank[119] and by Zinoveva and Peshkov[120] at 0·83 K. The phase-boundary curve has its maximum close to the equimolar composition and coincides with the λ-point curve (as a function of composition) for mole fractions of ^{3}He above 0·7. The complete phase diagram is one of the most complicated known for a binary system, since we have not only liquid–liquid equilibrium but also azeotropy[121], a λ-surface[122] which is a function of p, T and x, and freezing of both components at higher pressures to more than one solid phase[122].

Perhaps the most remarkable feature of the system is that at zero temperature the compositions of the phases do not approach those of the pure components[123]. The limiting mole fractions of ^{3}He are 1·000 and 0·0637 $\pm$ 0·0005. At first sight this result appears to be in conflict with the third law of thermodynamics, but theoretical analysis suggests that this is not so[124].

Phase separation in isotopic mixtures is caused primarily by differences in mass and not in quantal statistics[118]. It is, therefore, not surprising that immiscibility is found also in liquid mixtures of neon with the different forms of hydrogen. The following U.C.S.T. have been reported[125]:

Ne $+$ n-H$_2$	U.C.S.T.	29·0 K
Ne $+$ p-H$_2$	U.C.S.T.	ca. 33 K
Ne $+$ n-D$_2$	U.C.S.T.	26·0 K

References

[1] Prigogine, I. and Defay, R. *Chemical Thermodynamics* (trans. Everett, D. H.), Ch. 15, London (Longmans) 1954

[2] Rice, O. K. *Chem. Rev.* 44 (1949) 65

[3] Copp, J. L. and Everett, D. H. *Discuss. Faraday Soc.* 15 (1953) 174

[4] Zimm, B. H. *J. phys. Chem.* 54 (1950) 1306

[5] Rice, O. K. *J. chem. Phys.* 23 (1955) 164; Thompson, D. R. and Rice, O. K. *J. Am. chem. Soc.* 86 (1964) 3547; Irani, N. F. and Rice, O. K. *Trans. Faraday Soc.* 63 (1967) 2158

[6] Cox, J. D. and Herington, E. F. G. *Trans. Faraday Soc.* 52 (1956) 926

7 Hildebrand, J. H. and Scott, R. L. *Regular Solutions*, p. 140–141, New Jersey (Prentice-Hall) 1962

8 Zimm, B. H. *J. chem. Phys.* 20 (1952) 538

9 Copp, J. L. and Everett, D. H. *Trans. Faraday Soc.* 53 (1957) 9

10 Andon, R. J. L., Cox, J. D. and Herington, E. F. G. *Trans. Faraday Soc.* 53 (1957) 410

11 Jura, G., Fraga, D., Maki, G. and Hildebrand, J. H. *Proc. natn. Acad. Sci. U.S.A.* 39 (1953) 19

12 Semenchenko, V. K. and Skripov, V. K. *Dokl. Akad. Nauk SSSR* 85 (1953) 1325; *Zh. fiz. Khim.* 25 (1951) 362; 29 (1955) 174; Amirkhanov, Kh., Gurvich, I. G. and Matizen, E. M. *Dokl. Akad. Nauk SSSR* 100 (1955) 735

13 Kohnstamm, P. and Timmermans, J. *Proc. Sect. Sci. K. ned. Akad. Wet.* 15 (1912/13) 1021

14 Claesson, S. and Sunderlof, L.-O. *J. Chim. phys.* 54 (1957) 914; Jacox, M. E., MacQueen, J. T. and Rice, O. K. *J. phys. Chem.* 64 (1960) 972

15 Rowlinson, J. S., in *Critical Phenomena* (ed. Green, M. S. and Sengers, J. V.) *Misc. Publs Bur. Stand.* No. 273 p. 9, 1966

16 Dunlap, R. D. and Furrow, S. D. *J. phys. Chem.* 70 (1966) 1331

17 Myers, D. B., Smith, R. A., Katz, J. and Scott, R. L. *J. phys. Chem.* 70 (1966) 3341

18 Francis, A. W. *Critical Solution Temperatures*, Washington (Am. chem. Soc.) 1961; *Liquid–liquid equilibriums*, New York (Interscience) 1963; *J. phys. Chem.* 58 (1954) 1099; 60 (1956) 20; 62 (1958) 579; 63 (1959) 753; *J. chem. Engng Data* 10 (1965) 45, 145, 260, 327; 11 (1966) 96, 234, 557; 12 (1967) 269, 380; *Chem. Engng Sci.* 22 (1967) 627, 707, 737

19 Thorp, N. and Scott, R. L. *J. phys. Chem.* 60 (1956) 670, 1441; Croll, I. M. and Scott, R. L. 62 (1958) 954; 68 (1964) 3853; Scatchard, G. and Wilson, G. M. *J. Am. chem. Soc.* 86 (1964) 133

20 Williamson, A. G. and Scott, R. L. *J. phys. Chem.* 65 (1961) 275

21 Gilmour, J. B., Zwicker, J. O., Katz, J. and Scott, R. L. *J. phys. Chem.* 71 (1967) 3259

22 Dunlap, R. D. and Scott, R. L. *J. phys. Chem.* 66 (1962) 631

23 Rotariu, G. J., Hanrahan, R. J. and Fruin, R. E. *J. Am. chem. Soc.* 76 (1954) 3752; Yen, L. C. and Reed, T. M. *J. chem. Engng Data* 4 (1959) 102; Fujishiro, R. and Hildebrand, J. H. *J. phys. Chem.* 66 (1962) 573

24 Hildebrand, J. H., with Cochran, D. R. F. *J. Am. chem. Soc.* 71 (1949) 22; with Fisher, B. B. and Benesi, H. A. 72 (1950) 4348; Carson, J. L., Knight, R. J., Watson, I. D. and Williamson, A. G. *J. phys. Chem.* 69 (1965) 3200

25 Campbell, D. N. and Hickman, J. B. *J. Am. chem. Soc.* 75 (1953) 2879

26 Newcome, M. M. and Cady, G. H. *J. Am. chem. Soc.* 78 (1956) 5216

27 Rowlinson, J. S. and Thacker, R. *Trans. Faraday Soc.* 53 (1957) 1; Dyke, D. E. L., Rowlinson, J. S. and Thacker, R. 55 (1959) 903

28 Munson, M. S. B. *J. phys. Chem.* 68 (1964) 796

29 Patrick, C. R. and Prosser, G. S. *Nature, Lond.* 187 (1960) 1021; McLaughlin, E. and Messer, C. E. *J. chem. Soc. A* (1966) 1106

30 Duncan, W. A. and Swinton, F. L. *J. phys. Chem.* 70 (1966) 2417; *Trans.*

Faraday Soc. 62 (1966) 1082; Duncan, W. A., Sheridan, J. P. and Swinton, F. L. *ibid.* 1090

[31] Fenby, D. V., McLure, I. A. and Scott, R. L. *J. phys. Chem.* 70 (1966) 602; Fenby, D. V. and Scott, R. L. 71 (1967) 4103

[32] Gaw, W. J. and Swinton, F. L., *Nature, Lond.* 212 (1966) 283; *Trans. Faraday Soc.* 64 (1968) 637, 2023

[33] Morcom, K. W. and Pollack, J. M., private communication

[34] Williamson, A. G. and Scott, R. L. *J. phys. Chem.* 65 (1961) 275; with Anderson, D. L., Smith, R. A., Myers, D. B. and Alley, S. K. 66 (1962) 621

[35] Scott, R. L., and Fenby, D. V. *Ann. Rev. phys. Chem.* 20 (1969) 111

[36] Steele, D., Gates, P. N. and Wheatley, W., paper read before the Chemical Society, Exeter, 1967

[37] Brown, C., with Franson, K. D. *J. chem. Phys.* 21 (1953) 917; with Berger, A. W. and Hersh, C. K. 23 (1955) 1340

[38] Jenkins, A. C., with Birdsall, C. M. *J. chem. Phys.* 22 (1954) 1779; and with DiPaolo, F. S. 23 (1955) 2049; with DiPaolo, F. S. 25 (1956) 296

[39] Stokes, C. S. and Streng, A. G. *J. chem. Phys.* 37 (1962) 920

[40] Streng, A. G. and Kirshenbaum, A. D. *J. chem. Engng Data* 4 (1959) 127

[41] McKinley, C. and Wang, E. S. *J. Adv. cryogen. Engng* 4 (1960) 11

[42] Streng, L. V. and Streng, A. G. *J. chem. Phys.* 38 (1963) 1788

[43] Streng, A. G. and Grosse, A. V. *J. inorg. nucl. Chem.* 9 (1959) 315

[44] Brown, I., with Smith, F. *Aust. J. Chem.* 7 (1954) 269; 8 (1955) 62; with Fock, W. 9 (1956) 180

[45] Orye, R. V. and Prausnitz, J. M. *Trans. Faraday Soc.* 61 (1965) 1338

[46] Brown, I. and Smith, F. *Aust. J. Chem.* 13 (1960) 30; 15 (1962) 9; Van Ness, H. C. and Kochar, N. K. *J. chem. Engng Data* 12 (1967) 38

[47] Brown, I., with Fock, W. *Aust. J. Chem.* 10 (1957) 417; with Smith, F. *ibid.* 423

[48] Schäfer, K. and Rohr, F. J. *Z. phys. Chem. Frankf. Ausg.* 24 (1960) 130; Edwards, J. L. and Schäfer, K. *Z. Naturf.* 19 (1964) 136

[49] Brown, I. and Smith, F. *Aust. J. Chem.* 8 (1955) 501; 9 (1956) 141

[50] Schneider, W. G. *J. phys. Chem.* 66 (1962) 2653

[51] Kortüm, G. and Freier, H.-J. *Mh. Chem.* 85 (1954) 693; *Chemie-Ingr-Tech.* 26 (1954) 670

[52] Röck, H. and Schneider, G. *Z. phys. Chem. Frankf. Ausg.* 8 (1956) 154; Schneider, G. 24 (1960) 165

[53] Keyes, D. B. and Hildebrand, J. H. *J. Am. chem. Soc.* 39 (1917) 2126

[54] Pannetier, G., Abello, L. and Kern, M. *Annls Chim. Phys.* 10 (1965) 403

[55] Hosseini, S. M. and Schneider, G. *Z. phys. Chem. Frankf. Ausg.* 36 (1963) 137

[56] Kehiaian, H. and Sosnkowska-Kehiaian, K. *Trans. Faraday Soc.* 62 (1966) 838

[57] Deshpande, D. D. and Pandya, M. V. *Trans. Faraday Soc.* 61 (1965) 1858

[58] Kehiaian, H. *Bull. Acad. pol. Sci. Sér. chim. geol. geogr.* 14 (1966) 703; Sosnkowska-Kehiaian, K., Orzel, K. and Kehiaian, H. *ibid.* 711; Kehiaian, H., paper read before the Chemical Society, Exeter, 1967

[59] Kiser, R. W., Johnson, G. D. and Shetlar, M. D. *J. chem. Engng Data* 6 (1961) 338

[60] Savini, C. G., Winterhalter, D. R. and Van Ness, H. C. *J. chem. Engng Data* 10 (1965) 168, 171; Sinor, J. E. and Weber, J. H. 5 (1960) 243; Renon, H. and Prausnitz, J. M. *Chem. Engng Sci.* 22 (1967) 299

[61] Wolf, K. L. *Trans. Faraday Soc.* 33 (1937) 179

[62] Harms, H. Z. *phys. Chem.* B53 (1943) 280; Staveley, L. A. K. and Spice, B. *J. chem. Soc.* (1952) 406

[63] Scatchard, G., with Ticknor, L. B. *J. Am. chem. Soc.* 74 (1952) 3724; and with Goates, J. R. and McCartney, E. R. *ibid.* 3721; with Satkiewicz, F. G. 86 (1964) 130

[64] Goates, J. R. and Snow, R. L., with James, M. R. *J. phys. Chem.* 65 (1961) 335; with Ott, J. B. 66 (1962) 1301

[65] Mrazek, R. V. and Van Ness, H. C. *A.I.Ch.E.Jl* 7 (1961) 190

[66] Williamson, A. G. and Scott, R. L. *J. phys. Chem.* 64 (1960) 440

[67] Brown, I., with Fock, W. *Aust. J. Chem.* 14 (1961) 387; with Smith, F. 15 (1962) 1

[68] Moelwyn-Hughes, E. A. and Missen, R. W. *J. phys. Chem.* 61 (1957) 518; Paraskevopoulos, G. C. and Missen, R. W. *Trans. Faraday Soc.* 58 (1962) 869; Otterstedt, J.-E. A. and Missen, R. W. *ibid.* 879

[69] Grosse-Wortmann, H., Jost, W. and Wagner, H. G. *Z. phys. Chem. Frankf. Ausg.* 49 (1966) 74; Klesper, I. 51 (1966) 1

[70] Brown, I. and Fock, W. *Aust. J. Chem.* 8 (1955) 361; 9 (1956) 141; with Smith, F. *ibid.* 364

[71] Brown, I., Fock, W. and Smith, F. *Aust. J. Chem.* 17 (1964) 1106

[72] Washburn, E. R. and Handorf, B. H. *J. Am. chem. Soc.* 57 (1935) 441

[73] Pardo, F. and Van Ness, H. C. *J. chem. Engng Data* 10 (1965) 163

[74] Hwa, S. C. P. and Ziegler, W. T. *J. phys. Chem.* 70 (1966) 2572

[75] Brown, I. and Smith, F. *Aust. J. Chem.* 7 (1954) 264; 9 (1956) 141

[76] Savini, C. G., Winterhalter, D. R., Kovach, L. H. and Van Ness, H. C. *J. chem. Engng Data* 11 (1966) 40

[77] Jones, H. K. DeQ. and Lu, B. C.-Y. *J. chem. Engng Data* 11 (1966) 488

[78] Barker, J. A., Brown, I. and Smith, F. *Discuss. Faraday Soc.* 15 (1953) 142

[79] Münster, A. *Trans. Faraday Soc.* 46 (1950) 165

[80] Tompa, H. *J. chem. Phys.* 21 (1953) 250

[81] Barker, J. A. *J. chem. Phys.* 20 (1952) 794, 1526; 21 (1953) 1391; with Smith, F. 22 (1954) 375; Dacre, B. and Benson, G. C. *Can. J. Chem.* 41 (1963) 278

[82] Washburn, E. W. *Trans. Am. electrochem. Soc.* 22 (1912) 330 (quoted Haase, R. *Discuss. Faraday Soc.* 15 (1953) 270)

[83] Prigogine, I. *The Molecular Theory of Solutions*, Ch. 15, Amsterdam (North-Holland) 1957

[84] Freymann, R. *C. r. hebd. Séanc. Acad. Sci., Paris* 193 (1931) 928; 195 (1932) 39

[85] Mecke, R. *Z. Elektrochem.* 52 (1948) 107, 269

[86] Errara, J. and Mollet, P. *C. r. hebd. Séanc. Acad. Sci., Paris* 204 (1937) 259; Errara, J. *Trans. Faraday Soc.* 33 (1937) 120; with Sack, H. 34 (1938) 728; with Gaspart, R. and Sack, H. *J. chem. Phys.* 8 (1940) 63

REFERENCES

[87] Orgel, L. E. *Rev. mod. Phys.* 31 (1959) 100; Hadzi, D. and Thompson, H. W. (eds.) *Hydrogen Bonding*, London (Pergamon) 1959; Pimentel, G. C. and McClellan, A. L. *The Hydrogen Bond*, San Francisco (Freeman) 1960

[88] Davies, M. M. and Sutherland, G. B. B. M. *J. chem. Phys.* 6 (1938) 755, 767

[89] Liddel, U. and Becker, E. D. *Spectrochim. Acta* 10 (1957–1958) 70; Becker, E. D., Liddel, U. and Shoolery, J. N. *J. molec. Spectrosc.* 2 (1958) 1

[90] Staveley, L. A. K., Tupman, W. I. and Hart, K. R. *Trans. Faraday Soc.* 51 (1955) 323; Morcom, K. W. and Travers, D. N. 61 (1965) 230; Röck, H. and Schröder, W. *Z. phys. Chem. Frankf. Ausg.* 11 (1957) 41; Mueller, C. R. and Kearns, E. R. *J. phys. Chem.* 62 (1958) 1441; Kearns, E. R. 65 (1961) 314; Campbell, A. N., Kartzmark, E. M. and Friesen, H. *Can. J. Chem.* 39 (1961) 735

[91] Schmidt, G. C. *Z. phys. Chem.* 121 (1926) 221; McGlashan, M. L. and Rastogi, R. P. *Trans. Faraday Soc.* 54 (1958) 496; Goates, J. R., Ott, J. B. and Mangelson, N. F. *J. phys. Chem.* 67 (1963) 2874; Winterhalter, D. R. and Van Ness, H. C. *J. chem. Engng Data* 11 (1966) 189

[92] Creswell, C. J. and Allred, A. L. *J. phys. Chem.* 66 (1962) 1469

[93] Gordy, W. *J. chem. Phys.* 7 (1939) 93; with Stanford, S. C. 8 (1940) 170

[94] Thacker, R. and Rowlinson, J. S. *Trans. Faraday Soc.* 50 (1954) 1036

[95] Kreglewski, A. *Bull. Acad. pol. Sci. Sér. Sci. chim. geol. geogr.* 11 (1963) 301; Wyrzykowska-Stankiewicz, D. and Kreglewski, A. *ibid.* 465; Kreglewski, A. and Woycicki, W. *ibid.* 645; Woycicki, W. and Trebicka, B. 12 (1964) 319

[96] Othmer, D. F., with Josefowitz, S. *Indust. Engng Chem.* 39 (1947) 1175; with Chudgar, M. M. and Levy, S. L. 44 (1952) 1872; Vierk, A.-L. *Z. anorg. allg. Chem.* 261 (1950) 283; Chirikova, Z. P., Galata, L. A., Kotova, Z. N. and Kofman, L. S. *Russ. J. phys. Chem.* 40 (1966) 493; Armitage, D. A., Blandamer, M. J., Foster, M. J., Hidden, N. J., Morcom, K. W., Symons, M. C. R. and Wootten, M. J. *Trans. Faraday Soc.* 64 (1968) 1193; *J. chem. Thermodynamics* 1 (1969) 503

[97] Hanson, D. O. and Van Winkle, M. *J. chem. Engng Data* 5 (1960) 30; Nicholson, D. E. *ibid.* 309; Kurtz, S. S., Wikingsson, A. E., Camin, D. L. and Thompson, A. R. 10 (1965) 330, 335

[98] Malcolm, G. N. and Rowlinson, J. S. *Trans. Faraday Soc.* 53 (1957) 921

[99] Ben-Naim, A. *J. phys. Chem.* 69 (1965) 1922; Franks, F. and Ives, D. J. G. *Q. Rev. chem. Soc.* 20 (1966) 1

[100] Mitchell, A. G. and Wynne-Jones, W. F. K. *Discuss. Faraday Soc.* 15 (1953) 161

[101] Lama, R. F. and Lu, B. C.-Y. *J. chem. Engng Data* 10 (1965) 216; Boyne, J. A. and Williamson, A. G. 12 (1967) 318; Arnett, E. M., Bentrude, W. G., Burke, J. J. and Duggleby, P. M. *J. Am. chem. Soc.* 87 (1965) 1541; Bertrand, G. L., Millero, F. J., Wu, C.-H. and Hepler, L. G. *J. phys. Chem.* 70 (1966) 699

[102] Butler, J. A. V., Thomson, D. W. and Maclennan, W. H. *J. chem. Soc.* (1933) 674; Dimmling, W. and Lange, E. *Z. Elektrochem.* 55 (1951) 322

[103] Katayama, T. *Chem. Engng, Tokyo* 26 (1962) 361

[104] Hill, A. E. *J. Am. chem. Soc.* 45 (1923) 1143; with Malisoff, W. M. 48 (1926) 918

[105] Jänecke, E. *Z. phys. Chem.* A164 (1933) 401

[106] Benjamin, L. and Benson, G. C. *J. phys. Chem.* 67 (1963) 858

[107] Cox, H. L. and Cretcher, L. H. *J. Am. chem. Soc.* 48 (1926) 451; with Nelson, W. L. 49 (1927) 1080

[108] Schneider, G. and Wilhelm, G. *Z. phys. Chem. Frankf. Ausg.* 20 (1959) 219

[109] Stedman, D. F. *Trans. Faraday Soc.* 24 (1928) 289

[110] Kohler, F. *Mh. Chem.* 82 (1951) 913; Bellemans, A. *J. chem. Phys.* 21 (1953) 368; Copp, J. L. *Trans. Faraday Soc.* 51 (1955) 1056; Matizen, E. V. and Kushova, N. V. *Russ. J. phys. Chem.* 34 (1960) 1056

[111] Andon, R. J. L. and Cox, J. D. *J. chem. Soc.* (1952) 4601; Cox, J. D. *ibid.* 4606; Andon, R. J. L., Cox, J. D. and Herington, E. F. G. (1954) 3188; *Discuss. Faraday Soc.* 15 (1953) 168; *Trans. Faraday Soc.* 53 (1957) 410

[112] Giguère, P. A., with Maass, O. *Can. J. Res.* 18B (1940) 181; with Morissette, B. G., Olmos, A. W. and Knop, O. *Can. J. Chem.* 33 (1955) 804; with Knop, O. and Falk, M. 36 (1958) 883; with Carmichael, J. L. *J. chem. Engng Data* 7 (1962) 526

[113] Scatchard, G., Kavanagh, G. M. and Ticknor, L. B. *J. Am. chem. Soc.* 74 (1952) 3715

[114] Wilson, R. Q., Munger, H. P. and Clegg, J. W. *Chem. Engng Prog. Symp. Ser.* 48 (1952) No. 3, 115

[115] Cornish, R. E., Archibald, R. C., Murphy, E. A. and Evans, H. M. *Indust. Engng Chem.* 26 (1934) 397; Wilson, A. L. 27 (1935) 867

[116] Taylor, J. B. and Rowlinson, J. S. *Trans. Faraday Soc.* 51 (1955) 1183

[117] Fricke, R. and Lüke, J. *Z. Elektrochem.* 36 (1930) 309; Gee, G. *Q. Rev. chem. Soc.* 1 (1947) 265

[118] Prigogine, I., Bingen, R. and Bellemans, A. *Physica* 20 (1954) 633

[119] Walters, G. K. and Fairbank, W. N. *Phys. Rev.* 103 (1956) 262

[120] Zinoveva, K. N. and Peshkov, V. P. *Soviet Phys. JETP* 5 (1957) 1024; 10 (1960) 22; 17 (1963) 1235

[121] Tedrow, P. M. and Lee, D. M. *Low Temperature Physics LT9* (ed. Daunt, J. G., Edward, D. O., Milford, F. J. and Yaqub, M.), Part A, p. 248, New York (Plenum Press) 1965

[122] Le Pair, C., Taconis, K. W., de Bruyn Ouboter, R. and Das, P. *Physica* 28 (1962) 305; with De Jong, E. 31 (1965) 764; *Cryogenics* 3 (1963) 112

[123] Edwards, D. O., Brewer, D. F., Seligman, P., Skertic, M. M. and Yaqub, M. *Phys. Rev. Lett.* 15 (1965) 773; Ifft, E. M., Edwards, D. O., Sarwinski, R. E. and Skertic, M. M. 19 (1967) 831; Betts, D. S. *Contemp. Phys.* 9 (1968) 97

[124] Bardeen, J., Baym, G. and Pines, D. *Phys. Rev.* 156 (1967) 207; Ebner, C. *ibid.* 222

[125] Simon, M. *Phys. Rev. Lett.* 2 (1962) 234; 5 (1963) 319; *Physica* 29 (1963) 1079; Brouwer, J. P., Hermans, L. J. F., Knaap, H. F. P. and Beenakker, J. J. M. 30 (1964) 1409; Beenakker, J. J. M. and Knaap, H. F. P. *Progress in Low Temperature Physics* (ed. Gorter, C. J.), Vol. 5 p. 287, Amsterdam (North-Holland) 1967; Streett, W. B. and Jones, C. H. *J. chem. Phys.* 42 (1965) 3989; Heck, C. K. and Barrick, P. L. *Adv. cryogen. Engng* 11 (1966) 349

LIQUID MIXTURES AT HIGH PRESSURES

6.1 CONSISTENCY

It has been shown that the discussion of liquid mixtures in terms of the excess thermodynamic functions is possible only for mixtures with vapour pressures below about 3 bar. However, many of the most interesting properties of liquid mixtures arise from the equilibria between two or three fluid phases at pressures above atmospheric, and in particular near the gas–liquid critical point.

The consistency of measurements of liquid–vapour equilibrium was discussed in Chapter 4. The test of consistency is to see that the Gibbs–Duhem equation is satisfied in a mixture at constant temperature and pressure; in practice, it is usual to assume that the pressure is sufficiently small for the liquid phases to be treated, at all compositions, as if they were at zero pressure. The Gibbs–Duhem equation holds also at higher pressures, but it is no longer so easy to use it, either in differential or integral form. First, the explicit effect of pressure on the chemical potentials can no longer be neglected in either phase and, secondly, there is difficulty in specifying real and accessible standard states for both components in both phases (see Section 4.3). In principle, both difficulties can be surmounted, the first by measuring the equations of state of both homogeneous phases, at all compositions, and the second by defining 'unsymmetrical' activity coefficients in which the standard state for the less volatile component is its pure liquid state, and that for the more volatile component its infinitely dilute solution in the first component. The second activity coefficient is sometimes called the *Henry's law constant*, since it governs the initial solubility of the gas in the liquid.

Methods of testing for consistency at high pressures are, therefore, far from simple and require more supplementary thermodynamic information on the homogeneous phases than is generally available. Nevertheless, some suitable methods have been developed and applied in a few favourable cases[1,2].

If there are two fluid phases in a binary mixture, then the small equilibrium displacements dp, dT, dx' and dx'' must satisfy the two conditions that the chemical potentials of each substance in one phase (μ_1' and μ_2') must equal those in the second phase (μ_1'' and μ_2''). The two equations connecting dp, dT, dx' and dx'' are, therefore,

177

(5.13) and (5.14), from which follow

$$\left(\frac{\partial x_2}{\partial T}\right)'_{p,\sigma} = -\frac{\Delta h_1 x''_1 + \Delta h_2 x''_2}{T g'_{2x} \Delta x_2} = \frac{1}{T g'_{2x}}\left[\left(\frac{\partial h}{\partial x_2}\right)'_{p,T} - \frac{\Delta h}{\Delta x_2}\right] \quad (6.1)$$

$$\left(\frac{\partial x_2}{\partial p}\right)'_{T,\sigma} = \frac{\Delta v_1 x''_1 + \Delta v_2 x''_2}{g'_{2x} \Delta x_2} = -\frac{1}{g'_{2x}}\left[\left(\frac{\partial v}{\partial x_2}\right)'_{p,T} - \frac{\Delta v}{\Delta x_2}\right] \quad (6.2)$$

where the symbol Δ again denotes the value in *phase'* less that in *phase"*. The first of these equations was used in the last Chapter to discuss the equilibrium between two partially immiscible liquids in the absence of a vapour phase and at constant pressure. However, they are applicable to the equilibrium between any pair of phases in a binary system, if the meaning of σ is extended to denote any displacement that maintains equilibrium between the phases. The suffixes prime and double-prime are used to denote any pair of phases, and, in particular, gas and liquid, respectively.

A useful test of consistency in dilute solution has been obtained from these equations by Wang[3]. He observes that in the limit of infinitely dilute solution g_{2x} is dominated by the term $RT/x_1 x_2$. If this expression is substituted in (6.1) and the limit $x'_2 = x''_2 = 0$ is taken, then we have

$$\lim_{x_2=0}\left[\left(\frac{\partial x'_2}{\partial T}\right)_{p,\sigma}(1 - \alpha_{12})\right] = -\frac{\Delta h_1^0}{RT^2} \quad (6.3)$$

where α_{12} is the volatility ratio (4.57) which is here equal to x''_2/x'_2, and Δh_1^0 is the molar latent heat of evaporation of pure component 1. This heat is often known accurately, and so the equation provides a check on the initial slopes of x'_2 and x''_2 as a function of T at constant p. A similar equation for constant T can be obtained from (6.2).

6.2 Azeotropy

Figure 6.1 shows the (p, T, x) surface and the (v, x) projection of a (p, v, x) surface for a binary mixture. The two equations above are the slopes of one side of a (p, T, x) surface in directions perpendicular to the p and T axes. The slopes of the other surface (*phase"*) are found by substituting x'' for x', etc. A third pair of equations, for slopes at constant x' and x'', may be obtained from these and the corresponding equations for *phase"*. The first of this pair is

$$\left(\frac{\partial p}{\partial T}\right)'_{x_2,\sigma} = \frac{\Delta h_1 x''_1 + \Delta h_2 x''_2}{T(\Delta v_1 x''_1 + \Delta v_2 x''_2)} \quad (6.4)$$

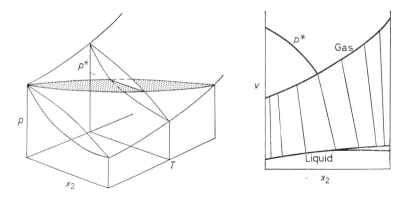

Figure 6.1. The (p, T, x) surface and the (v, x) projection of the (p, v, x) surface (at constant temperature) of a simple binary mixture. The shaded cut on the (p, T, x) surface shows the boiling and condensation points at a given pressure. The isobar p^* on the (v, x) diagram is shown in the gas, liquid and two-phase region, the other isobars only in the latter

The compositions of the two phases can become equal in two different ways. If x' approaches x'', as h' approaches h'' and v' approaches v'', etc., then the point of identity is a critical point. If, however, x' becomes equal to x'' without h' being equal to h'', etc., then the system is at an *azeotropic point*. Azeotropic systems are discussed in this Section and critical systems in Section 6.4. A system is azeotropic when it can be distilled (or condensed) without change of composition.

It follows directly from the first parts of (6.1) and (6.2) that, if x' is equal to x'', whilst Δh and Δv, etc. remain non-zero, then the slopes $(\partial p/\partial x_2)'_\sigma$, $(\partial p/\partial x_2)''_\sigma$, $(\partial T/\partial x_2)'_\sigma$ and $(\partial T/\partial x_2)''_\sigma$ are all zero. That is, the vapour pressure (at constant temperature) and the boiling point (at constant pressure) are either maxima or minima with respect to changes in composition. A maximum in the vapour pressure is always accompanied by a minimum in the boiling point, as Δh and Δv have the same signs. It also follows from these equations that $(\partial p/\partial x_2)'_\sigma$ and $(\partial p/\partial x_2)''_\sigma$ become equal as they approach zero, and similarly with the temperature derivatives.

These deductions are known collectively as the *Gibbs–Konowalow laws*. It is conventional to describe an azeotrope with a maximum vapour pressure and a minimum boiling point as a positive azeotrope, and the converse as a negative azeotrope. The former are much the more common, and *Figure 6.2* shows the (p, T, x) surface and the (v, x) diagram for this azeotrope. The minimum volume of

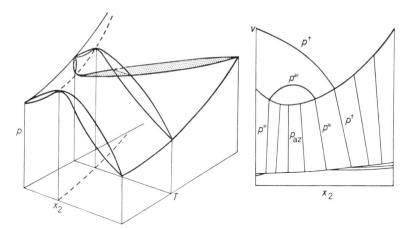

Figure 6.2. The (p, T, x) surface and the (v, x) projection of the (p, v, x) surface (at constant temperature) for a mixture that forms a positive azeotrope. The conventions are as in *Figure 6.1*. The dashed line is the locus of the azeotrope. The order of increasing pressure of the isobars on the (v, x) diagram is $p_2^0 < p\dagger < p_1^0 < p^* < p_{az}$

the gas phase is at the azeotropic composition if the vapour is a perfect gas mixture.

A system of two phases and two components has two degrees of freedom. Hence, for a displacement on a (p, T, x) surface

$$dp = (\partial p/\partial T)_{x,\sigma}\, dT + (\partial p/\partial x)_{T,\sigma}\, dx \qquad (6.5)$$

The last term is zero for an azeotrope and so, putting x' equal to x'' in (6.4),

$$\frac{dp_{az}}{dT} = \left(\frac{\partial p}{\partial T}\right)_{x,\sigma} = \frac{\Delta h}{T\,\Delta v} = \frac{\Delta s}{\Delta v} \qquad (6.6)$$

This equation is the same as Clapeyron's equation for a system of one component, and indeed, an azeotrope has many of the characteristics of a pure substance. The logarithm of the azeotropic pressure is almost a linear function of $(1/T)$. An approximate derivation of this statement follows from (6.6) in the same way as (2.78) follows from (2.76). *Figure 6.3* shows the azeotropic pressure and composition for the system ethanol + water[4]. The agreement of the several observers is good for the vapour pressure but poor for the less readily measurable azeotropic composition.

Successive or fractional distillation of a mixture which forms a positive azeotrope leads to a distillate of the composition of the latter and a residue of the pure component that was initially present

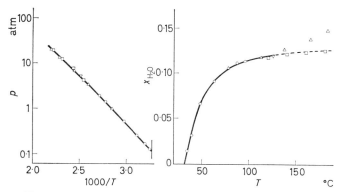

Figure 6.3. The vapour pressure and composition of the azeotrope of ethanol + water. Circles, Wade and Merriman (0·13–1·91 atm); squares, Kleinert (4·3–19·5 atm); triangles, Otsuki and Williams (1·0–20.4 atm); inverted triangle, Othmer and Levy (5·1 atm)[4]

in excess. Straight distillation of a mixture which forms a negative azeotrope leads eventually to a residue of the azeotropic composition and a distillate from which one of the pure components can be separated by fractionation. Thus a negative azeotrope can be separated by straight distillation from a mixture of arbitrary composition, but a positive azeotrope only by fractional distillation.

The former, although less common, were therefore studied and analysed about fifty years before there was any systematic study of the latter. The earliest workers thought that negative azeotropes were chemical compounds because of their low vapour pressures and reproducible compositions. This was disproved by Roscoe and Dittmar[5] in 1860 when they showed that the composition of the azeotrope formed from hydrogen chloride and water changed with the pressure under which the distillation was performed. Their results agree remarkably well with the best modern work of Bonner and his colleagues[5] (*Table 6.1*). Roscoe later extended his work to other aqueous acids.

A positive azeotrope is at a maximum of the p–x graph and is, therefore, at low vapour pressures, a mixture of positive excess free

Table 6.1. Composition and boiling points of the hydrogen chloride + water azeotrope

p (mmHg)	50	760	1000	2500
t (°C) (Bonner & Wallace)	48·72	108·58$_4$	116·18$_5$	—
Wt.% HCl (Roscoe & Dittmar)	23·2	20·24	19·7	18·0
Wt.% HCl (Bonner & Titus)	23·42	20·222	19·734	—

energy. Conversely, a negative azeotrope has a negative excess free energy. There is, however, no direct correlation between the sizes of the excess free energies and the occurrence or absence of azeotropy, as this depends also on the ratio of the vapour pressures of the pure components. Elementary reasoning from the properties of the (p, T, x) surface leads to the following generalizations.

(1) The closer the vapour pressures of the components the more likely is azeotropy. It is inevitable at any temperature at which the vapour pressures are the same. (Such a temperature and pressure is often called a *Bancroft point*.)

(2) If the excess free energy is symmetrical in the composition, then a positive azeotrope is richer in the component of higher vapour pressure, and conversely for a negative azeotrope.

(3) An increase of temperature and of vapour pressure in a positive azeotrope increases the mole fraction of the component whose vapour pressure increases the more rapidly with temperature. The converse holds for a negative azeotrope.

(4) The closer the vapour pressures of the pure components, the more rapidly does the azeotropic composition change with temperature.

These generalizations are not without exceptions but are usually an adequate guide to the properties of a system. If a mixture is *quadratic*, and if its vapour is a perfect gas mixture, then the azeotropic pressure and composition at a given temperature can be calculated from the vapour pressures of the pure components and the excess free energy. Conversely, a knowledge of the composition and pressure at a given temperature (or even of the composition and temperature at a given pressure) is sufficient for an estimate of the excess free energy[6]. Such estimates are unlikely to be badly in error, since the excess free energy is notably the most symmetric of all the excess functions. The composition of an azeotrope formed by a quadratic mixture is approximately a linear function of the temperature[6,7].

There have been few systematic measurements of the pressure, temperature and composition of an azeotrope over the whole of the liquid range, but it is often possible to obtain an adequate knowledge of a system by combining several sets of measurements. There are four possibilities. A binary mixture can form an azeotrope, (1) over the whole of the liquid range, (2) over a range bounded above by a return to normal behaviour, (3) over a range similarly bounded below, or (4) over a range bounded above and below. The first type of behaviour is called *absolute azeotropy* and the others *limited azeotropy*. Simple mixtures furnish examples of both.

No mixtures of inert gases or of simple diatomic molecules form azeotropes, except for the unusual behaviour of the systems ^{3}He + ^{4}He and H_2 + Ne, which were discussed in the last Chapter. The classical system that approaches most closely to azeotropy is argon + oxygen which has a positive excess free energy (Section 4.6). The most simple binary mixtures in which azeotropy occurs extensively are those formed from carbon dioxide, nitrous oxide, ethane, ethylene and acetylene.

Carbon dioxide + nitrous oxide

Cook[8] found that there is no azeotrope formed from 20°C to the gas–liquid critical points (31–36°C). It is possible that one is formed at the triple point of carbon dioxide as the vapour pressures are here 5·17 bar (CO_2) and 4·99 bar (N_2O) and as the system has positive deviations from Raoult's law.

Carbon dioxide + ethane

The system forms a positive azeotrope over the whole of the liquid range. It would have a mole fraction[9] of about 0·5 at the normal boiling point of about −98°C, if the carbon dioxide did not solidify at −93°C. The proportion of carbon dioxide increases slowly with increasing vapour pressure to a mole fraction[10] of 0·53 at 9 bar, and to 0·65–0·70 near the gas–liquid critical point[11] at about 50 bar.

Carbon dioxide + ethylene

This system does not form an azeotrope near the normal boiling point[9] but does so in the critical region[12]. The composition changes from a mole fraction of carbon dioxide of 0·25 at −30°C to one of about 0·45 at the critical point. The system is an example of limited azeotropy over a range of vapour pressure from about 4 bar to the critical point.

Carbon dioxide + acetylene

This system is unusual in forming a negative azeotrope of a mole fraction of 0·33 in carbon dioxide at the normal boiling point[13] of −85°C. This temperature is below those of the triple points of the pure components but above that of the eutectic mixture which has almost the same composition. The system does not form an azeotrope between 5°C and the critical points[11] (31–36°C), but nothing is known of the change of azeotropic composition with vapour pressure between 1 and 30 bar.

Nitrous oxide + ethane

There is an azeotrope at the critical point[14] with a mole fraction of nitrous oxide of 0·7. Nothing is known of the behaviour at lower temperatures.

Nitrous oxide + ethylene

There is no azeotrope at the critical point[15]. The system has not been studied at low temperatures.

Nitrous oxide + acetylene

This is the only one of the ten systems that has not been studied.

Ethane + ethylene

This system does not form an azeotrope at any temperature[9,16–18].

Ethane + acetylene

This system forms an azeotrope over the whole of the liquid range. The mole fraction of the ethane changes from 0·59 at 1·07 bar to 0·52 at the critical point[11,13,19]. The vapour-pressure curves cross at −35°C (9 bar), above which acetylene is the more volatile.

Ethylene + acetylene

The system forms an azeotrope at the critical point[20] with a mole fraction of ethylene of 0·8. This has risen to almost 0·95 at −17·8°C (26·7 bar)[21], and there is no azeotrope at the normal boiling point[13].

A ternary azeotrope is a mixture of three components whose vapour pressure is greater (or less) than that of any of the pure components and of the binary mixtures. It has been shown that none of the three ternary systems, *carbon dioxide + nitrous oxide + ethylene*[15], *carbon dioxide + ethane + ethylene*[9], and *ethane + ethylene + acetylene*[16,21], forms a ternary azeotrope.

Few other systems have been studied over the whole of the liquid range, and so proved cases of absolute azeotropy are rare. The best authenticated, apart from the two above, are *benzene + cyclohexane*[22], *n-propanol + water*[10,23], and *hydrogen chloride + methyl ether*[24]. This last is a negative azeotropy, and one of the few cases known of negative azeotropy persisting to the critical point. Two other examples of this behaviour also have an acidic component, *acetic acid + pyridine*[25] and *sulphur trioxide + water*[26]. Systems with negative excess free energies are usually far from quadratic and the compositions of their azeotropes change rapidly with temperature. The system *chloroform + acetone* is a well-known negative azeotrope at its normal boiling point but it is probably no longer azeotropic at the critical point[10,25].

Such limited azeotropy is quite common and occurs also with the negative azeotrope *carbon dioxide + acetylene* (discussed above) and with the positive azeotropes *methanol + benzene*[7] (in which the mole fraction of benzene in the azeotrope probably becomes zero at 210°C), *ethyl acetate + carbon tetrachloride*[7] (where that of carbon tetrachloride becomes zero at about 115°C), and *methanol + methyl ethyl ketone*[27] (in which that of the ketone becomes zero at about 110°C).

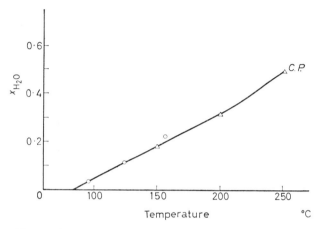

Figure 6.4. The composition of the azeotrope of acetone + water up to the gas–liquid critical point. Circles, Othmer and Morley; triangles, Griswold and Wong[28]

These three examples of limited positive azeotropy are mixtures of a highly polar and a less polar substance, in which the vapour pressures of the pure substances are not parallel on a graph of $\log p$ against $1/T$. Mixtures in which the azeotropy is limited by a minimum temperature, below which the behaviour is normal, include *carbon dioxide + ethylene*, *ethylene + acetylene*, *water + ethanol* (all discussed above) and *acetone + water*. This last system does not form an azeotrope at the normal boiling point but does so above 2·4 bar (85°C). The mole fraction of the water increases with temperature to 0·445 at the critical point[28] (*Figure 6.4*).

Limited azeotropy that is bounded above and below occurs only if the vapour-pressure curves of the two components cross at a *Bancroft point*. Any departure from Raoult's law necessarily produces an azeotrope at this point, and if the departure is small, then the azeotropy will be limited to a range of temperature around it.

If the departures from Raoult's law are small, then the components must be similar. The two isomeric heptanes[29], *2.4-dimethylpentane* and *2,2,3-trimethylbutane*, have the same vapour pressure at about 0·7 bar and at some temperature between 64 and 68°C. (The vapour curves are almost identical, and so the point of intersection is hard to determine.) Their equimolar mixture is a negative azeotrope with a boiling point 0·13°K above that of the pure components. The azeotropy is limited to the range 55°C (pure 2,4-dimethylpentane) to 75°C (pure 2,2,3-trimethylbutane), as is shown schematically in *Figure 6.5.*

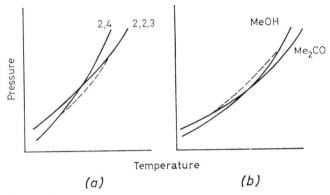

Figure 6.5. Limited azeotropy bounded above and below: (*a*) negative azeotropy of 2,4-dimethylpentane + 2,2,3-trimethylbutane, and (*b*) positive azeotropy of methanol + acetone. The dashed lines are the vapour pressures of the azeotropes (schematic only)

A mixture of an aliphatic and an aromatic hydrocarbon has a large excess free energy, so that a crossing of the vapour-pressure curves leads to absolute azeotropy, or at least to azeotropy that extends over a considerable range of temperature. The vapour-pressure curves[30] of *benzene* and *cyclohexane* cross at 52·4°C (0·396 bar), above which point benzene is the more volatile. Here the azeotropy is almost certainly absolute. A polar mixture that exhibits limited positive azeotropy around a Bancroft point is *methanol* + *acetone*[27]. The lower limit is at 20°C (0·25 bar, pure acetone) and the upper at about 145°C (20 bar, pure methanol). The vapour-pressure curves are sketched in *Figure 6.5.* No case is known of limited azeotropy bounded above and below by the same pure component, but the system *phenol* + *water* may prove to be an exception. Aring and von Weber[31] have shown that the azeotropy is bounded below by pure water at about 20°C. The azeotrope contains less phenol than the aqueous phase in equilibrium with water-saturated phenol, see Section 6.5. The mole fraction of phenol increases with rising temperature to a maximum of about 0·022 at 160°C and then falls to 0·01 at 280°C. It probably returns to zero before the system reaches the gas–liquid critical point of water at 374°C, but this question is still to be settled.

It has been shown in Chapters 4 and 5 that g^E is usually close to quadratic in form, although h^E and s^E may be cubic. Hence it is rare indeed for a system to exhibit, at one temperature, both positive and negative azeotropy. If we exclude reacting systems such as[32] $N_2O_5 + H_2O$ (which is more properly regarded as two separate systems 'side-by-side', $N_2O_5 + HNO_3$ and $HNO_3 + H_2O$), then there is only one known case of double azeotropy, the system $C_6F_6 + C_6H_6$ which was discussed in the last Chapter. At 70°C, the vapour pressures are

x_F	0·0000	0·1847	0·7852	1·0000
p/bar	0·7341	0·7432	0·7129	0·7185

The presence of a positive azeotrope at a mole fraction of about 0·2 and of a negative at one of about 0·8 is seen clearly from these figures, which are a selection from those found by Gaw and Swinton[33].

Lecat[34] was for many years the leading compiler of lists of systems that are known to form azeotropes. His *Tables Azéotropiques** list 6253 binary systems that form azeotropes at the normal boiling point (which he calls *orthobaric azeotropes*) and 6978 systems that do not. More recently Horsley has published lists of 16 175 binary and 659 ternary systems in which he records briefly the properties of the azeotrope, wherever one is formed. His lists[34] are not restricted to atmospheric pressure, but nevertheless owe a lot to Lecat's earlier work. Many of his references are to one of the 90 or so papers and books of Lecat, not to the original work.

The extensive work on azeotropy of the Polish school of physical chemists has been reviewed by Swietoslawski and by Malesinski[35].

6.3 LATENT HEATS OF BINARY MIXTURES

The latent heat of evaporation of a pure substance is the heat required to transfer one mole from the liquid to the gas under

* References for this publication are to be found only in the two associated volumes of *Bibliographie* (Lamertin, Brussels, 1932 and 1942). There is no second volume of the *Tables*.

equilibrium conditions, that is, at constant pressure and temperature. The differential latent heat may be formally expressed as $T(\partial S/\partial m)_{p,T}$ where dm is the number of moles vaporized. The differential heat is equal to the integral heat needed for the evaporation of a finite amount of liquid, as neither pressure nor temperature are changed by the passage of dm moles. The latent heat of a binary mixture is not so readily specified for, in general, changes of pressure and temperature occur whenever liquid is evaporated. It is therefore possible to define an infinite number of latent heats and, in particular, latent heats of evaporation at constant temperature, pressure or composition of one of the phases. The first two are of some interest.

Consider one mole of a mixture formed of two phases, prime and double-prime. Let the molar masses and equilibrium compositions at a given pressure and temperature be m', x_1', x_2' and m'', x_1'', x_2'', where

$$m' + m'' = 1, \qquad x_1' + x_2' = 1, \text{ etc.} \qquad \text{and} \qquad x_2'' > x_2' \qquad (6.7)$$

Now let δm moles be transferred at constant temperature from *phase''* to *phase'*, let the composition of this drop be (x_1, x_2) and the pressure change required to maintain equilibrium be δp. Let $\delta x_1'$, etc. be the increase in x_1', etc. caused by this transfer. Then

$$\delta x_1' = -\delta x_2' = (x_1 - x_1')\left(\frac{\delta m}{m'}\right) = \left(\frac{\partial x_1}{\partial p}\right)_{T,\sigma}' \delta p = -\left(\frac{\partial x_2}{\partial p}\right)_{T,\sigma}' \delta p \qquad (6.8)$$

$$\delta x_1'' = -\delta x_2'' = -(x_1 - x_1'')\left(\frac{\delta m}{m''}\right) = \left(\frac{\partial x_1}{\partial p}\right)_{T,\sigma}'' \delta p = -\left(\frac{\partial x_2}{\partial p}\right)_{T,\sigma}'' \delta p \qquad (6.9)$$

These equations may be solved to give the composition of the drop (x_1, x_2) and δp, in terms of an arbitrary change δm. The differential latent heat, $T(\partial s/\partial m)_{T,\sigma}$, may now be written down. It is formed of two terms, called by Strickland-Constable[36] the *direct* and *indirect* terms. The direct term is related to the difference in the partial molar entropies of the two phases

$$\text{Direct latent heat} = Tx_1\,\Delta s_1 + Tx_2\,\Delta s_2 \qquad (6.10)$$

where, as before, Δs_1, is $s_1' - s_1''$, etc. The indirect term is related to the change in the entropy of the two phases caused by the consequent change δp required to maintain equilibrium.

Indirect latent heat

$$= T(\partial p/\partial m)_{T,\sigma}[m'(\partial s/\partial p)_{T,x}' + m''(\partial s/\partial p)_{T,x}''] \qquad (6.11)$$

$$= -T(\partial p/\partial m)_{T,\sigma}[m'(\partial v/\partial T)_{p,x}' + m''(\partial v/\partial T)_{p,x}''] \qquad (6.12)$$

The composition of the drop (x_1, x_2) and δp may now be eliminated by using (6.8) and (6.9). The entropy differences $\Delta s_1 = (\Delta h_1/T)$, etc. may be eliminated in favour of Δv_1, etc. by using (6.1) and (6.2). The latent heat then becomes:

Direct differential latent heat at constant temperature

$$= - \frac{Tm'(\partial x_1/\partial T)'_{p,\sigma}(\Delta v_1 x_1'' + \Delta v_2 x_2'') + Tm''(\partial x_1/\partial T)''_{p,\sigma}(\Delta v_1 x_1' + \Delta v_2 x_2')}{m'(\partial x_1/\partial p)'_{T,\sigma} + m''(\partial x_1/\partial p)''_{T,\sigma}}$$

(6.13)

Indirect differential latent heat at constant temperature

$$= \frac{T \Delta x_1 [m'(\partial v/\partial T)'_{p,x} + m''(\partial v/\partial T)''_{p,x}]}{m'(\partial x_1/\partial p)'_{T,\sigma} + m''(\partial x_1/\partial p)''_{T,\sigma}}$$

(6.14)

All the quantities in these two equations can be obtained experimentally from a knowledge of the change of v with pressure, temperature and composition in the two phases, and from the slopes of phase-boundary curves such as $(\partial x_1/\partial p)'_{T,\sigma}$, etc. They are, therefore, the closest analogue for a binary mixture of Clapeyron's equation which, for a system of one component, similarly expresses the latent heat in terms of purely mechanical properties.

The indirect term is generally negligible at the bubble point, as the coefficient of thermal expansion of the liquid is much smaller than that of the vapour. It may be appreciable at the dew point, however, even if the total vapour pressure is low. Strickland-Constable[36] quotes as an example the direct and indirect terms for an equimolar mixture of carbon dioxide and propylene at 0°C, where the pressure changes from 21 to 42 bar between dew- and bubble-point. The indirect term changes from 1970 to 80 J mol⁻¹ and the direct term from 13 700 to 10 900 J mol⁻¹ between these points. The total *integral latent heat* for the complete isothermal expansion of such a mixture is obtained by integration of the differential heats between dew- and bubble-points, and is 13 500 J mol⁻¹.

The direct and indirect differential latent heats for evaporation at constant pressure may be found similarly. There are two equations analogous to (6.8) and (6.9) in which δT and $(\partial x_1/\partial T)'_{p,\sigma}$, etc. replace δp and $(\partial x_1/\partial p)'_{T,\sigma}$, etc. The direct term is again given by (6.10) and the indirect term by

$$T(\partial T/\partial m)_{p,\sigma}[m'(\partial s/\partial T)'_{p,x} + m''(\partial s/\partial T)''_{p,x}]$$

(6.15)

$$= (\partial T/\partial m)_{p,\sigma}[m'c_p' + m''c_p'']$$

(6.16)

The composition of the drop and the change δT may now be found, as before, in terms of δm, and the following expressions obtained for the two terms:

Direct differential latent heat at constant pressure

$$= \frac{\begin{array}{c}Tm'(\partial x_1/\partial T)'_{p,\sigma}(\partial p/\partial T)'_{x,\sigma}(\Delta v_1 x_1'' + \Delta v_2 x_2'') \\ + Tm''(\partial x_1/\partial T)''_{p,\sigma}(\partial p/\partial T)''_{x,\sigma}(\Delta v_1 x_1' + \Delta v_2 x_2')\end{array}}{m'(\partial x_1/\partial T)'_{p,\sigma} + m''(\partial x_1/\partial T)''_{p,\sigma}} \quad (6.17)$$

Indirect differential latent heat at constant pressure

$$= - \frac{\Delta x_1 [m' c_p' + m'' c_p'']}{m'(\partial x_1/\partial T)'_{p,\sigma} + m''(\partial x_1/\partial T)''_{p,\sigma}} \quad (6.18)$$

The integral latent heat at constant temperature is that required for flash distillation as, for example, in the pipe-stills of the petroleum industry. The integral latent heat at constant pressure is that required for the usual laboratory or technical distillation, or for the first step of a fractional distillation. Only the former can be related to the mechanical properties of the mixture. The calculation of the indirect term of the latter requires a knowledge of the heat capacities of the two phases.

The indirect terms vanish if the mixture is an azeotrope, as Δx is zero. The direct terms at constant pressure and at constant temperature are then both equal to $T \Delta v (\mathrm{d}p_{az}/\mathrm{d}T)$ where p_{az} is the vapour pressure of the azeotrope. This is identical with Clapeyron's equation for a pure substance.

6.4 GAS–LIQUID CRITICAL STATES OF SIMPLE MIXTURES

If a homogeneous liquid mixture in equilibrium with an equal volume of vapour is heated, and if the pressure is adjusted to maintain the equality of volumes, then the system must come eventually to a critical point at which all the intensive properties of the co-existing phases have become the same. Such a critical point is physically but not thermodynamically analogous to the gas–liquid critical point of a pure substance.

It will become clear in the next Section that there is often no absolute distinction between gas–liquid and liquid–liquid critical points in mixtures, for both are points of incipient material but not of mechanical instability. Thus the critical points described in this Section, although having many of the qualities of the gas–liquid critical points of pure substances, are described by the equations of Section 5.2.

The proof of the statement that these critical points are not ones of mechanical instability can be obtained only by discussing the behaviour of the system on a (a, v, x) surface, at constant temperature, for the molar Helmholtz free energy is (classically) a continuous differentiable function of v and x in regions of both material and mechanical instability. The (g, p, x) surface, at constant temperature, cannot properly be used until it has been shown that the system is mechanically stable.

The use of a (a, v, x) surface for the discussion of the critical point of a binary mixture is formally identical with the use, in Chapter 3, of a (U, S, V) surface for that of a pure substance, and so is given here only in outline. The conditions of equilibrium at constant temperature of two phases, prime and double-prime, may be written

$$p' = p'' \tag{6.19}$$

$$\mu_1' - \mu_2' = \mu_1'' - \mu_2'' \tag{6.20}$$

$$\mu_2' = \mu_2'' \tag{6.21}$$

or, in terms of a and its derivatives,

$$a_v' = a_v'' \qquad \text{(cf. 3.20)} \tag{6.22}$$

$$a_x' = a_x'' \qquad \text{(cf. 3.21)} \tag{6.23}$$

$$a' - v'a_v' - x'a_x' = a'' - v''a_v'' - x''a_x'' \qquad \text{(cf. 3.22)} \tag{6.24}$$

If the mixture is to be stable under fluctuations of density and composition, then the determinant

$$D = \begin{vmatrix} a_{2v} & a_{xv} \\ a_{xv} & a_{2x} \end{vmatrix} \qquad \text{(cf. 3.23)} \tag{6.25}$$

must be positive. This condition requires that a_{2x} is positive (a condition that is always satisfied in simple systems such as those discussed in this Section and is formally analogous to U_{2V} being positive in a system of one component) and that a_{2v} is positive (the condition of mechanical stability and the analogue of thermal stability in a system of one component). It requires also that

$$D = - (\partial p / \partial v)_x (\partial^2 g / \partial x^2)_p > 0 \tag{6.26}$$

This equation alone suggests that D could be zero by the system becoming either mechanically or materially unstable.

However, as before, it is easy to show that only one of these limits is reached at a critical point (with the exception of a special case discussed below). Consider the Taylor expansion of a about its value at the critical point in powers of $\delta x(= x - x^c)$ and $\delta v(= v - v^c)$. Substitution of the first terms of this expansion and of its differentiated forms into (6.22) and (6.23) gives

$$a_{xv} \, \Delta x + a_{2v} \, \Delta v = 0 \qquad \text{(cf. 3.27)} \qquad (6.27)$$

$$a_{2x} \, \Delta x + a_{xv} \, \Delta v = 0 \qquad \text{(cf. 3.28)} \qquad (6.28)$$

where Δx is $x' - x''$. Either of these equations gives the slope of the tie-line joining (v', x') to (v'', x'') on the (v, x) projection of the (a, v, x) surface. At the critical point, this tie-line becomes the tangent to the curve bounding the unstable region, that is, to the curve along which D is zero. The equation for the tangent is, therefore, any one of the three

$$a_{xv} \, dx + a_{2v} \, dv = 0 \qquad \text{(cf. 3.29)} \qquad (6.29)$$

$$a_{2x} \, dx + a_{xv} \, dv = 0 \qquad \text{(cf. 3.30)} \qquad (6.30)$$

$$D_x \, dx + D_v \, dv = 0 \qquad \text{(cf. 3.31)} \qquad (6.31)$$

The first two may be written

$$\left[-\left(\frac{\partial p}{\partial x} \right)_v \right] dx + \left[-\left(\frac{\partial p}{\partial v} \right)_x \right] dv = 0 \quad \text{(cf. 3.32)} \qquad (6.32)$$

$$\left[\left(\frac{\partial^2 g}{\partial x^2} \right)_p - \left(\frac{\partial p}{\partial x} \right)_v^2 \Big/ \left(\frac{\partial p}{\partial v} \right)_x \right] dx + \left[-\left(\frac{\partial p}{\partial x} \right)_v \right] dv = 0$$

$$\text{(cf. 3.33)} \qquad (6.33)$$

If these two equations are to represent the same tangent, then it is clear that $(\partial^2 g/\partial x^2)_p$ must be zero, whatever the value of $(\partial p/\partial v)_x$. The third equation, (6.31), gives

$$a_{3x} - 3a_{2xv} \left(\frac{a_{xv}}{a_{2v}} \right) + 3a_{x2v} \left(\frac{a_{xv}}{a_{2v}} \right)^2 - a_{3v} \left(\frac{a_{vx}}{a_{2v}} \right)^3 = 0 \qquad (6.34)$$

or

$$(\partial^3 g/\partial x^3)_p = 0 \qquad (6.35)$$

Figure 6.6 shows the (v, x) projection[37] of the (p, v, x) surface, which may be derived from the (a, v, x) surface by differentiation. Three boundary curves are shown. The outermost is that of the co-existing or equilibrium volumes and was called the *connodal* or *binodal curve* by van der Waals and his school. The next is the boundary curve for material instability which is tangential to the equilibrium curve at the critical point. It is the *spinodal curve* of van der Waals. The innermost is the boundary curve for mechanical stability, that is, the locus of the maxima and minima of the lines representing the hypothetical continuous variation of p with v, at constant x, through the two-phase region. This curve does not go near the critical point but meets that of material instability at

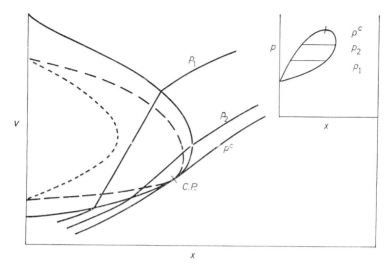

Figure 6.6. The (v, x) projection of a (p, v, x) surface at a temperature above the critical point of the components
Boundary curves:
———— co-existence curve
– – – – limit of material stability
- - - - - limit of mechanical stability
Three isobars are shown, the highest of which passes through the critical point (C.P.). The inset shows the (p, x) projection of the surface

$x = 0$. This meeting follows directly from (6.25) which shows that D can be zero for a pure substance only if a_{2x} is zero, as a_{2v} becomes infinite as x approaches zero (or unity).

The separation between the curves of mechanical and material stability justifies the treatment of the critical point of binary mixtures by means of a (g, p, x) surface at constant temperature or a (g, T, x) surface at constant pressure, and (5.2)–(5.29) are applicable equally to a gas–liquid and to a liquid–liquid critical point in a binary mixture. The following conclusions follow from these equations:

(1) The derivatives $(\partial p/\partial x)'_{T,\sigma}$ and $(\partial T/\partial x)'_{p,\sigma}$ vanish at the critical point and have opposite signs to $(\partial p/\partial x)''_{T,\sigma}$ and $(\partial T/\partial x)''_{p,\sigma}$, respectively. The equation for the temperature derivatives is (5.29); the analogous one for the pressure derivatives is

$$\left(\frac{\partial x}{\partial p}\right)'_{T,\sigma} = -\left(\frac{\partial x}{\partial p}\right)''_{T,\sigma} = -\frac{6v^c_{2x}}{\Delta x \, g^c_{4x}} \qquad (6.36)$$

193

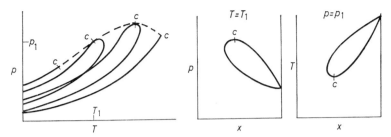

Figure 6.7. The (p, T) projection and (p, x) and (T, x) sections of the (p, T, x) surface. The critical line is shown dashed, and critical points are marked C

The (p, x) and (T, x) loops for a typical system in which $p_2^c > p_1^c$ and $T_2^c > T_1^c$ are shown in *Figure 6.7(b)* and (c). The critical point is always at an extreme value of p (at constant T) and of T (at constant p)

(2) The derivative $(\partial p / \partial T)_{x,\sigma}$ is generally non-zero at the critical point, which is neither at the maximum temperature nor at the maximum pressure of the (p, T) loop at constant x. This a necessary consequence of the rounded ends of the (p, x) and (T, x) loops. All critical points lie on the envelope of the (p, T) loops, as is readily seen in *Figure 6.7(a)* by considering neighbouring loops of infinitesimally different compositions. *Figure 6.8* combines *Figure 6.7(a)*, (b) and (c) into a three-dimensional sketch.

(3) The critical point is not generally at the end of the (v, x) curve of *Figure 6.6*, as the tie-lines do not connect phases of equal composition. An azeotrope is an exception to this and is discussed separately below. The derivative $(\partial p / \partial x)_{T,\sigma}$ is infinite at the end of

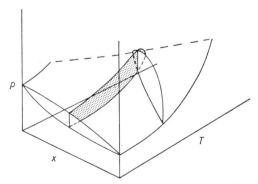

Figure 6.8. The (p, T, x) surface. The two sections drawn have a common critical point

194

this loop and so, by (6.2)

$$(\partial v/\partial x)_{p,T} = \Delta v/\Delta x \qquad (6.37)$$

That is, the isobar that passes through this point (p_2 in *Figure 6.6*) is colinear with the tie-line.

It is seen that there is nothing thermodynamically unusual about the shape of the (p, x), (T, x) or (p, T) loops. Their rounded ends are a natural and necessary consequence of the assumption that the Helmholtz free energy is a continuous differentiable function of v and x. Nevertheless, the shape of these loops gives rise to experimental behaviour which is, at first sight, odd.

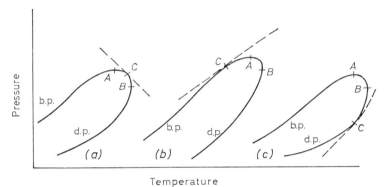

Figure 6.9. The three types of (p, T) loop

Consider the head of a (p, T) loop of constant composition such as that shown in *Figure 6.9(a)*. The critical point, C, is neither the point of maximum pressure, A, nor that of maximum temperature, B. If a mixture of this composition is compressed isothermally at a temperature below C, then normal condensation occurs. The first drop of liquid appears at the dew-point (d.p.) and the last bubble of gas vanishes at the bubble-point (b.p.). If, however, the temperature is between C and B, then complete condensation never occurs. The critical point C is the meeting point of the dew- and bubble-point curves, and so a line of increasing pressure at a temperature between C and B cuts the (p, T) loop at two dew-points.

On compression, the amount of liquid increases to a maximum and then falls again to a second dew-point. This evaporation of a liquid by an isothermal increase of pressure is the opposite of the normal behaviour of a mixture and of the invariable behaviour of a pure substance. The phenomenon was therefore called *retrograde condensation* by Kuenen[38] who was the first to observe it under equilibrium conditions and to interpret it correctly.

Figure 6.10 shows some of Kuenen's original observations on a mixture of carbon dioxide and methyl chloride with a mole fraction of the former of 0·41, and at a temperature of 105·0°C. This lies between the critical point, *C*, of 102°C and the maximum of the (*p*, *T*) loop, *B*, of 106·5°C. The sudden onset of retrograde behaviour at 81·6 atm is very marked. However, the critical point need not necessarily lie between *A* and *B* but can lie outside them on either side, as is shown in *Figure 6.9(b)* and (*c*). If the order of the points is *C*, *A*, *B* then retrograde behaviour between two dew-points occurs again, as is clear from *Figure 6.9(b)*. Isotherms that pass through two dew-points were said by Kuenen to show *retrograde behaviour of the first kind*. An isotherm that passes through two bubble-points exhibits *retrograde behaviour of the second kind*. This is less common but occurs when the order of the three points is *A*, *B*, *C* as in *Figure 6.9(c)*. Similarly unorthodox behaviour is found on changing the temperature at constant pressure. Retrograde isobars can join a pair of dew-points, as in *Figure 6.9(b)*, or one of bubble-points, as in *Figure 6.9(a)* and (*c*).

There are no agreed names for the points *A*, *B*, and *C* of *Figure 6.9*. Point *C* is the only one properly called a critical point, since it is a state of the system in which the two phases have become identical. It was called a *plait point* by van der Waals and his school, since it is the point at which a plait or fold first develops in the (*a*, *v*, *x*) surface. Kuenen calls point *B* the *critical point of contact*, which he unfortunately sometimes shortens to *critical point*. This is not a happy choice, as *B* is not a critical point in the usual sense of that term.

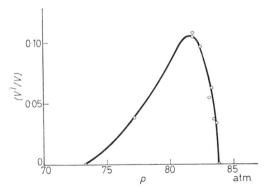

Figure 6.10. Retrograde condensation. The proportion of the volume occupied by the liquid phase in a mixture of carbon dioxide + methyl chloride on isothermal compression at 105·0°C. The dew-points are at 73·3 and 83·9 atm (calculated from the results of Kuenen[38])

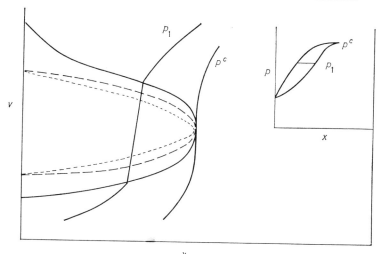

Figure 6.11. The gas–liquid critical point of an azeotrope. The (v, x) projection and, inset, the (p, x) projection. The conventions are those of *Figure 6.6*

Sage and Lacey[39] suggested the names *cricondenbar* and *cricondentherm* for A and B, respectively.

An interesting situation arises if the critical point is at the end of the (v, x) loop, as in *Figure 6.11*. The co-existence curve on this figure is the (v, x) projection of a line in a three-dimensional (p, v, x) space. The line has the following properties. First, the value of the pressure at the critical point is an extremum—usually a maximum. This follows directly from the fact that the tie-lines are perpendicular to the (p) axis and converge to zero length at the critical point. Secondly, the bubble-point pressure always exceeds the dew-point pressure. That is, for any given composition, x^*, the equilibrium pressure $p''(x^*)$ is greater than $p'(x^*)$ in *Figure 6.11*. These two properties of the (p, v, x) line require that $(\partial p/\partial x)'_{T,\sigma}$ and $(\partial p/\partial x)''_{T,\sigma}$ both approach zero at the critical point. It is clear from the diagram that $(\partial v/\partial x)'_{T,\sigma}$ and $(\partial v/\partial x)''_{T,\sigma}$ are both infinite at this point and therefore $(\partial p/\partial x)^c_{v,T}$ is zero and $(\partial v/\partial x)^c_{p,T}$ is infinite. Hence

$$\left(\frac{\partial p}{\partial v}\right)^c_{x,T} = -\frac{(\partial p/\partial x)^c_{v,T}}{(\partial v/\partial x)^c_{p,T}} = 0 \qquad (6.38)$$

or

$$a^c_{xv} = 0, \qquad a^c_{2x} = 0, \qquad D^c = 0 \qquad (6.39)$$

Thus the critical point is now both materially and mechanically unstable and the fluid near this point behaves as a pure substance. For example, mechanical stability near the critical point requires that a_{3v}^c is also zero. Such a system cannot be discussed on a (g, p, x) surface, since the infinity in $(\partial v/\partial x)_{p,T}$ produces a discontinuity.

This behaviour is found whenever an azeotrope persists up to the critical point. The (p, x) loop now ends in a cusp and not with a rounded end, for the only one of the three functions (6.22)–(6.24) that retains any first-order terms is a_x for which the leading terms are

$$a_x = a_x^c + a_{2x}^c(\delta x) + \tfrac{1}{2}a_{3x}^c(\delta x)^2 + a_{2xv}^c(\delta x)(\delta v) + \tfrac{1}{2}a_{x2v}^c(\delta v)^2 + \cdots \tag{6.40}$$

or

$$0 = a_{2x}^c[\delta x' - \delta x''] + \tfrac{1}{2}a_{x2v}^c[(\delta v')^2 - (\delta v'')^2] + \cdots \tag{6.41}$$

Hence $\delta x'$ is equal to $+\delta x''$ and is of the order of $(\delta v)^2$. This differs from the normal critical mixture for which $\delta x'$ is equal to $-\delta x''$ and is of the order of δv. The shape of the cusp is shown in *Figure 6.11*.

If the critical point moves farther round the (v, x) loop to larger volumes, then the critical point again becomes normal, that is, non-azeotropic, but is now at a minimum of the (p, x) loop, not a maximum. The system now forms an azeotrope at a pressure above the critical for that temperature and at a different composition. The transition, with changing temperature, from normal behaviour, through the critical azeotrope, to this inverted behaviour is shown in *Figure 6.12*, which is based on the system carbon dioxide + ethylene[12]. The critical line in such a diagram is the locus of the extrema of the (p, x) loops (or cusp) and not, as has often been misleadingly shown in published diagrams[40], the envelope of these loops. Such an envelope has little significance, for only on the (p, T) projection is it the critical line. Thus the coincidence of an azeotropic and a critical point leads to simultaneous mechanical and material instability, whereas one of these points without the other produces one type of instability only.

The description of the gas–liquid critical point given above is a classical description; that is, it is based on the assumption that A is everywhere analytic. It was shown in Chapter 3 that there is good reason to believe that such classical descriptions are wrong, both numerically and in principle, for the gas–liquid critical point of a one-component system. In the last Chapter it was suggested that they were wrong also for binary liquid–liquid critical points, although the evidence is less compelling. Nothing is known directly about the singularities at the gas–liquid critical point of a binary system, but they are presumed to be the same as those at a liquid–liquid critical point, unless there is an azeotrope, when they behave

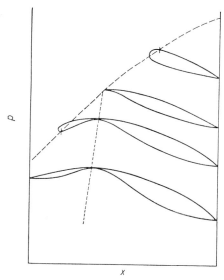

Figure 6.12. Intersection of an azeotropic line (dotted) and a critical
line (dashed). Four isotherms are shown

as a one-component system. This presumption is based on the
identity of description in analytic thermodynamics and on the fact
(see next Section) that gas–liquid and liquid–liquid critical points
are formally indistinguishable in some systems.

It is found experimentally that positive critical azeotropy is
generally associated with a minimum in the critical temperature on a
(T^c, x) graph and with a maximum in the critical pressure on a
(p^c, x) graph. Negative critical azeotropy is very rare but is
associated with a maximum critical temperature. None of these
associations is a thermodynamic necessity, but such maxima and
minima make azeotropy most likely.

This is best made clear by the (p, T) projections of three systems
that, first, show normal behaviour (carbon dioxide + n-butane[41]),
secondly, positive azeotropy (carbon dioxide + ethane[11]) and,
thirdly, negative azeotropy (hydrogen chloride + methyl ether[24]).
The azeotropic line is a tangent to the critical line in such projections
(*Figure 6.13*).

It is seen that a maximum in the pressure, unaccompanied by a
minimum in the temperature, does not necessarily produce azeotropy. In fact, such maxima are the rule in mixtures of hydrocarbons of very different numbers of carbon atoms. It will be shown
in Chapter 9 that the association of a minimum critical temperature

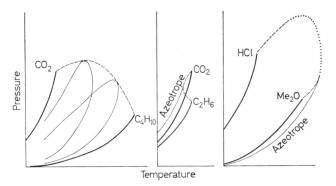

Figure 6.13. The (p, T) diagrams of three systems. The first is normal, the second has a positive, the third a negative azeotrope. The critical lines are dashed (or dotted where not determined experimentally). Two (p, T) loops for mixtures of fixed composition are shown in the first diagram, and the azeotropic lines in the second and third

with positive and a maximum critical temperature with negative azeotropy has a simple theoretical basis, for the critical temperature of a simple mixture is one of the most direct sources of information on the energy of interaction of two unlike molecules.

There is now an immense body of information on liquid–vapour equilibria at high pressures, much of which extends to the critical region. The importance of this field has increased with the greater use of natural gas, the principal constituents of which are methane and nitrogen, together with smaller amounts of hydrogen, the higher hydrocarbons and, occasionally, hydrogen sulphide. Much of the experimental work has been in the temperature range of 0–150°C, and so our information on any one system is often incomplete. However, the (simple) systems listed below are those for which it is believed that there is a continuous gas–liquid critical curve joining the critical points of the two pure components; those that are known to be immiscible in the liquid phase are deferred to the next Section. The systems below may, however, be azeotropic or one of the components may solidify above the critical point of the other. The latter are excluded from this Section only if there is evidence that liquid immiscibility would occur if the solid state did not intervene.

The following list is, of course, not complete but is offered as a set of important systems whose liquid–vapour equilibria have been studied to high pressures, and in most cases to the critical line. Some of the references will be found to contain results on ternary systems also. As usual in this book, systems containing helium and hydrogen are omitted.

Argon + nitrogen[43,44], oxygen[43,44], carbon monoxide[43], methane[43]
Nitrogen + oxygen[43–45], carbon monoxide[43,46], methane[18,41,43,47–50]
Oxygen + carbon monoxide[43], carbon dioxide[52], methane[43]
Carbon monoxide + methane[43,53]
Carbon dioxide + methane[54–56], ethane[9–11], ethylene[9,12,57], acetylene[11,13], propane[41], n-butane[41], n-pentane[41], nitrous oxide[8], methyl chloride[24]
Methane + ethane[18,47,48,58,59,66], ethylene[18,60,61], propane[58,62–65], n-butane[51,59,62,63,64], i-butane[67], n-pentane[63,65], i-pentane[68]
Ethane + ethylene[9,16–18], acetylene[11,13,16,19], propane[18,58,63,69], propylene[18,70], n-butane[59,65,71,72], n-pentane[59,65,73,74], n-heptane[58,65,72,73,75], n-decane[76], cyclohexane[77], benzene[77], hydrogen chloride[78], hydrogen sulphide[78], nitrous oxide[14], perfluoro-n-heptane[86], acetone[85]
Ethylene + acetylene[20,21], propylene[57], n-heptane[80], nitrous oxide[15]
Propane + n-butane[63,81], n-pentane[63,65,81], i-pentane[82], n-heptane[58], n-decane[83], benzene[84], hydrogen sulphide[85], sulphur hexafluoride[86], perfluoro-n-heptane[86], acetone[85]
n-Butane + n-pentane[63,65], n-hexane[63], n-heptane[65,80], n-decane[87,94], perfluoro-n-heptane[86], acetone[85]
n-Pentane + n-hexane[88], n-heptane[89], cyclohexane[88], benzene[88], toluene[88], hydrogen sulphide[90], perfluoro-n-heptane[86], acetone[85]
n-Hexane + cyclohexane[88], benzene[88], toluene[88,91], perfluoro-n-heptane[86], acetone[85]
Cyclohexane + benzene[88], toluene[88], perfluorocyclohexane[92]
Benzene + toluene[88], methanol[93], ethanol[93], perfluorobenzene[33]
Hydrogen chloride + dimethyl ether[24]

The team of Reamer, Sage and Lacey has contributed heavily to the work listed above. A fuller account of their work on both binary and multicomponent systems is to be found in a recent book by Sage[94].

Most of these systems are simple mixtures of non-polar substances in which the critical curve is a continuous curve in (p, T, x) space from the critical point of one pure component to that of the other. Some of the mixtures contain polar components, such as hydrogen chloride, hydrogen sulphide, methyl chloride and methyl ether, but the critical line is still continuous. A study of the complete lines in the list leads to the following generalizations:

(1) The (T^c, x) graph is often close to a straight line for mixtures of similar critical constants, for example nitrogen + oxygen, carbon dioxide + nitrous oxide and ethane + ethylene. Such straight lines are associated with small departures from Raoult's law.

(2) Large differences in the critical temperatures or volumes of pure components (the two generally go together) lead to lines that are predominantly convex upwards but which may be sigmoid. There is a clear increase in curvature along the series ethane + benzene, ethane + cyclohexane, ethane + n-heptane and ethylene + n-heptane. The ratio of the critical volumes

201

(or molecular sizes) of the pure components also increases along this series.

(*3*) (T^c, *x*) graphs are concave upwards, or even show minima, where there are large positive deviations from Raoult's law, as in mixtures of a polar and non-polar substance and in some of aliphatic and aromatic hydrocarbons. For example, ethane + hydrogen chloride, ethane + hydrogen sulphide, propane + hydrogen sulphide, methanol + benzene, n-hexane + benzene, n-hexane + toluene, cyclohexane + benzene and cyclohexane + toluene. Six of the eight mixtures containing fluorine compounds also have minima.

6.5 CRITICAL POINTS IN MIXTURES OF COMPLEX LIQUIDS

Many of the pairs of liquids chosen for discussion in Chapter 5 were only partially miscible at low vapour pressures. The effects of increased pressure and temperature on such immiscibility are examined qualitatively in this Section. The behaviour of these systems can be both complex and unfamiliar, for many of the results that were discovered between 1895 and 1915 have since been omitted from most textbooks of physics and chemistry, including many of those on the phase rule, whilst much of the more recent work has been undertaken by engineers and so has not been assimilated into current chemistry and physics. The possible types of phase behaviour may be set out in order of the increasing complexity of their description in (*p*, *T*, *x*) space:

(*1*) Systems with an upper and a lower critical solution temperature, both of which lie between the melting points of the solids and the critical points of the liquids. They have two distinct critical curves in (*p*, *T*, *x*) space, one of which connects the U.C.S.T. to the L.C.S.T., the other the two gas–liquid critical points of the pure substances. The former may be called, unambiguously, a liquid–liquid critical curve and the latter a gas–liquid critical curve. This behaviour may or may not be combined with azeotropy.

(*2*) Systems with a U.C.S.T. only in which the range of liquid–liquid immiscibility is terminated by the solidification of one of the components. Again the gas–liquid critical curve is entirely separate from the liquid–liquid curve, and again azeotropy may be present.

(*3*) Systems in which the melting point of one pure component is above the critical temperature of the other and in which the gas–liquid critical curve is broken at two *critical end points* in

(p, T, x) space by the vapour-pressure curve of the saturated solution.

(4) Systems in which the region of liquid–liquid immiscibility extends to, or is found only in, that of the gas–liquid critical curve. Again the curve joining the critical points of the two pure components is broken by the appearance of a third phase at a critical end point. (This is the largest and most complex class, and is sub-divided in the discussion below.)

(5) Systems which formally belong to class (3) but would belong to class (4) if the solid phase did not intervene first.

The (p, x) graphs in the region of two liquid phases may be of four types, irrespective of the class to which the system belongs, as shown in *Figure 6.14(a–d)*. The first type is a system in which the pressure of the three-phase line (liquid + liquid + gas) is between the saturated vapour pressures of the pure components, so that no azeotrope is formed. In the second a homogeneous positive azeotrope is formed outside the composition range of immiscibility. In the third, a heterogeneous azeotrope (or *hetero-azeotrope*) is

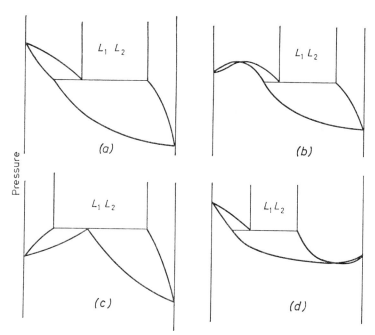

Figure 6.14. The four types of (p, x) curves found with partially miscible liquids. The area L_1L_2 is the region of two liquid phases

formed in which the pressure of the three-phase line is the highest at which vapour can exist. Here the composition of the vapour lies between those of the immiscible liquids and not, as in *Figure 6.14(a)* and (*b*), outside them. The fourth diagram shows a homogeneous negative azeotrope at a composition well removed from those of the immiscible liquids.

The first of these four types of (*p, x*) diagram is that of immiscible pairs in which the pure components have very different volatilities, for example, n-pentane + nitrobenzene[95], n-hexane + aniline[96], carbon dioxide + water[97], propylene oxide + water[98], ammonia + toluene[99], benzene + sulphur[95] and water + nicotine[100] from the L.C.S.T. at 61°C up to 85°C.

The second type—*Figure 6.14(b)*—is less common but occurs with a few aqueous mixtures, for example, water + phenol[95,101] (see also Section 6.2), water + nicotine[100] above 85°C, and water + methyl ethyl ketone[102].

The third type (*Figure 6.14(c)*) is probably the commonest and is found whenever two liquids of similar vapour pressure are only partially miscible. Mixtures of a fluorocarbon and the corresponding hydrocarbon are of this type (see Section 5.3). Other examples are methanol + cyclohexane[103], water + triethylamine[104], water + aniline[101], water + i-butanol[105], and water + ethyl acetate[106]. These systems all revert to type (*b*) in the immediate neighbourhood of the critical solution point. This must necessarily happen unless, by chance, the composition of the azeotrope is that of the liquid phases at their critical point. In general this does not happen (*Figure 6.15*).

Examples of the fourth type (*Figure 6.14(d)*) are very rare, since its occurrence at low vapour pressures implies that the excess free energy is negative at the azeotrope but positive at the immiscibility. The best known examples are the aqueous solutions of hydrogen chloride, hydrogen bromide and sulphur dioxide, in which the properties of the mixtures are quite different at the two extremes of composition. Weak solutions are ionic and the systems form negative azeotropes because of the large heat of solvation of the ions. However, mixtures very rich in hydrogen chloride, hydrogen bromide or sulphur dioxide are little ionized, and Roozeboom showed in 1888 that the three liquids were only partially miscible with water at high concentrations, and therefore at high vapour pressures[107]. More recently the system acetic acid + triethylamine, in which the components are acid and base, has been found to behave similarly[108].

The first of the five classes of phase behaviour set out at the beginning of this Section presents no difficulty, as the region of

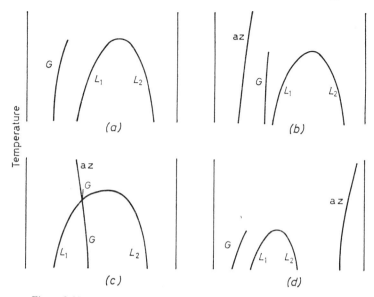

Figure 6.15. The (T, x) projections of the four types of system shown in *Figure 6.14.* It is assumed that all the liquid boundary curves, L_1 and L_2, meet at U.C.S.T. The lines marked G are the compositions of the gas phases in equilibrium with the immiscible liquids, and those marked 'az' the compositions of the homogeneous azeotropes

liquid immiscibility lies wholly within the liquid ranges of the pure components. The effect of pressure on the U.C.S.T. and L.C.S.T. has been studied systematically by Timmermans who worked on this subject first with Kohnstamm at Amsterdam and later with his own group at Brussels[109], and by Schneider[110]. If G is analytic at the critical point, then the effect is related to the second derivatives of the excess volume and entropy by (5.37). If neither v^E nor s^E have points of inflection, then the sign of $(d T^c/dp)$ is that of the ratio $(v^E/s^E)^c$. Now at a U.C.S.T. the excess entropy is generally positive and the second derivative s_{2x} is always negative. Hence if v^E is also positive, an increase of pressure leads to an increase in the critical temperature.

This behaviour is shown by most systems in which the pure components have similar boiling points, as for example[109,110], acetonitrile + cyclohexane, acetic anhydride + cyclohexane, nitromethane + cyclohexane, methanol + cyclohexane, phenol + water and aniline + n-decane. The slopes are about 0·02 K bar^{-1}, and the critical line continues to rise until it is interrupted by the

205

separation of a solid phase, as in the second of the five classes above. In nitromethane + carbon tetrachloride the excess volume is almost zero, and so T^c is practically independent of pressure.

If the boiling points of the pure components are widely separated, or if both components are polar, then v^E is often negative at a U.C.S.T., and the temperature falls with increasing pressure. Falling critical temperatures have been found[109,110] in aniline + n-octane, nitrobenzene + n-hexane, nitrobenzene + n-decane, phenol + n-hexane, water + methyl ethyl ketone, and water + s-butanol. A L.C.S.T. is always raised by an increase of temperature as s^E is necessarily negative and v^E is so in all known cases. No examples need be quoted, as all the L.C.S.T. discussed in Section 5.4 exhibit

Table 6.2. Critical curves which meet at an upper critical pressure.

System	U.C.S.T. at sat. vapour pressure	L.C.S.T.	Upper critical pressure	
Water + methyl ethyl ketone	141°C	(−10°C)	83°C	1080 bar
Water + s-butanol	114°C	(−10°C)	65°C	810 bar

this behaviour, and in many of these cases Timmermans has shown by direct experiment that the critical temperature is raised. In two systems a meeting of the critical curves has been found at an upper critical pressure, above which the fluids are miscible in all proportions.

The results of Timmermans's measurements on water + methyl ethyl ketone and water + s-butanol are shown in Table 6.2. The temperatures shown in brackets as L.C.S.T. at saturated vapour pressures are those at which ice separates. The true liquid–liquid critical points can only be realized under metastable conditions and are at about −20°C. However, a closed dome of immiscibility in (p, T, x) space, lying wholly above the melting points, has been demonstrated for water + n-butyl glycol[110] (Figure 6.16).

Some methyl pyridines have closed solubility curves at saturation pressure. On raising the pressure the U.C.S.T. falls and the L.C.S.T. rises but they do not always meet to form a closed dome. They can diverge again above about 2 kbar, and at high pressures the miscibility is decreasing with rising pressure[110].

The second class is that in which there is a U.C.S.T. only and the region of liquid immiscibility is bounded below by the separation of a solid phase. Before discussing such systems it is better to consider the phase diagram for the simpler case of two miscible liquids freezing to immiscible solids[111,112].

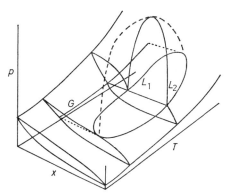

Figure 6.16. The dome of immiscibility in (p, T, x) space for a pair
of liquids whose range of immiscibility lies wholly between the
melting points and the gas–liquid critical points
– – – locus of the upper critical solution pressures

This is shown in *Figure 6.17*. The (T, x) projection of A (the
triple point of component 1), of B (that of component 2), of C, D
(the eutectic point) and F gives the usual diagram for two solids
melting to form a miscible liquid. The composition of the vapour
in equilibrium with the two solids and the liquid is shown at E, and
the (p, T) projection of C, D, E and F is the *quadruple point* of the

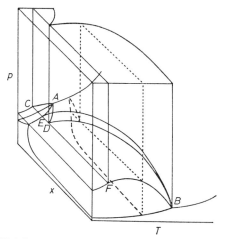

Figure 6.17. The (p, T, x) surface of two immiscible solids that
melt to form a miscible liquid. The dashed lines show a (p, x)
section at a temperature lying between those of the triple points,
A and B

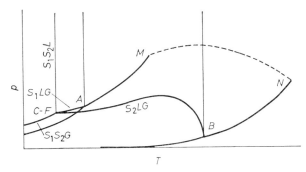

Figure 6.18. The (p, T) projection of a system of the kind shown in *Figure 6.17*. M and N are the gas–liquid critical points of the pure substances, and the dashed line is the locus of those of the mixtures. The three-phase lines only are marked S_1S_2G, etc. to show the nature of the phases in equilibrium

system—an invariant point at which solid + solid + liquid + gas are in equilibrium. The (p, T) projection of the whole figure, including the gas–liquid critical line, is shown in *Figure 6.18*. The two lines DB and EB of *Figure 6.17* have the same projection in *Figure 6.18*, as this line is a univariant system of three phases, solid + liquid (DB) + gas (EB). Similarly, DA and EA represent the liquid and gas in equilibrium with the other pure component.

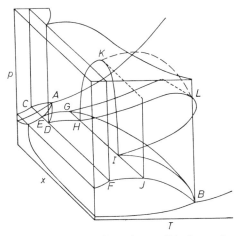

Figure 6.19. The (p, T, x) surface of two solids that melt to partially miscible liquids. Here the dome of immiscibility of *Figure 6.16* abuts on to the melting plane at HIK. The dashed line KL is the locus of the upper critical solution pressures

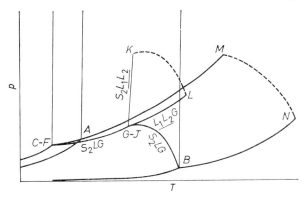

Figure 6.20. The (p, T) projection of *Figure 6.19.* The two dashed lines KL and MN are, respectively, the liquid–liquid and the gas–liquid critical lines. On the three-phase lines which end in critical points the pair of phases that become identical are underlined

The melting of two solids to partially miscible liquids[113] is shown in (p, T, x) space in *Figure 6.19,* as a (p, T) projection in *Figure 6.20,* and as a (p, x) section in *Figure 6.21.* There are now two quadruple points in the (p, T) projection. The lower, C, D, E, F, is the same as that in *Figure 6.18,* namely the equilibrium between

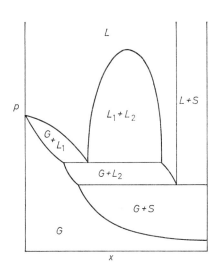

Figure 6.21. A (p, x) section of *Figure 6.19* at a temperature lying between the quadruple axis G, H, I, J and the triple point B

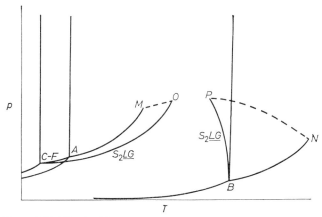

Figure 6.22. The (p, T) projection of a system in which the solubility of the solid component in the liquid is low. The saturated vapour-pressure curve of *Figure 6.18* (DB) now cuts the critical line at the lower and upper critical end points, O and P

solid + solid + liquid + gas. However, the two lines EG and DH do not now move continuously with increasing x_2 until they reach the triple point B, but as the liquid mixture becomes richer in the second component, the limit of miscibility is reached at a second quadruple point, G, H, I, J. Here the four phases are gas + liquid + liquid + solid. It can happen that the equilibrium lines solid + liquid + liquid that arise from H and I in *Figure 6.19* do not end in a critical point of upper critical pressure, as shown, but continue until they meet the line of solid + solid + liquid that arises from D, in a third quadruple point of solid + solid + liquid + liquid. However, only one example of this is known, the system acetonitrile + water[114], which has a quadruple point of this kind at $-24.2°$C and 1240 bar, although there is evidence that aniline + water[114] behaves similarly.

Hetero-azeotropes give similar (p, T, x) diagrams but have the line L_1L_2G of *Figure 6.20* at a pressure higher than the vapour-pressure curves of the pure components.

The third class of system is that in which the melting point of the second component is above the critical point of the first, and where the solubility of the solid in the liquid mixture is low. If the solubility is high, then the (p, T) projection of the phase diagram is as shown in *Figure 6.18*. If it is low, then the (p, T) projection of the vapour-pressure curves DB and EB lies close to the vapour pressure of the more volatile component and cuts the gas–liquid critical

210

curve at two *critical end points* (*Figure 6.22*). There is now a temperature gap between O and P, the lower and upper end points in which the pure solid second component is in equilibrium with one homogeneous mixed fluid phase at all pressures. This solubility of solids in compressed gases has been reviewed elsewhere[112] and need not be discussed here, as there is no liquid phase in such systems.

The fourth of the five classes distinguished at the beginning of this Section is that in which the liquid–liquid immiscibility extends into the region of (p, T, x) space of the gas–liquid critical curve. This class is both large and complicated, and further classification is needed if the variety of observed behaviour is to be reduced to some order. The classification chosen here is based upon a concept of a monotonically increasing departure from the behaviour of the simple systems discussed in Section 6.4. This receives some support from the recent work of Scott[115] on the phase diagrams of mixtures that conform to van der Waals's equation and is summarized in *Figure 6.23*.

In a simple mixture there is a continuous gas–liquid critical line, e.g. *MN* in *Figure 6.18*. The simplest type of break in this line is shown in *Figure 6.23a* in which it is near the critical point of the more volatile component. It is caused by the appearance of two liquid phases over a short range of temperature. Kuenen[97] was the first to discover behaviour of this kind with mixtures of ethane with ethanol, n-propanol and n-butanol. These alcohols are completely miscible with liquid ethane at 25°C but separation occurs near the critical temperature of pure ethane (32°C). *Figure 6.24* shows the (p, T, x) surface for ethane + n-propanol. It is seen that the three-phase line extends here only over 3 K and is bounded below by a liquid–liquid and above by a gas–liquid critical end point; at the latter the gas and the liquid phase rich in ethane become identical. The critical line that starts from the former point assumes more and more the character of a gas–liquid critical line and ends at the critical point of pure propanol. It provides a clear example of the confusion that can arise from a careless use of the words *gas* and *liquid* in the critical region of a mixture.

Over the years a variety of similar systems have come to light. Examples in which both critical end points have been located are carbon dioxide (T^c, 31°C) + nitrobenzene[116] (liquids immiscible from 30–40°C), carbon dioxide + o-nitrophenol[95,117] (26–40°C), ethylene (T^c, 9°C) + p-dichlorobenzene[118,119] (26·0–26·5°C), ethane (T^c, 32°C) + 1,3,5-trichlorobenzene[117,119] (40·3–46·8°C).

More interesting perhaps has been the recent discovery that immiscibility of this type can occur in mixtures of hydrocarbons if the two components differ sufficiently in chain length. Thus

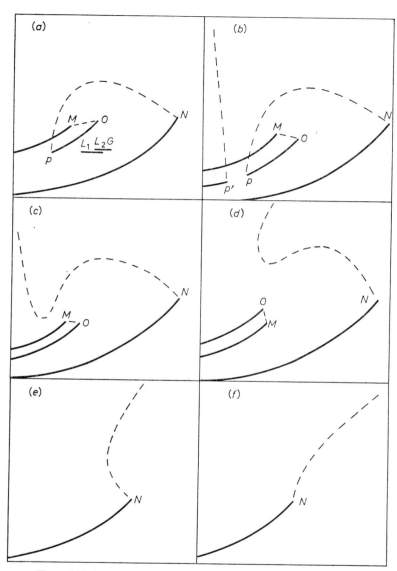

Figure 6.23. The (p, T) projection of the critical lines of systems in which there is immiscibility of the liquid phases at temperatures up to the critical point of the more volatile component. For three-dimensional sketches of (a), (c) and (e) see *Figures 6.24, 6.26* and *6.28*

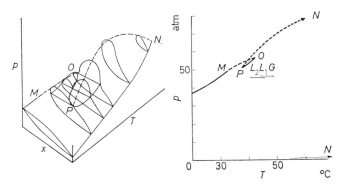

Figure 6.24. The (p, T, x) surface and the (p, T) projection of ethane + n-propanol[97]. Here the three-phase region that lies between the critical end points O and P is wholly above the critical point of pure ethane, M. Often, with systems of this type, the end point P lies 10–20 K below M

methane is miscible at all temperatures up to the gas–liquid critical line with the normal paraffins up to pentane (cf. Section 6.4). However, it is immiscible with n-hexane[120] above a critical end point of 183 K, which is 7 K below the critical point of pure methane. Toluene and n-heptane[120–122] are immiscible with methane over the whole liquid range from a quadruple point (solid + liquid + liquid + gas) to a critical end point at 191·7 K (cf. *Figure 6.25*).

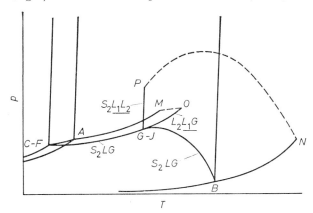

Figure 6.25. The (p, T) projection of a system in which the range of liquid immiscibility (H and I to O) is bounded at its lower end by the separation of a solid phase. In the absence of the solid the critical line NP would cut the vapour-pressure curve of the system liquid + liquid + gas to give a diagram of the kind shown in *Figure 6.24*

213

Above this point, these and similar systems behave quite normally, as is clear from *Figure 6.23a*, and so measurements at higher temperatures do not reveal the anomalies[50,58,123–125].

It is characteristic of the systems with short breaks in the critical line that the temperature of the liquid–liquid end point is very sensitive to changes of structure in the heavier hydrocarbon. Thus branched hydrocarbons are more soluble than straight-chain, and cyclic ones are less so[120,122,123,126]. n-Octane[127], n-nonane[128] and n-decane[123] resemble n-heptane in freezing before complete miscibility occurs, but some of their isomers can be cooled below the liquid–liquid end point.

If ethane is substituted for methane, then similar systems can be found[129], but is is now necessary to go to $n-C_{19}H_{40}$ before the normal paraffins show immiscibility[130], and even for this hydrocarbon the two critical end points are separated by only 1·2 K. Kohn[130] has shown that this break is absent with $n-C_{17}H_{36}$ and with $n-C_{18}H_{38}$, and that it increases to 2·9 K at $n-C_{20}H_{42}$. Higher normal paraffins, such as[130] $n-C_{28}H_{58}$, melt above the critical temperature of ethane (32°C) and so show no immiscibility, but it has been found in branched paraffins[129] up to $C_{37}H_{76}$. Propane is apparently miscible with all hydrocarbons up to $C_{37}H_{76}$ but immiscible with higher hydrocarbons (lubricating oils[131]) and with long-chain acids and esters[132].

The ratio of chain length in the binary mixture of normal paraffins which first shows liquid immiscibility is 6 for methane solutions, 9·5 for ethane and over 13 for propane. If the solvent has 6 or more carbon atoms, then phase separation of this type occurs only if the solute is a polymer. This has been demonstrated[133] for many polymer-solvent systems, and it has been found that it is quite common for the L.C.S.T. to be 100 K or more below the critical point of the pure solvent. Again the L.C.S.T. is sensitive to small changes in chain length and branching, but a detailed discussion of such solutions is outside the scope of this book.

Liquid nitrogen is a poorer solvent than liquid methane for the higher hydrocarbons. Immiscibility starts here with ethane, but again measurements at temperatures well above the critical point of the more volatile component do not reveal the break in the critical line, and our knowledge of these systems is less complete than that of the methane solutions[47,48,50,64,71].

An interesting variation on this class of systems is shown in *Figure 6.23b*. Here the liquid mixture has two regions of immiscibility, one bounded above and below by the critical end points and one bounded above by a conventional U.C.S.T. and below by solidification at a quadruple point. Clearly such behaviour occurs only when there is a nice balance of intermolecular forces, but several examples are now known. One is methane + 1-hexene[120] where the range of complete miscibility lies between the U.C.S.T. at 133·8 K and the critical end point at 179·6 K. A second is benzene + polyisobutene[133] where the range of miscibility is from 23°C to about 260°C (not[134] 160°C, as stated previously[133]), and a third cyclohexane + polystyrene[133] (30–180°C).

It should be noted that the systems sulphur + benzene, sulphur + toluene, sulphur + triphenylmethane, etc. are not of this type[135,136]. Such systems are immiscible at low temperatures, pass through a U.C.S.T. on heating and then change in character at the polymerization temperature (159°C in pure sulphur). Above this temperature they are physically and chemically quite different solutions and commonly become immiscible again on heating further. In triphenylmethane the two temperatures are 147°C (U.C.S.T.) and 199°C (L.C.S.T.). These come together on raising the pressure, and above 700 bar there are two liquid phases at all temperatures[135].

Figure 6.23c can be regarded as a diagram that has evolved from *Figure 6.23b* by the raising of the minimum in the gas–liquid critical line so that it no longer 'cuts' the three-phase line. The two liquids are now immiscible at all temperatures, and such behaviour is associated with a greater disparity in intermolecular forces than *Figures 6.23a* and *b*. Thus ethane yields diagrams of the type of *Figure 6.23a* when mixed with ethanol and n-propanol but one like *Figure 6.23c* with the more polar methanol[137]. *Figure 6.26* shows the (p, T, x) surface and its (p, T) projection. Here the critical end point O at which the ethane-rich liquid layer becomes identical with the gas is only 3·2 K above the critical temperature of pure ethane. The system methane + hydrogen sulphide behaves similarly[138].

Mixtures of carbon dioxide with the lower paraffins show no anomalies, that is, the critical points of the pure components are joined by a continuous line. However, from $n-C_7H_{16}$ upwards there is a U.C.S.T. which lies between the triple and critical points of CO_2. The liquid–liquid critical line which starts from this point rises with a positive slope and probably meets the solid surface to give a diagram that is topologically the same as *Figure 6.20*. The gas–liquid critical points are still joined by a continuous line, as Reamer and Sage[41] showed for $CO_2 + n-C_{10}H_{22}$. Schneider and Franck[110,139] have found, however, that the U.C.S.T. moves to higher temperatures as the chain length increases and reaches the critical point of CO_2 at $n-C_{13}H_{28}$, which is immiscible at all temperatures. Formally it has the same phase diagram as *Figure 6.23c*, although in this case it cannot be described as having 'evolved' from *Figure 6.23b*. The minimum of the critical line is so low that its (p, T)

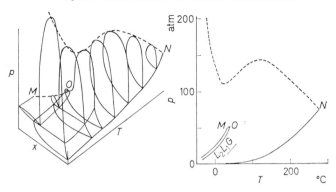

Figure 6.26. A sketch of the (p, T, x) surface and the (p, T) projection of the system ethane and methanol[137]. The critical lines are shown dashed. M and N are the critical points of pure ethane and methanol, respectively, and O is the critical end point where the gas phase and the liquid phase rich in ethane have the same composition

projection appears to cut the vapour-pressure curve of pure methane. The minimum moves to higher temperatures and pressures as the chain length increases and is at 40°C and 180 bar with n-$C_{16}H_{34}$. These critical lines rise steeply as the mole fraction of CO_2 increases beyond that at the minimum and eventually take on a positive slope. That for CO_2 + n-$C_{16}H_{34}$ has been followed to 53°C and 2250 bar.

Figure 6.23d differs from *Figure 6.23c* in two respects. First, the system has a hetero-azeotrope, and secondly, the critical line that starts from the critical point of the less volatile component has a shallower minimum and a more pronounced positive slope at high pressures. These two features are often but not always found to go together, particularly in aqueous mixtures. The critical end point O can lie at higher or lower temperatures than the point M; the two cases are distinguished in more detail in *Figure 6.27*. The former is found in aqueous mixtures with ethyl ether[140], propylene[141] and 1-butene[142], the latter with most other hydrocarbons such as ethane[143], propane[144], n-butane[143,145], n-pentane[146], n-hexane[147,148], cyclohexane[148] and benzene[146,149,150].

A remarkable feature of these systems is that the pressure of the three-phase line, liquid + liquid + gas, near the critical end point is greater than the sum of the vapour pressures of the pure components at the same temperature. Thus for n-hexane + water at 200°C:

Pure hexane 18·2 bar, pure water 15·5 bar: sum, 33·7 bar

Mixed liquids on three-phase line 35·3 bar

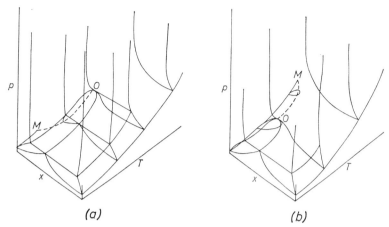

Figure 6.27. The (p, T, x) surfaces of heterogeneous azeotropes in the critical region. In (a) the critical end point, O, lies between the critical temperatures of the pure components (e.g. water + ethyl ether[1 0]) and in (b) it is at a temperature lower than those of both the components (e.g. water + n-hexane[147])

Such behaviour is commonly thought to be thermodynamically impossible (that is, materially unstable), but this would be so only if the vapours in equilibrium with the pure and mixed liquids were perfect gases. Clearly they are not, and so thermodynamic propriety is maintained.

The critical line that starts from N changes in shape from that of *Figure 6.23e* to *Figure 6.23f* as the disparity of the molecules increases in size or chemical type. Alwani and Schneider[149] showed that benzene + water resembles *Figure 6.23d*, but aqueous mixtures with aliphatic hydrocarbons are usually closer to *Figure 6.23e*. This has been demonstrated for ethane[143], n-butane[143], n-pentane[150] and n-heptane[150], and for carbon dioxide[151].

The upper critical lines of systems of this type have been studied only quite recently, since they often rise to very high pressures indeed. The best studied is nitrogen + ammonia, a system that is formed of two of the reactants in the Haber synthesis of ammonia. Krichevski and his colleagues[152] have found that the critical line starts from the critical point of ammonia (132°C, 112 bar), moves first to lower temperatures, but at 87°C and 1100 bar it becomes vertical (that is, $(\mathrm{d}T^c/\mathrm{d}p) = 0$) and then moves back to higher temperatures. The slope $(\mathrm{d}T^c/\mathrm{d}p)$ is still positive at the highest point reached, 180°C and 15 kbar. Lindroos and Dodge and others[153] have confirmed their results.

The (p, T, x) diagram of this system is shown in *Figure 6.28*, and its appearance suggests that sufficiently high pressures will cause the fluids to separate at all temperatures, even at those above the critical point of pure ammonia. Here the heterogeneous region is bounded at a constant pressure by a U.C.S.T. and at a constant temperature by a lower critical solution pressure.

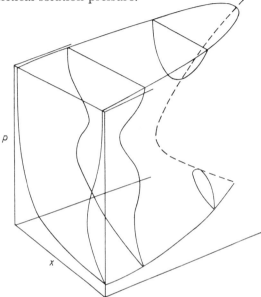

Figure 6.28. The (p, T, x) surface of systems[152] such as nitrogen + ammonia and methane + ammonia, at temperatures near to the critical point of the less volatile component

This system and argon + ammonia[153] are remarkable also for the fact that above 1800 bar the 'gaseous' phase becomes more dense than the 'liquid' phase and sinks to the bottom of the vessel. This effect is a consequence only of the great difference between the molecular weights and is not of any fundamental significance. The molar density is still lower in the gas than in the liquid, that is, the phase richer in ammonia.

The system methane + ammonia[152] has a similar phase diagram but does not show the gravitational inversion*. It is seen that the (p, x) loops at temperatures below the *point of double contact* are of an

* Such inversion of the phases was first found by Kamerlingh Onnes[154] in 1906 when he compressed helium in contact with liquid hydrogen. The system is again one where the molecular weight of the gaseous component is about twice that of the liquid.

unusual 'waisted' shape that implies that the solubility of the gas in the liquid component passes through a maximum with increasing pressure. Such a maximum was found for the solubility of nitrogen in water in measurements up to 3 kbar by Basset and Dodé[155], and it was the consideration of such results that led Krichevski to look for the double loops in the mixtures of nitrogen and ammonia. Helium + nitrogen, neon + nitrogen and neon + argon behave similarly[42].

Systems in which the disparity between the molecules is even greater have a critical line that rises monotonically from the critical point of the less volatile component, so that (dT^c/dp) is always positive. Tsiklis and others have found this behaviour in mixtures of helium with carbon dioxide[156], ethylene[156], propane[157], n-butane[158], cyclohexane[159], benzene[159] and xenon[160,161] and in argon + water[143]. The phrase *immiscibility of two gases* has been applied to this phase separation at temperatures above the critical points of both components.

This phrase was used by Kamerlingh Onnes and Keesom[154] when they predicted, on the basis of van der Waals's equation, that such separation was possible. Their prediction was not always accepted[162] and, even after its vindication in 1940, there have been several writers[163-165] who have deprecated the phrase *immiscibility of gases*. This is graphic but can be misleading if these critical lines are not put into their proper context, for there is a continuous change from the type of behaviour shown by ethane + methanol, through that shown by nitrogen + ammonia, to that of helium + ammonia, and in each case the cause of the immiscibility is the same, namely the relative weakness of the forces between the unlike molecules.

However, it is probable that the (p, x) loops are open at the top (high pressures) at all temperatures, and that those writers[160,163] who suggest that the critical line must eventually make its way to the critical point of the more volatile component are almost certainly wrong.

Finally, there is the fifth class of systems distinguished at the beginning of this Section. These belong, formally, to the third class, for the critical line is formed of two parts, each of which ends at a critical end point in equilibrium with a pure solid phase. However, it is clear from the positions of these two parts in (p, T, x) space that they could never join to give a continuous critical line even in a metastable system in which there was no solid phase. That is, these are systems which would be immiscible in the liquid state (either at all temperatures or else only in the critical region of the volatile component) were it not for the solidification of the less volatile component.

The (p, T) projection of a system of this type is shown in *Figure 6.29*. The first to be found were carbon dioxide $(T^c, 31°C)$ + diphenylamine[95,166] (m.p. 53°C), and ethane $(T^c, 32°C)$ + naphthalene[167] (m.p. 80°C). Scheffer, Diepen and their colleagues have discovered a large number of similar systems, such as methane + naphthalene[168], and ethylene + n-$C_{28}H_{58}$[169], n-$C_{36}H_{74}$[169], diphenyl[169], naphthalene[170], anthracene[170] and hexachloroethane[170].

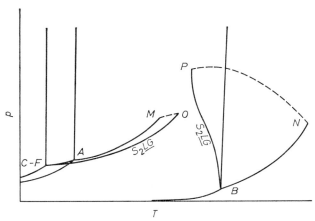

Figure 6.29. The (p, T) projection of a system such as ethylene + naphthalene[170]. This phase diagram is formally of the same type as *Figure 6.22*, but here the two critical lines *MO* and *NP* could never join to give a continuous critical line from *M* to *N* in the absence of the solid phase. If the triple point *B* were at a lower temperature, the diagram would resemble *Figure 6.25*

The elucidation of the phase behaviour of liquid systems near critical points was due mainly to the schools at Amsterdam and Leiden that owed their inspiration to van der Waals. He did not take part in the experimental work but continued, even after the publication of his famous work on *Continuity*, to interpret, as far as possible, the new experimental results. His theoretical work was based on the (a, v, x) surface and on his equation of state whenever he needed an explicit function for the free energy. This work, which Scott[115] has recast in more modern terms (see Section 9.6), is to be found in a series of papers[171] entitled 'The Theory of Binary Mixtures' published between 1906 and 1912.

Other notable series of papers are the experimental and thermodynamic papers of Kuenen, first from Leiden and later from Dundee, which are discussed fully in his book[37], and the sixteen papers[172] of Kamerlingh Onnes and his colleagues at Leiden with the general title 'Contributions to the knowledge of van der Waals ψ surface' (where ψ is the Helmholtz free energy).

Katz and Rzasa[173] have published a useful bibliography of this field in which they give abstracts of all papers published before 1910 (with facsimile reproduction of a few of the more important) and the titles of those published since. There are only a few gaps in the first part, which is the more useful, but the list of titles is by no means complete. Muckleroy[173] has continued their list down to 1960 with titles taken principally from American journals.

In all the (p, T) projections in this Section it is seen that a three-phase system of a binary mixture is represented by a line, in the same way as the two-phase systems of the pure components. It is appropriate, therefore, to finish this Chapter by quoting Gibbs's extension[174] of Clapeyron's equation to this univariant three-phase line.

Consider a system in which the compositions of the three phases are x_2', x_2'' and x_2'''. A small change at equilibrium of pressure, temperature and the three compositions must give equal increments of μ_1', μ_1'' and μ_1''' and of μ_2', μ_2'' and μ_2'''. Equating these increments gives four equations for the five unknowns, δp, δT, $\delta x_2'$, $\delta x_2''$ and $\delta x_2'''$. The equations may, therefore, be solved to give the ratio of any two of the unknowns, in particular

$$\left(\frac{\partial p}{\partial T}\right)_\sigma = \begin{vmatrix} x_2' & s' & 1 \\ x_2'' & s'' & 1 \\ x_2''' & s''' & 1 \end{vmatrix} \bigg/ \begin{vmatrix} x_2' & v' & 1 \\ x_2'' & v'' & 1 \\ x_2''' & v''' & 1 \end{vmatrix} \tag{6.42}$$

This may be compared with Clapeyron's equation for two phases and one component by writing the latter

$$\left(\frac{\partial p}{\partial T}\right)_\sigma = \begin{vmatrix} s' & 1 \\ s'' & 1 \end{vmatrix} \bigg/ \begin{vmatrix} v' & 1 \\ v'' & 1 \end{vmatrix} \tag{6.43}$$

These equations may be generalized for any univariant system of n components and $(n + 1)$ phases.

REFERENCES

[1] Adler, S. B., Friend, L., Pigford, R. L. and Rosselli, G. M. *A.I.Ch.E. Jl* 6(1960) 104; Thompson, R. E. and Edmister, W. C. 11(1965) 457

[2] Prausnitz, J. M. *Chem. Engng Sci.* 18 (1963) 613; Chueh, P. L., Muirbrook, N. K. and Prausnitz, J. M. *A.I.Ch.E. Jl* 11 (1965) 1092, 1097

[3] Wang, D. I. J. *Adv. cryogen. Engng* 3 (1960) 294

[4] Wade, J. and Merriman, R. W. *J. chem. Soc.* 99 (1911) 997; Kleinert, T. *Angew. Chem.* 46 (1933) 18; Otsuki, H. and Williams, F. C., and

Othmer, D. F. and Levy, S. L. *Chem. Engng Prog. Symp. Ser.* 49 (1953) No. 6, 55, 64

5 Roscoe, H. E. and Dittmar, W. *J. chem. Soc.* 12 (1860) 128; Roscoe, H. E. 13 (1861) 146; 15 (1862) 270; Bonner, W. D., with Titus, A. C. *J. Am. chem. Soc.* 52 (1930) 633; with Wallace, R. E. *ibid.* 1747

6 Prigogine, I. and Defay, R. *Chemical Thermodynamics* (trans. Everett, D. H.), Ch. 28, London (Longmans) 1954

7 Skolnik, H. *Indust. Engng Chem.* 43 (1951) 172

8 Cook, D. *Proc. R. Soc.* A219 (1953) 245

9 Clark, A. M. and Din, F. *Discuss. Faraday Soc.* 15 (1953) 202

10 Kuenen, J. P. and Robson, W. G. *Phil. Mag.* 3 (1902) 149, 622; 4 (1902) 116

11 Kuenen, J. P. *Phil. Mag.* 44 (1897) 174

12 Haselden, G. G., Newitt, D. M. and Shah, S. M. *Proc. R. Soc.* A209 (1951) 1

13 Clark, A. M. and Din, F. *Trans. Faraday Soc.* 46 (1950) 901

14 Kuenen, J. P. *Phil. Mag.* 40 (1895) 173

15 Rowlinson, J. S., Sutton, J. R. and Weston, J. F. *Thermodynamic and Transport Properties of Fluids*, p. 10, London (Instn. Mech. Engrs) 1958

16 McCurdy, J. L. and Katz, D. L. *Indust. Engng Chem.* 36 (1944) 674

17 Hanson, G. H., Hogan, R. J., Ruehlen, F. N. and Cines, M. R. *Chem. Engng Prog. Symp. Ser.* 49 (1953) No. 6, 37

18 Moran, D. W. *Ph.D. Thesis*, Univ. London, 1959

19 McMillan, W. A. *J. Am. chem. Soc.* 58 (1936) 1345

20 Churchill, S. W., Collamore, W. G. and Katz, D. L. *Oil Gas J.* 41 (1942) 33, 36

21 Hogan, R. J., Nelson, W. T., Hanson, G. H. and Cines, M. R. *Indust. Engng Chem.* 47 (1955) 2210

22 Rao, V. N. K., Swami, D. R. and Rao, M. N. *A.I.Ch.E. Jl* 3 (1957) 191

23 Barr-David, F. and Dodge, B. F. *J. chem. Engng Data* 4 (1959) 107

24 Kuenen, J. P. *Phil. Mag.* 1 (1901) 593

25 Swietoslawski, W. and Kreglewski, A. *Bull. Acad. pol. Sci. Sér. Sci. chim. geol. geogr.* 2 (1954) 77

26 Thomas, J. S. and Barker, W. F. *J. chem. Soc.* 127 (1925) 2820; Luchinskii, C. P. *Zh. fiz. Khim.* 30 (1956) 1207; Stuckey, J. E. and Secoy, C. H. *J. chem. Engng Data* 8 (1963) 386

27 Britton, E. C., Nutting, H. S. and Horsley, L. H. *Analyt. Chem.* 19 (1947) 601

28 Othmer, D. F. and Morley, F. R. *Indust. Engng Chem.* 38 (1946) 751; Griswold J. and Wong, S. Y. *Chem. Engng Prog. Symp. Ser.* 48 (1952) No. 3, 18

29 Forziati, A. F., Norris, W. R. and Rossini, F. D. *J. Res. natn. Bur. Stand.* 43 (1949) 555; Calingaert, G. and Wojciechowski, M. *J. Am. chem. Soc.* 72 (1950) 5310

30 Willingham, C. B., Taylor, W. J., Pignocco, J. M. and Rossini, F. D. *J. Res. natn. Bur. Stand.* 35 (1945) 219

31 Aring, H. and von Weber, U. *J. prakt. Chem.* 30 (1965) 295

32 Lloyd, L. and Wyatt, P. A. H. *J. chem. Soc.* (1955) 2248

REFERENCES

[33] Gaw, W. J. and Swinton, F. L. *Nature, Lond.* 212 (1966) 283; private communication

[34] Lecat, M. *Tables Azéotropiques, Tome Premier, Azéotropes binaires orthobares* (2nd ed., publ. by the author), Brussels, 1949; Horsley, L. H. *Azeotropic Data*, Washington (Am. chem. Soc.), Part 1, 1952, Part 2, 1962

[35] Swietoslawski, W. *Azeotropy and Polyazeotropy*, Oxford (Pergamon) 1963; Malesinski, W. *Azeotropy and other Theoretical Problems of Vapour–Liquid Equilibrium*, London (Wiley) 1965

[36] Strickland-Constable, R. F. *Proc. R. Soc.* A209 (1951) 14; 214 (1952) 36

[37] Kuenen, J. P. *Theorie der Verdampfung und Verflüssigung von Gemischen, Figure 23*, p. 69, Leipzig (Barth) 1906

[38] Kuenen, J. P. *Communs phys. Lab. Univ. Leiden* No. 4 (1892)

[39] Sage, B. H., Lacey, W. N. and Schaafsma, J. G. *Indust. Engng Chem.* 26 (1934) 214

[40] Roozeboom, H. W. B. *Die Heterogenen Gleichgewichte 2. Systeme aus zwei Komponenten*, Part 1, *Figs. 46–54*, pp. 98–101, Brunswick (Vieweg) 1904; Kuenen, J. P. *Theorie der Verdampfung und Verflüssigung von Gemischen, Figs. 27 and 28*, p. 77, Leipzig (Barth) 1906; Zernike, J. *Chemical Phase Theory, Fig. 24*, p. 126, Antwerp (Kluwer) 1956

[41] Poettmann, F. H. and Katz, D. L. *Indust. Engng Chem.* 37 (1945) 847; Reamer, H. H., Sage, B. H. and Lacey, W. N. 43 (1951) 2515; *J. chem. Engng Data* 8 (1963) 508; Akers, W. W., Kelley, R. E. and Lipscomb, T. G. *Indust. Engng Chem.* 46 (1954) 2535; Brandt, L. W. and Stroud, L. 50 (1958) 849; Cines, M. R., Roach, J. T., Hogan, R. J. and Roland, C. H. *Chem. Engng Prog. Symp. Ser.* 49 (1953) No. 6, 1

[42] Burch, R. J. *J. chem. Engng Data* 9 (1964) 19; Streett, W. B. 13 (1968) 218; *J. chem. Phys.* 42 (1965) 500; 46 (1967) 3282; *Chem. Engng Prog. Symp. Ser.* 63 (1967) No. 81, 37; *Cryogenics* 8 (1968) 88

[43] Jones, I. W. and Rowlinson, J. S. *Trans. Faraday Soc.* 59 (1963) 1702

[44] Wilson, G. M., Silverberg, P. M. and Zellner, M. G. *International Advances in Cryogenic Engineering* (ed. Timmerhaus, K. D.), p. 192, New York (Plenum Press) 1965; Thorpe, P. L. *Trans. Faraday Soc.* 64 (1968) 2273

[45] Kuenen, J. P., with Clark, A. L. *Communs phys. Lab. Univ. Leiden* No. 150 b (1917); with Verschoyle, T. and van Urk, A. T. No. 161 (1922)

[46] Akers, W. W. and Eubanks, L. S. *Adv. cryogen. Engng* 3 (1960) 275

[47] Ellington, R. T., Eakin, B. E., Parent, J. D., Gami, D. C. and Bloomer, R. T. *Thermodynamic and Transport Properties of Gases, Liquids and Solids*, p. 180, New York (Am. Soc. mech. Engrs) 1959

[48] Cosway, H. F. and Katz, D. L. *A.I.Ch.E. Jl* 5 (1959) 46; Chang, S.-D. and Lu, B. C.-Y. *Chem. Engng Prog. Symp. Ser.* 63 (1967) No. 81, 18

[49] Omar, M. H., Dokoupil, Z. and Schroten, H. G. M. *Physica* 28 (1962) 309

[50] Roberts, L. R. and McKetta, J. J. *J. chem. Engng Data* 8 (1963) 161; Azarnoosh, A. and McKetta, J. J. *ibid.* 513; Poston, R. S. and McKetta, J. J. 11 (1966) 362; *A.I.Ch.E. Jl* 11 (1965) 917

[51] Keesom, W. H. *Communs phys. Lab. Univ. Leiden* No. 88 (1903); Booth, H. S. and Carter, J. M. *J. phys. Chem.* 34 (1930) 2801; Nederbragt,

G. W. *Indust. Engng Chem.* 30 (1938) 587
[52] Zenner, G. H. and Dana, L. I. *Chem. Engng Prog. Symp. Ser.* 59 (1963) No. 44, 36
[53] Toyama, A., Chappelear, P. S., Leland, T. W. and Kobayashi, R. *Adv. cryogen. Engng* 7 (1962) 125
[54] Donnelly, H. G. and Katz, D. L. *Indust. Engng Chem.* 46 (1954) 511; Sterner, C. J. *Adv. cryogen. Engng* 6 (1961) 467
[55] Pikaar, M. J. *Ph.D. Thesis*, Univ. London, 1959
[56] Davis, J. A., Rodewald, N. and Kurata, F. *A.I.Ch.E. Jl* 8 (1962) 537
[57] Haselden, G. G., Holland, F. A., King, M. B. and Strickland-Constable, R. F. *Proc. R. Soc.* A240 (1957) 1
[58] Price, A. R. and Kobayashi, R. *J. chem. Engng Data* 4 (1959) 40; Van Horn, L. D. and Kobayashi, R. 12 (1967) 294
[59] Cota, H. M. and Thodos, G. *J. chem. Engng Data* 7 (1962) 62; Forman, J. C. and Thodos, G. *A.I.Ch.E. Jl* 8 (1962) 209
[60] Guter, M., Newitt, D. M. and Ruhemann, M. *Proc. R. Soc.* A176 (1940) 140
[61] Tully, P. C. and Edmister, W. C. *A.I.Ch.E. Jl* 13 (1967) 155
[62] Reamer, H. H., Sage, B. H. and Lacey, W. N. *Indust. Engng Chem.* 42 (1950) 534, 1258; Akers, W. W., Burns, J. F. and Fairchild, W. R. 46 (1954) 2531
[63] Etter, D. O. and Kay, W. B. *J. chem. Engng Data* 6 (1961) 409, 537
[64] Roof, J. G. and Baron, J. D. *J. chem. Engng Data* 12 (1967) 292
[65] Mehra, V. S. and Thodos, G. *J. chem. Engng Data* 7 (1962) 497; 8 (1963) 1; 10 (1965) 307; 11 (1966) 365; 13 (1968) 155
[66] Roberts, L. R., Wang, R. H., Azarnoosh, A. and McKetta, J. J. *J. chem. Engng Data* 7 (1962) 484
[67] Olds, R. H., Sage, B. H. and Lacey, W. N. *Indust. Engng Chem.* 34 (1942) 1008
[68] Amick, E. H., Johnson, W. B. and Dodge, B. F. *Chem. Engng Prog. Symp. Ser.* 48 (1952) No. 3, 65
[69] Matschke, D. E. and Thodos, G. *J. chem. Engng Data* 7 (1962) 232
[70] Lu, H., Newitt, D. M. and Ruhemann, M. *Proc. R. Soc.* A178 (1941) 506; McKay, R. A., Reamer, H. H., Sage, B. H. and Lacey, W. N. *Indust. Engng Chem.* 43 (1951) 2112
[71] Lehigh, W. R. and McKetta, J. J. *J. chem. Engng Data* 11 (1966) 180
[72] Kay, W. B. *Indust. Engng Chem.* 30 (1938) 459; 32 (1940) 353
[73] Ekiner, O. and Thodos, G. *J. chem. Engng Data* 11 (1966) 154, 457; 13 (1968) 304; *Can. J. Chem.* 43 (1966) 205
[74] Reamer, H. H., with Sage, B. H. and Lacey, W. N. *J. chem. Engng Data* 5 (1960) 44, 364; with Berry, V. and Sage, B. H. 6 (1961) 184
[75] Weber, J. H. *J. chem. Engng Data* 4 (1959) 301
[76] Reamer, H. H., with Sage, B. H. *J. chem. Engng Data* 7 (1962) 161; and with Berry, V. *ibid.* 486
[77] Kay, W. B., with Nevens, T. D. *Chem. Engng Prog. Symp. Ser.* 48 (1952) No. 3, 108; with Albert, R. E. *Indust. Engng Chem.* 48 (1956) 422
[78] Quint, N. *Proc. Sect. Sci. K. ned. Akad. Wet.* 2 (1899) 40; Ashley, J. H. and Brown, G. M. *Chem. Engng Prog. Symp. Ser.* 50 (1954) No. 10, 129

REFERENCES

[79] Kay, W. B. and Brice, D. B. *Indust. Engng Chem.* 45 (1953) 615; Brewer, J., Rodewald, N. and Kurata, F. *A. I. Ch. E. Jl* 7 (1961) 13

[80] Kay, W. B. *Indust. Engng Chem.* 40 (1948) 1459; 41 (1949) 484

[81] Nysewander, C. N., Sage, B. H. and Lacey, W. N. *Indust. Engng Chem.* 32 (1940) 118; Sage, B. H. and Lacey, W. N. *ibid.* 992

[82] Vaughan, W. E. and Collins, F. C. *Indust. Engng Chem.* 34 (1942) 885

[83] Reamer, H. H. and Sage, B. H. *J. chem. Engng Data* 11 (1966) 17; Graue, D. J. and Sage, B. H. 12 (1967) 49

[84] Glanville, J. W., Sage, B. H. and Lacey, W. N. *Indust. Engng Chem.* 42 (1950) 508

[85] Kay, W. B. and Rambosek, G. M. *Indust. Engng Chem.* 45 (1953) 221; *J. phys. Chem.* 68 (1964) 827

[86] Clegg, H. P. and Rowlinson, J. S. *Trans. Faraday Soc.* 51 (1955) 1333; Jordan, L. W. and Kay, W. B. *Chem. Engng Prog. Symp. Ser.* 59 (1963) No. 44, 46

[87] Reamer, H. H. and Sage, B. H. *J. chem. Engng Data* 9 (1964) 24

[88] Partington, E. J., Rowlinson, J. S. and Weston, J. F. *Trans. Faraday Soc.* 56 (1960) 479

[89] Cummings, L. W. T., Stones, F. W. and Volante, M. A. *Indust. Engng Chem.* 25 (1933) 728

[90] Reamer, H. H., Sage, B. H. and Lacey, W. N. *Indust. Engng Chem.* 45 (1953) 1805

[91] Watson, L. M. and Dodge, B. F. *Chem. Engng Prog. Symp. Ser.* 48 (1952) No. 3, 73

[92] Dyke, D. E. L., Rowlinson, J. S. and Thacker, R. *Trans. Faraday Soc.* 55 (1959) 903

[93] McCracken, P. G. and Smith, J. M. *A.I.Ch.E. Jl* 2 (1956) 498; with Storvick, T. S. *J. chem. Engng Data* 5 (1960) 130

[94] Sage, B. H. *Thermodynamics of Multicomponent Systems*, New York (Reinhold) 1965

[95] Büchner, E. H. *Z. phys. Chem.* 54 (1906) 665; 56 (1906) 257

[96] Keyes, D. B. and Hildebrand, J. H. *J. Am. chem. Soc.* 39 (1917) 2126

[97] Kuenen, J. P. and Robson, W. G. *Phil. Mag.* 48 (1899) 180

[98] Wickert, J. N., Tamplin, W. S. and Shank, R. L. *Chem. Engng Prog. Symp. Ser.* 48 (1952) No. 2, 92

[99] Kraus, C. A. and Zeitfuchs, E. H. *J. Am. chem. Soc.* 44 (1922) 1249

[100] Fowler, R. T. *J. Soc. chem. Ind., Lond.* 69 (1950) S. 65; Campbell, A. N., Kartzmark, E. M. and Falloner, W. E. *Can. J. Chem.* 36 (1958) 1475

[101] Schreinemakers, F. A. H. *Proc. Sect. Sci. K. ned. Akad. Wet.* 3 (1900–01)1

[102] Marshall, A. *J. chem. Soc.* 89 (1906) 1350

[103] Wood, S. E. *J. Am. chem. Soc.* 68 (1946) 1963

[104] Kohler, F. *Mh. Chem.* 82 (1951) 913

[105] Jänecke, E. *Z. phys. Chem.* A164 (1933) 401

[106] Merriman, R. W. *J. chem. Soc.* 103 (1913) 1790, 1801; Wuyts, H. *Bull. Soc. chim. Belg.* 33 (1924) 168

[107] Roozeboom, H. W. B. *Z. phys. Chem.* 2 (1888) 449; Rupert, F. F. *J. Am. chem. Soc.* 31 (1909) 860; Haase, R., Naas, H. and Thumm, H. *Z. phys. Chem. Frankf. Ausg.* 37 (1963) 210; Spall, B. C. *Can. J. chem.*

Engng 41 (1963) 79; Butcher, K. L., Hanson, C. and Plewes, J. A. *Chem. Inds, Lond.* (1962) 355; (1963) 249

[108] Van Klooster, H. S. and Douglas, W. A. *J. phys. Chem.* 49 (1945) 67

[109] Timmermans, J. and Kohnstamm, P. *Proc. Sect. Sci. K. ned. Akad. Wet.* 12 (1909–10) 234; 15 (1912–13) 1021; 13 (1910–11) 507; *J. Chim. phys.* 20 (1923) 491; Poppe, G. *Bull. Soc. chim. Belg.* 44 (1935) 640

[110] Schneider, G. *Z. phys. Chem. Frankf. Ausg.* 37 (1963) 333; 39 (1963) 187; Roth, K., Schneider, G. and Franck, E. U. *Abh. dt. Bunsen-Ges.* 70 (1966) 5; Schneider, G. *ibid.* 10, 497; with Russo, C. *ibid.* 1008

[111] Roozeboom, H. W. B. *Die Heterogenen Gleichgewichte 2, Systeme aus zwei Komponenten,* Part 1, Plates I and II, Brunswick (Vieweg) 1904; Zernike, J. *Chemical Phase Theory, Fig. 20-4,* Antwerp (Kluwer) 1956

[112] Rowlinson, J. S. and Richardson, M. J. *Adv. chem. Phys.* 2 (1958) 85

[113] Roozeboom, H. W. B. *Die Heterogenen Gleichgewichte 2. Systeme mit zwei flüssigen Phasen,* Part 2, End Plate (by Büchner, E. H.), Brunswick (Vieweg) 1918; Zernike, J. *Chemical Phase Theory, Figs. 23-11* and *23-16,* Antwerp (Kluwer) 1956

[114] Schneider, G. *Z. phys. Chem. Frankf. Ausg.* 41 (1964) 327

[115] Scott, R. L., private communication

[116] Kohnstamm, P. and Reeders, J. C. *Proc. Sect. Sci. K. ned. Akad. Wet.* 14 (1911–12) 270

[117] Scheffer, F. E. C. and Smittenberg, J. *Recl Trav. chim. Pays-Bas Belg.* 52 (1933) 1, 982

[118] Diepen, G. A. M. and Scheffer, F. E. C. *J. Am. chem. Soc.* 70 (1948) 4081

[119] Todd, D. B. and Elgin, J. C. *A.I.Ch.E. Jl* 1 (1955) 20; Chappelear, D. C. and Elgin, J. C. *J. chem. Engng Data* 6 (1961) 415

[120] Davenport, A. J. and Rowlinson, J. S. *Trans. Faraday Soc.* 59 (1963) 78; with Saville, G. 62 (1966) 322; Guy, K. W. A., Malanowski, S. K. and Rowlinson, J. S. *Chem. Engng Sci.* 22 (1967) 801

[121] Kohn, J. P. *A.I.Ch.E. Jl* 7 (1961) 514; *Chem. Engng Prog. Symp. Ser.* 63 (1967) No. 81, 57

[122] Chang, H. L., with Hurt, L. J. and Kobayashi, R. *A.I.Ch.E. Jl* 12 (1966) 1212; with Kobayashi, R. *J. chem. Engng Data* 12 (1967) 517, 520

[123] Shim, J. and Kohn, J. P. *J. chem. Engng Data* 7 (1962) 3; Beaudoin, J. M. and Kohn, J. P. 12 (1967) 189; Kohn, J. P. and Haggin, J. H. S. *ibid.* 313

[124] Reamer, H. H. and Sage, B. H. *J. chem. Engng Data* 4 (1959) 98; Berry, V. and Sage, B. H. *ibid.* 204

[125] Koonce, K. T. and Kobayashi, R. *J. chem. Engng Data* 9 (1964) 490, 494

[126] Schneider, G. *Z. phys. Chem. Frankf. Ausg.* 46 (1965) 375

[127] Kohn, J. P. and Bradish, W. F. *J. chem. Engng Data* 9 (1964) 5

[128] Shipman, L. M. and Kohn, J. P. *J. chem. Engng Data* 11 (1966) 176

[129] Rowlinson, J. S. and Freeman, P. I. *Pure appl. Chem.* 2 (1961) 329

[130] Kohn, J. P., Kim, Y. J. and Pan, Y. C. *J. chem. Engng Data* 11 (1966) 333; Rodrigues, A. B. and Kohn, J. P. 12 (1967) 191; Kim, Y. J., Carfagno, J. A., McCaffrey, D. S. and Kohn, J. P. *ibid.* 289; Wagner, J. R., McCaffrey, D. S. and Kohn, J. P. 13 (1968) 22

REFERENCES

131 Wilson, R. E., Keith, P. C. and Haylett, R. E. *Indust. Engng Chem.* 28 (1936) 1065

132 Hixson, A. W., with Hixson, A. N. *Trans. Am. Inst. chem. Engrs* 37 (1941) 927; with Bockelmann, J. B. 38 (1942) 891; Drew, D. A. and Hixson, A. N. 40 (1944) 675

133 Freeman, P. I. and Rowlinson, J. S. *Polymer* 1 (1960) 20; Baker, C. H., Byers Brown, W., Gee, G., Rowlinson, J. S., Stubley, D. and Yeadon, R. E. 3 (1962) 215; Allen, G. and Baker, C. H. 6 (1965) 181; Myrat, C. D. and Rowlinson, J. S. *ibid.* 645

134 Patterson, D. and Swinton, F. L., private communications

135 Schneider, G. *Z. phys. Chem. Frankf. Ausg.* 41 (1964) 110

136 Scott, R. L. *J. phys. Chem.* 69 (1965) 261; Larkin, J. A., Katz J. and Scott, R. L. 71 (1967) 352

137 Kuenen, J. P. *Phil. Mag.* 6 (1903) 637; Ma, Y. H. and Kohn, J. P. *J. chem. Engng Data* 9 (1964) 3

138 Kohn, J. P. and Kurata, F. *A.I.Ch.E. Jl* 4 (1958) 211; *J. chem. Engng Data* 4 (1959) 33

139 Schneider, G., Alwani, Z., Heim, W., Horvath, E. and Franck, E. U. *Chemie-Ingr-Tech.* 39 (1967) 649

140 Scheffer, F. E. C. *Proc. Sect. Sci. K. ned. Akad. Wet.* 15 (1912–13) 380

141 Azarnoosh, A. and McKetta, J. J. *J. chem. Engng Data* 4 (1959) 211; Li, C. C. and McKetta, J. J. 8 (1963) 271

142 Leland, T. W., McKetta, J. J. and Kobe, K. A. *Indust. Engng Chem.* 47 (1955) 1265; Wehe, A. H. and McKetta, J. J. *J. chem. Engng Data* 6 (1961) 167

143 Danneil, A., Tödheide, K. and Franck, E. U. *Chemie-Ingr-Tech.* 39 (1967) 816; Lentz, H. and Franck, E. U. *Abh. dt. Bunsen-Ges.*, 73 (1969) 28

144 Kobayashi, R. and Katz, D. L. *Indust. Engng Chem.* 45 (1953) 440

145 Reamer, H. H., Olds, R. H., Sage, B. H. and Lacey, W. N. *Indust. Engng Chem.* 36 (1944) 381

146 Scheffer, F. E. C. *Proc. Sect. Sci. K. ned. Akad. Wet.* 17 (1914–15) 834

147 Scheffer, F. E. C. *Proc. Sect. Sci. K. ned. Akad. Wet.* 16 (1913–14) 404

148 Rebert, C. J. and Hayworth, K. E. *A.I.Ch.E. Jl* 13 (1967) 118

149 Rebert, C. J. and Kay, W. B. *A.I.Ch.E. Jl* 5 (1959) 285; O'Grady, T. M. *J. chem. Engng Data* 12 (1967) 9; Alwani, Z. and Schneider, G. *Abh. dt. Bunsen-Ges.* 71 (1967) 633

150 Connolly, J. F. *J. chem. Engng Data* 11 (1966) 13

151 Tödheide, K. and Franck, E. U. *Z. phys. Chem. Frankf. Ausg.* 37 (1963) 387

152 Krichevski, I. R. *Acta phys.-chim. URSS* 12 (1940) 480; with Bolshakov, P. E. 14 (1941) 353; with Tsiklis, D. S. 18 (1943) 264; Tsiklis, D. S. *Dokl. Akad. Nauk SSSR* 86 (1952) 993

153 Lindroos, A. E. and Dodge, B. F. *Chem. Engng Prog. Symp. Ser.* 48 (1952) No. 3, 10; Reamer, H. H. and Sage, B. H. *J. chem. Engng Data* 4 (1959) 152, 303; Michels, A., Dumoulin, E. and van Dijk, J. J. Th. *Physica* 25 (1959) 840; 27 (1961) 886

154 Onnes, H. K. and Keesom, W. H. *Communs phys. Lab. Univ. Leiden* No. 96a, 96b, 96c (1906); Suppl. No. 15, 16 (1907)

[155] Basset, J. and Dodé, M. *C. r. hebd. Séanc. Acad. Sci., Paris* 203 (1936) 775; Krichevski, I. R. *J. Am. chem. Soc.* 59 (1937) 596

[156] Tsiklis, D. S. *Dokl. Akad. Nauk SSSR* 86 (1952) 1159; 91 (1953) 1361; with Vasiliev, J. N. *Physics and Chemistry of High Pressures*, p. 25, London (Soc. chem. Indust.) 1962

[157] Tsiklis, D. S. *Dokl. Akad. Nauk SSSR* 101 (1955) 129

[158] Jones, A. E. and Kay, W. B. *A.I.Ch.E. Jl* 13 (1967) 717, 720

[159] Tsiklis, D. S. and Maslennikova, V. Ya. *Dokl. Akad. Nauk SSSR* 157 (1964) 426

[160] de Swaan Arons, J. and Diepen, G. A. M. *J. chem. Phys.* 44 (1966) 2322

[161] Zandbergen, P., Knaap, H. F. P. and Beenakker, J. J. M. *Physica* 33 (1967) 379

[162] Randall, M. and Sosnick, B. *J. Am. chem. Soc.* 50 (1928) 967

[163] Zernike, J. *Chemical Phase Theory*, pp. 143–144, Antwerp (Kluwer) 1956

[164] Bridgman, P. W. *Rev. mod. Phys.* 18 (1946) 1

[165] Din, F. *Nature, Lond.* 181 (1958) 587

[166] Roozeboom, H. W. B. and Büchner, E. H. *Proc. Sect. Sci. K. ned. Akad. Wet.* 7 (1904–5) 556

[167] Prins, A. *Proc. Sect. Sci. K. ned. Akad. Wet.* 17 (1914–5) 1095; van Welie, G. S. A. and Diepen, G. A. M. *J. phys. Chem.* 67 (1963) 755

[168] van Hest, J. A. M. and Diepen, G. A. M. *Physics and Chemistry of High Pressures*, p. 10, London (Soc. chem. Indust.) 1962

[169] Diepen, G. A. M. and Scheffer, F. E. C. *J. Am. chem. Soc.* 70 (1948) 4085

[170] van Gunst, C. A., Scheffer, F. E. C. and Diepen, G. A. M. *J. phys. Chem.* 57 (1953) 578; van Welie, G. S. A. and Diepen, G. A. M. *Recl Trav. chim. Pays-Bas Belg.* 80 (1961) 659, 666, 673

[171] van der Waals, J. D. *Proc. Sect. Sci. K. ned. Akad. Wet.* 9 (1906–7) 621, 727, 826; 10 (1907–8) 56, 123, 183; 11 (1908–9) 146, 187–201, 317, 426, 477, 698, 816, 890; 14 (1911–2) 504, 655, 875, 1049, 1217; 15 (1912–3) 602

[172] Onnes, H. K. *et al.*, *Communs phys. Lab. Univ. Leiden* No. 59a, 59b, 64 (1900); No. 65, 75, Suppl. No. 5 (1901); No. 79, 81, Suppl. No. 6 (1902); Suppl. No. 7 (1903); Suppl. No. 8 (1904); No. 96a, 96b, 96c, Suppl. No. 11 (1906); Suppl. No. 14, 15, 16 (1907)

[173] Katz, D. L. and Rzasa, M. L. *Bibliography for Physical Behavior of Hydrocarbons under Pressure and Related Phenomena*, Ann Arbor (Edwards) 1946; Muckleroy, J. A. *Bibliography on Hydrocarbons, 1946–1960*, Tulsa, Oklahoma (Natural Gas Processors Assoc.) 1962

[174] Gibbs, J. W. *Collected Works*, Vol. 1, pp. 97-8, New Haven (Yale) 1928

7

INTERMOLECULAR FORCES

7.1 INTRODUCTION

The third part of this book is given to the interpretation of some of the experimental results discussed in the first six Chapters. The important link between the experimental work and the theories developed by the methods of statistical mechanics is a good knowledge of the potential energy of the assembly of molecules as a function of their positions and orientations. The study of liquids has contributed little to our knowledge of this energy. Rather, one must gather as much information as possible from other sources before attempting the interpretation of the properties of liquids.

The three main sources have been, first, the direct calculation of intermolecular forces by the methods of quantum mechanics and of classical electrostatic theory; secondly, the measurement of the few macroscopic properties that can be related directly to the intermolecular potential energy; thirdly, and most recently, the study of the interactions of molecules in pairs by experiments on the scattering of molecular beams.

The direct calculations can be performed only for simpler atoms and molecules than those discussed in this book, but nevertheless they are believed to be a good guide to the functional dependence of the energy on molecular positions and orientations even for complex molecules.

Model potentials of a reasonably correct functional form may, therefore, be constructed for a pair of molecules of interest, but they will contain two or more incalculable parameters. They can be used for the rigorous calculation only of the macroscopic properties of assemblies of molecules that are either almost completely disordered, as in a dilute gas, or almost completely ordered, as in a crystal near the absolute zero of temperature. The equilibrium properties of these two extreme forms of matter can be calculated for model potentials of almost any complexity, but the transport properties of a dilute gas can, in practice, be calculated exactly only for molecules of spherical symmetry. The comparison of these calculations with the experimental results is the principal source of our knowledge of intermolecular forces.

From the work on molecular beams we have learnt much about the energies of interaction of a metallic and a non-metallic atom or molecule, but for technical reasons, it has been less easy to study interactions of the kind of interest in this book. Nevertheless, one useful contribution has been made which is mentioned below.

Here a very brief account is given of the types of force, of the most commonly used model potentials, and of the conclusions reached after comparing the calculations with experiment. More space than usual is given to the dependence of the potentials on the orientations of the molecules, as this is more important in the liquid state than in the gas. The theory of intermolecular forces is outside the scope of this book. It is discussed at great length in a book of Hirschfelder, Curtiss and Bird[1], in a volume of *Advances in Chemical Physics* edited by Hirschfelder[1] and in recent reviews[2].

7.2 The Form of the Intermolecular Potential

It is a simple deduction from the properties of matter that two molecules must attract each other at large separations (otherwise gases would not condense to liquids) and that this attraction must be replaced by a repulsion at small separations (otherwise the compressibilities of liquids and solids would not be so small and the volume of matter at all temperatures would be zero). Furthermore, it is readily shown that the pair potential $u_2(r)$ is nowhere negatively infinite and that it approaches zero at large r more rapidly than r^{-3}. It is, therefore, convenient to divide the intermolecular potential into two terms, one of which is negative and falls off moderately slowly with distance, and the other of which is positive and falls off rapidly with distance.

There are two assumptions in writing down such a potential as a preliminary to the discussion of the properties of matter in bulk. First, it is assumed that the potentials are additive; that is, it is legitimate to write the potential energy, $\mathcal{U}(\mathbf{r}_1 \ldots \mathbf{r}_N)$, of a macroscopic assembly of N molecules as the sum of pair potentials, $u_2(r)$, between all of the $N(N-1)/2$ possible pairs and, secondly, that such pair potentials can be separated into attractive and repulsive terms. The first assumption is discussed briefly below.

The positive term in the intermolecular potential arises from the overlap, and so repulsion, of the closed electron clouds of the two molecules. Quantal calculations[1,3] show that this term has the form $F(r)e^{-Br}$, at the comparatively large separations of molecules in liquids. Here $F(r)$ is a polynomial in r, the separation, and B is a positive parameter. A potential of this form is not easy to handle in calculations of bulk properties and, in practice, it is replaced in model potentials either by the exponential term alone or by an inverse power of the separation, λr^{-n}. Neither simplification gives a proper representation of the potential over all values of r, but the former is probably adequate in all collisions in which the kinetic energy of the molecules is no more than about $5\,kT$.

The limitations of the latter are discussed below. It is adequate for many of the properties of liquids but not for some of the more subtle properties of gases. Little is known of the dependence of these forces on the mutual orientation of the molecules except that their symmetry must follow that of the nuclear skeletons, and that it is reasonable to represent the repulsion of a pair of polyatomic molecules by the superposed repulsions of centres based on the nuclei of each.

The negative, or attractive, term in the potential may be divided further into three types. The first, and most important, is the attraction between the oscillating cloud of electrons in one molecule and those of another.

These forces are manifest only in the quantal description of the system and so they were the last type to be understood. They were first studied by London who named them *dispersion forces*, as the oscillations responsible for them lead also to the dispersion of light by the molecules. He showed that the energy could be expressed as a sum of terms that vary inversely with even powers of the separation, r^{-6}, r^{-8}, r^{-10}, etc. The coefficients of these terms can be calculated directly only for atomic and molecular hydrogen and for helium. Approximate calculations for larger systems have suggested the expression[4] for the r^{-6} term

$$-\nu_2 r^{-6} = -\tfrac{3}{4}(pa_0 A^3)^{1/2}e^2 r^{-6} \qquad (7.1)$$

where p is the number of electrons in the outer shell, a_0 the Bohr radius of the hydrogen atom ($0\cdot529$ Å), A the polarizability of the atom and e the electronic charge. This simple equation shows that this term increases rapidly with the size, and therefore the polarizability, of the atomic or molecular system. Much more accurate is the expression of the dispersion coefficient, ν_2, in terms of a sum over the dipole oscillator strengths for the excitation of the atom[5]. These strengths can be calculated reliably only for simple atoms such as hydrogen, helium and lithium, but fortunately can be determined experimentally[6-8] from a knowledge of the refractive index as a function of frequency or of the Verdet constant. This combination of a quantal expression with the experimental values for the coefficients is the most accurate way of obtaining ν_2; the accuracy is believed to be about 5 per cent for the interaction of two argon atoms. (Such semi-empirical methods are often valuable, for we can determine the magnitudes of several kinds of intermolecular force by introducing into the theoretical expressions not only oscillator strengths but ionization potentials, dipole and quadrupole moments and electron polarizabilities.) Each of the succeeding terms in r^{-8}, etc. is much smaller at the separations that are important in liquids, but their sum is comparable in size with the r^{-6} term at those near the minimum of the pair potential.

The importance of the dispersion forces is threefold. First, they act between all neighbouring atoms or molecules, and so can account for the existence of attractive forces between spherically symmetrical systems such as the inert gas molecules—forces that are beyond the

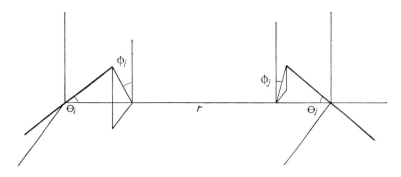

Figure 7.1. The four angles that describe the orientation of two axially symmetric molecules with respect to the line joining their centres

scope of classical electrostatics. Secondly, they have been shown to be additive, to a good approximation, and so permit the separation of the intermolecular energy of an assembly into the sum of pair potentials described above. Thirdly, they are usually much the most important negative term in the potential.

Again, little is known of the dependence of these forces on the orientation of non-spherical molecules. The most reliable calculations are those for molecular hydrogen[9]; de Boer considered the two extreme orientations, first, with the two molecules arranged with the four nuclei in one line ($\theta_i = \theta_j = 0$ or π in *Figure 7.1*) and, secondly, with the two molecules parallel ($\theta_i = \theta_j = \pi/2$ or $3\pi/2$ and $\varphi_i + \varphi_j = 0$ in *Figure 7.1*). The dispersion energy in the first position is greater than that in the second by a factor of about 1·4 for a given separation of the centres of the molecules. However, the repulsive part of the potential is greater in the first position by a factor of up to 10, owing to the closer approach of the electrons around the two near nuclei.

This means that, as is to be expected, the total energy passes through a deeper minimum at a closer separation of the molecular centres when the axes are parallel than when they are colinear. The deepest minimum is, in fact, found in neither of these positions but in a skew orientation. However, the principle remains that the deepest minimum in the energy is associated with the orientation in which the separation of the centres is least.

This principle has a useful application in devising model potentials for elliptical molecules. It is probable that the change of the dispersion energy with orientation can be estimated for more complex linear molecules from a knowledge of the polarizations parallel and perpendicular to the molecular axis.

A more important cause of the departure of the potential from spherical symmetry than the anisotropy of the repulsive or dispersion forces is the electrostatic potential that arises from a permanently unsymmetrical charge distribution within the molecules. This is the second type of attractive force mentioned above. The mutual electrostatic potential energy of any two discrete charge distributions can be expressed as an infinite series of inverse powers of the separation of any two points, one in each distribution.

This series is known as the *multipole expansion*[10] and converges as long as the two distributions do not overlap. The coefficients of the inverse powers, r^{-1}, r^{-2}, etc., are the product of two quantities. One is a pure function of the five angles needed to specify the relative orientation of two irregular molecules. The other is itself the product of the two quantities, one for each molecule, that are used to describe the charge distributions. These quantities are the *multipoles* and form a series of increasing complexity.

A description of a charge distribution may be made by specifying its multipoles—the more terms that are specified, the greater the information conveyed. The first of this series is simply the net (or ionic) charge of the distribution and is a scalar quantity. The second is the dipole moment, and is a vector, as it has both a magnitude and a direction with respect to any co-ordinate system set up within the molecule. The third and higher terms are tensors of increasing complexity and are called the quadrupole, octopole, 16-pole, etc. More formally the multipoles are defined by*

Net charge (Ion) $$C = \sum_i e_i \qquad (7.2)$$

Dipole $$\mu = \sum_i e_i \mathbf{r}_i \qquad (7.3)$$

Quadrupole $$Q = \tfrac{1}{2}\sum_i e_i(3\mathbf{r}_i\mathbf{r}_i - r_i^2\,U) \qquad \text{etc.} \qquad (7.4)$$

* See notation, p. xiii.

where e_i is the charge on the ith particle in the charge distribution, $\mathbf{r}_i$ the vector distance of this particle from an arbitrary centre and $\mathbf{U}$ the unit tensor. The summation is over all particles in the distribution and is naturally replaced by an integration if the time average of the charge distribution is a continuous function, as for the electrons in a molecule.

The first two of these equations present no difficulty and show the scalar character of the ionic charge and the vector character of the dipole with its three perpendicular components $\sum_i e_i x_i$, $\sum_i e_i y_i$ and $\sum_i e_i z_i$. $\sum_i e_i \mathbf{r}_i \mathbf{r}_i$ might be the more natural definition of a quadrupole, but it is convenient to define it as a traceless tensor, as in (7.4), since this simplifies the expressions for the intermolecular energies. In particular, it means that a spherical distribution of charge has no quadrupole. A simple case of a quadrupole is a linear distribution of charge. If the axis of the distribution is chosen to be the z-axis, then all x_i and y_i are zero. The second-order tensor is now reduced to one term only

$$q = Q_{zz} = \sum_i e_i z_i^2 \tag{7.5}$$

Similarly, for any molecule with a z-axis of three-fold symmetry (or greater), the quadrupole can be represented by one term only

$$q = Q_{zz} = -2Q_{xx} = -2Q_{yy} = \sum_i e_i(z_i^2 - x_i^2) = \sum_i e_i(z_i^2 - y_i^2) \tag{7.6}$$

The value of all but the first non-vanishing multipole depends on the origin from which $\mathbf{r}_i$, etc. are measured[10,11]. This is generally chosen to be the centre of electrical charge of the molecule (nuclei and electrons).

The expression for the energy of interaction of two charge distributions, which for simplicity are supposed to have axial symmetry, can be written in terms of these multipoles and the angles needed to specify the orientation (*Figure 7.1*). The angles θ and φ are reckoned for each molecule from an axis that is directed towards the centre of the other. Three of these angles are independent, θ_i, θ_j and the sum $(\varphi_i + \varphi_j)$. The energy, u, between two molecules i and j (of the same or different species) may be written[1]

$$u(r_{ij}, \theta_i, \theta_j, \varphi_i, \varphi_j) = \sum_{l_i=0} \sum_{l_j=0} \sum_m X^{l_i l_j m}(r_{ij})$$
$$S_{l_i m}(\theta_i, \varphi_i) S_{l_j m}(\theta_j, \varphi_j) \tag{7.7}$$

where X represent functions only of r_{ij}. They depend on the details of the two charge distributions and are zero if the modulus of m

exceeds l_i or l_j. S_{lm} are surface harmonics defined by

$$S_{lm}(\theta, \varphi) = \left[(2l + 1) \frac{(l - |m|)!}{(l + |m|)!} \right]^{1/2} P_l^m(\cos \theta)\, e^{im\varphi} \qquad (7.8)$$

where P_l^m is an associated Legendre function defined for positive m by

$$P_l^m(\cos \theta) = (\sin \theta)^m \frac{\mathrm{d}^m P_l(\cos \theta)}{\mathrm{d}(\cos \theta)^m} \qquad (7.9)$$

and where P_l^{-m} is equal to P_l^m. If the energy is to be a function only of $(\varphi_i + \varphi_j)$, then X must be unchanged on substituting $(-m)$ for m. This equation is capable of representing any type of potential between molecules of axial symmetry, including the terms of the multipole expansion. The first term X^{000} represents all the spherical components of the potential, as S_{00} is unity and so independent of the angles. The terms that describe the multipole expansion of molecules with zero net charge $(C_i = C_j = 0)$ are

$$X^{110} = 2X^{111} = \frac{2\mu_i\mu_j}{3r_{ij}^3} \qquad \text{Dipole}_i + \text{Dipole}_j \qquad (7.10)$$

$$X^{120} = \sqrt{3}X^{121} = \frac{\sqrt{3}\mu_i q_j}{\sqrt{5}r_{ij}^4} \qquad \text{Dipole}_i + \text{Quadrupole}_j \qquad (7.11)$$

$$X^{210} = \sqrt{3}X^{211} = \frac{\sqrt{3}q_i\mu_j}{\sqrt{5}r_{ij}^4} \qquad \text{Quadrupole}_i + \text{Dipole}_j \qquad (7.12)$$

$$X^{220} = \tfrac{3}{2}X^{221} = 6X^{222} = \frac{6q_iq_j}{5r_{ij}^5} \qquad \text{Quadrupole}_i + \text{Quadrupole}_j \qquad (7.13)$$

$$\text{also Dipole}_i + \text{Octopole}_j, \text{ etc.}$$

The successive terms of (7.7) can, therefore, be made to represent the interactions of the multipoles of two charge distributions by a suitable choice of the coefficients $X^{l_i l_j m}(r_{ij})$. The first term is the familiar dipole + dipole interaction. This is formed from those terms of (7.7) with $l_i = l_j = 1$ and m equal to $-1, 0$ and $+1$. The sum of these three terms, with the values of X given by (7.10), may be written in the simple form

$$\frac{\mu_i\mu_j}{r_{ij}^3} [2 \cos \theta_i \cos \theta_j + \sin \theta_i \sin \theta_j \cos (\varphi_i + \varphi_j)] \qquad (7.14)$$

This function of the angles can take all values between -2 and $+2$. Similarly, the dipole + quadrupole and quadrupole + quadrupole terms may be written out in full by substitution from (7.11)–(7.13) and using the explicit forms of the surface harmonics. If both net charges are zero, then there are no terms of the types X^{100} and X^{010}. It is shown in the next Chapter that the absence of these terms leads to a simplification of the statistical theory of assemblies of polar molecules.

The highest multipole used in this book is the quadrupole. This is sufficient to describe the charge distribution of most simple molecules, and Stogryn and Stogryn[12] have published a useful list of numerical values. In principle, the higher multipoles could be used to describe strongly localized interactions such as that in a hydrogen bond[13]. This has not often been tried in practice, as there is one question about hydrogen bonds that is not yet fully answered. It is not known how far a purely classical description is adequate to describe the final distribution of charge in a pair of hydrogen-bonded molecules. The energy of the molecules in the equilibrium bonded state is simply the classical (or coulombic) energy of the equilibrium array of nuclei and electron clouds, but it is not known how far specifically quantal effects determine the array.

All molecules are polarizable, and so there will be further forces arising from the interaction of the permanent multipoles of one molecule with the induced ones of the other. These forces are the third of the three types mentioned above. They are generally weak and depend little on orientation. The only term that is of any importance is the interaction of a permanent with an induced dipole. This may be represented by the following choice of coefficients in (7.7)

$$X^{000} = -\frac{\mu_i^2 A_j}{r_{ij}^6} \tag{7.15}$$

$$X^{200} = -\frac{\mu_i^2 A_j}{\sqrt{5}r_{ij}^6} \tag{7.16}$$

The first of these coefficients is the spherical and the second the angle-dependent part of the interaction of the dipole of molecule i with a molecule j of polarizability A_j.

This is as far as theory takes us, and for further information we must turn to experiment[14,15]. The useful results from molecular beam scattering are easily summarized[15,16]. For the more simple of the molecules discussed in this book they provide welcome confirmation of the correctness of the oscillator-strength calculation of the coefficient of the dispersion potential, ν_2, although the experiments are apparently of lower accuracy than the calculations. So far, however, these tell us little about the depth of the potential or about its shape near a collision diameter σ, defined by $u_2(\sigma) = 0$.

Much more substantial, if less specific, is the information obtained from the bulk physical properties. If we are to avoid any contamination by multibody potentials, then we must determine the pair potential $u_2(r)$ solely from the equilibrium and transport properties of the dilute gas. Argon is the substance most studied and is taken here as an example.

The second virial coefficient alone is insufficient to determine the whole of $u_2(r)$ but, in principle, is capable of yielding by means of a Laplace transform[17] unique values of the inverse functions $[r(u_2)]$ for $u_2 > 0$ and $[r_+^3(u_2) - r_-^3(u_2)]$ for $u_2 < 0$ where r_+ and r_- are the pair of separations that correspond to each negative value of u_2.

The second virial coefficient of argon at room temperature and above is reconcilable with a wide range of potentials of the bireciprocal or Lennard-Jones form

$$u_2(r) = \lambda_2 r^{-n} - \nu_2 r^{-m} \quad (n > m > 3) \qquad (7.17)$$

or with a similar potential in which the first term is replaced by an exponential expression of the form e^{-Br}. The Lennard-Jones potential, (7.17), is commonly used with the values $n = 12$ and $m = 6$, and it is found that, with this choice, it is possible to fit not only the second virial coefficient but also the viscosity and coefficient of diffusion at moderate and high temperatures with the same, or similar, values of λ_2 and ν_2. This $(12, 6)$ potential is often written

$$u(r) = 4\epsilon[(\sigma/r)^{12} - (\sigma/r)^6] = \epsilon[(r^*/r)^{12} - 2(r^*/r)^6] \quad (7.18)$$

where the subscript 2 is now omitted from u, etc. when it is clear that a pair potential is intended. The parameters ϵ, σ and r^* are, respectively, the minimum depth of u, the collision diameter and the separation at which u has its minimum (*Figure 7.2*).

This agreement between experiment and a model potential was taken for many years to be confirmation of the essential correctness of the form of (7.18), and corroboration was provided by the fact that the same potential could account also for the lattice parameters of solid argon[18]. This rosy view is now no longer tenable, for the following reasons:

(1) the coefficient of r^{-6} required by (7.18) is twice as large as that found by semi-empirical calculations from oscillator strengths, and confirmed by beam-scattering experiments.

(2) the observed coefficients of viscosity and thermal conductivity at low temperatures can also be related[19] to the coefficient of r^{-6} and are reconcilable with the calculated values but not with those from (7.18).

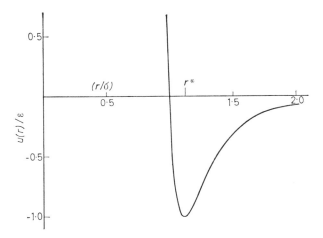

Figure 7.2. The Lennard-Jones (12,6) potential as a function of
(r/σ) where σ is the collision diameter, at which the energy is zero.
The maximum depth of the potential is ϵ and occurs at a distance r^*
which is $(2^{1/6}\,\sigma)$

(3) the second virial coefficient at low temperatures is irreconcilable with (7.18) and requires a potential with a deeper
minimum[20].

(4) theoretical calculations of the coefficient of r^{-8} show that
this term is not negligible[3].

Thus the experimental evidence now available requires a pair
potential which is shallower than (7.18) at large separations, where
the r^{-6} is dominant, but deeper and steeper near the minimum.
The higher terms in the dispersion energy in r^{-8}, etc. are neglected
in (7.18) but, in argon at least, their sum is probably as large as
the r^{-6} term alone at separations near the minimum. One widely
used empirical potential which differs from (7.18) in a way that
fits these requirements qualitatively is that due to Kihara[21]

$$u(r) = \lambda(r-\gamma)^{-12} - \nu(r-\gamma)^{-6} \qquad (r > \gamma)$$
$$u(r) = \infty \qquad\qquad\qquad (r < \gamma) \tag{7.19}$$

where the 'core', γ, is about $\frac{1}{10}$ of σ. This potential, although an
improvement on (7.18), has the undesirable feature of generating
spurious terms in r^{-7}, r^{-9}, etc. as well as the required terms in r^{-6},
r^{-8} and r^{-10}, etc.*

* Possibly $u(r) = \lambda(r^2 - \gamma^2)^{-6} - \nu(r^2 - \gamma^2)^{-3}$ would be better but it has,
apparently, not been tried.

So far, only the properties of the dilute gas have been used. If we now turn to more dense systems, then we find a paradox. The Kihara potential is a better representation than the Lennard-Jones of the true two-body potential of argon, but it does not reproduce so well the properties of the crystal and, in particular, leads to too high values for the lattice energy and Debye frequency, both of which are quite well represented by the Lennard-Jones potential.

Similar results are found for the few properties of a liquid that can be compared directly with the potential. Thus Monte Carlo calculations (see next Chapter) of the density and configurational energy of a liquid with a Lennard-Jones potential at low temperatures and zero pressure are in excellent agreement with experiment if the parameters are chosen to fit the second virial coefficient and viscosity at moderate and high temperatures. The computer results are not reconcilable with a Kihara pair potential.

A further discrepancy is revealed by a study of the isotopic separation factor between liquid and vapour. This can be expressed in terms of the second derivative of $u(r)$ and so can be used for testing model potentials. It is found[22] that the Kihara potential leads to a curvature near the minimum that is about 20 per cent greater than that observed experimentally, whilst the Lennard-Jones potential is about 4 per cent lower than experiment. In fact, as is shown in the next Chapter, the curvature of the Lennard-Jones potential is insufficient to satisfy a necessary (Schwarz) inequality, but nevertheless the liquid certainly behaves more as if it were a 'Lennard-Jones fluid' than a 'Kihara fluid'.

These paradoxes can be resolved only by the introduction of multibody potentials into the discussion of the properties of the condensed phases. That is, if we write the configurational energy, $\mathscr{U}$, as a convergent series

$$\mathscr{U}(\mathbf{r}_1 \ldots \mathbf{r}_N) = \sum_{i<j}\sum u_{ij} + \sum_{i<j<k}\sum\sum u_{ijk} + \ldots \qquad (7.20)$$

then it is insufficient to take only the first term on the right-hand side.

The results above are indirect evidence that u_{ijk} contributes between 5 and 10 per cent to the total energy of liquid argon at its triple point and that this contribution is positive; that is, it reduces the stability of the fluid. More direct evidence for the existence of this three-body potential comes from the third virial coefficient which is a direct measure of the interaction of molecules three at a time[23]. Little is known of the form of u_{ijk}, but the most important term is probably the dipole–dipole–dipole term first described by Axilrod and Teller[21,24]

$$v_3(1 + 3 \cos \theta_i \cos \theta_j \cos \theta_k)/r_{ij}^3 r_{ik}^3 r_{jk}^3 \qquad (7.21)$$

where r_{ij}, r_{ik} and r_{jk} are the sides and θ_i, θ_j and θ_k the angles of the triangle formed by the three particles. The coefficient v_3 is related[21,25] to the pair-coefficient v_2 by

$$v_3 = \tfrac{3}{4}Av_2 \qquad (7.22)$$

where A is the polarizability of one molecule. The term (7.21) is apparently capable of reconciling the best Kihara pair potential and the experimental third virial coefficient. Since v_3 is positive, it follows that (7.21) is positive for equilateral (and similar) triangles and negative for obtuse triangles and linear arrays of molecules. Hence the net contribution of (7.21) to the lattice energy of the crystal is positive, as is required to resolve the paradox above[26].

However, there is still some doubt if (7.21) is the only contribution to u_3 that must be taken into account, for it has been claimed that the three-body overlap forces are not negligible and that they may reduce substantially the effect of (7.21). It is too early to attempt to resolve the differences of opinion on this point[27], but certain that (7.21) is, at least, one of the most important contributions to u_3.

It can be concluded, therefore, that the true two-body potential in argon and other similar substances is closer to Kihara (7.19) than to Lennard-Jones (7.18) but that the Kihara potential cannot be used in the condensed states without explicit inclusion of a three-body potential of which (7.21) is a leading term. The Lennard-Jones potential is, however, a useful 'effective' two-body potential for the discussion of the cruder bulk properties of the condensed states, for example, the first derivatives of the free energy. It is so used in the next two Chapters.

Even the Lennard-Jones potential is too complicated for the discussion of many fundamental points of principle in the theory of liquids, and so more simple model potentials are used in examining statistical approximations. The two that are used most frequently in the remainder of this book are the hard and soft spherical potentials defined by the equations

Hard sphere

$$\begin{aligned} u(r) &= \infty \qquad & (r < \sigma) \\ u(r) &= 0 \qquad & (r > \sigma) \end{aligned} \qquad (7.23)$$

Soft sphere

$$u(r) = \epsilon(r/\sigma)^{-n} \qquad (n > 3) \qquad (7.24)$$

The soft sphere is characterized by two independent parameters, the index n and the parameter of strength or size $(\epsilon\sigma^n)$. Clearly one symbol, say λ, could be used for this combination, but it is useful to write the potential in the form (7.24), since we shall be interested in its limit as n becomes infinite. This limit is indefinite if $u(r)$ is written as λr^{-n}, whereas (7.24) approaches the hard sphere of diameter σ. The physical properties of an assembly of soft spheres depend, of course, only on the value of the combination of parameters $(\epsilon\sigma^n)$.

However, the inert gases are only a small proportion of the liquids whose properties await theoretical interpretation, and for more complex molecules several modifications of these simple model potentials are needed. These are of three kinds:

(1) The addition of the direct and induced electrostatic terms. The multipole expansions for these are given above.

(2) The representation of the 'shape' of molecules. These shapes arise mainly from the change with orientation of the repulsive forces. Pople[28] suggests that such change can be represented by two of the terms of (7.7)

$$X^{200} = X^{020} = \lambda' r^{-12} \tag{7.25}$$

where λ' is a parameter that governs the ellipticity of the molecules. Positive values of λ' make them prolate (or rod-like) and negative values oblate (or plate-like). If these terms are added to (7.18), then a potential is obtained that has its minimum energy at an orientation that allows this to occur at the closest separation. This association of the minimum of u with that of r was noticed above in the discussion of the potential between two hydrogen molecules. The same result may be achieved less realistically by ascribing the variation of potential with orientation entirely to the attractive forces, that is, by choosing terms of the kind

$$X^{l_i l_j m} = \nu'(l_i, l_j, m) r^{-6} \qquad (l_i, l_j \neq 0) \tag{7.26}$$

where the only restriction on the terms is that neither l_i nor l_j shall be zero. What such a potential loses in realism from, say, (7.25) it makes up by its greater usefulness. There are, in Chapters 8 and 9, several statistical problems that can be solved for the addition of (7.26) to a (12, 6) potential but not for (7.25).

(3) The third modification which is sometimes needed is an alteration of the exponents of the Lennard-Jones potential. In 'globular' molecules such as neopentane, carbon tetrachloride and sulphur hexafluoride, the origins of the attractive and repulsive forces are not the geometrical centres of the molecules but are in the atoms or groups disposed symmetrically about

this centre. This change of origin affects the potential in two ways. First, it is no longer spherically symmetrical. This departure can, if necessary, be treated by taking suitable terms from (7.7), but it is probably less important than the second effect. This is an alteration in the apparent exponents of the potential when this referred to the centres of the molecules. The simplest model for a globular molecule is to suppose that it is a spherical shell each part of which interacts with each of a neighbouring shell with a (12, 6) potential. This gives a total potential which is still spherical but much steeper than r^{-12} and r^{-6}, if r is the distance between the centres. The increase in the repulsive exponent is greater than in the attractive. Several calculations[29] of the equilibrium and transport properties of gases have been made for this model, and a few very rough ones for liquids. The most extensive are those of Hamann and Lambert[29] who used a (28,7) potential.

7.3 Forces Between Unlike Molecules

The potential energy between a pair of unlike molecules can be represented in the same way as that between one of the same species. The parameters of, say, (7.17) are determined by the chemical

Table 7.1. The coefficients of the dispersion energy, $(\nu \times 10^{79}$, in J m^6)

The like interactions are on the diagonal of the Table and the unlike interactions above it. Below the diagonal are shown, in brackets, the geometrical means of the like interactions.

	Ne	Ar	Kr	Xe
Ne	6·04	19	26	36
Ar	(19)	63	87	125
Kr	(28)	(87)	125	182
Xe	(39)	(127)	(180)	257

species of both molecules and so may be written more fully as $\lambda_{\alpha\beta}$ and $\nu_{\alpha\beta}$. In a binary mixture of components 1 and 2 there are three kinds of intermolecular potential, represented by (λ_{11}, ν_{11}), (λ_{12}, ν_{12}) and (λ_{22}, ν_{22}). It is natural to ask if the 'mixed' parameters, λ_{12} and ν_{12}, are related in any way to those of the pure substances. Theory can offer a little assistance here. London's theory of the dispersion forces suggests that ν_{12} is close to the geometric mean of ν_{11} and ν_{22}. This is shown in *Table 7.1* which is based on the semi-empirical calculations of Dalgarno and his colleagues[5,6]. It is seen that ν_{12} is equal to, or possibly a little less than, the geometric mean of ν_{11} and ν_{22}. Mason and Monchick[15] have adduced evidence, principally from beam-scattering at high energies[30], that there is a similar relation for λ_{12}.

A wide study of the properties of gaseous mixtures has suggested further two empirical rules for the calculation of the mixed parameters. These rules are usually set out in terms of ϵ and σ of (7.18), not for λ and ν:

$$\epsilon_{12} = \epsilon_{11}^{1/2}\epsilon_{22}^{1/2} \tag{7.27}$$

$$\sigma_{12} = \tfrac{1}{2}\sigma_{11} + \tfrac{1}{2}\sigma_{22} \tag{7.28}$$

The first equation is equivalent to London's rule for ν_{12} if the molecules all have the same σ, but its real justification is its empirical success. The second holds exactly for the collision diameter of hard spheres of different sizes, but again its justification lies in its success. This arithmetic mean rule was first proposed by Lorentz[31] in 1881 for the equivalent parameter, $b^{1/3}$ in van der Waals's equation, and the geometric mean for energies of interaction was used by Berthelot[32] in 1898. The name *Lorentz–Berthelot mixture* has therefore been suggested for a mixture of Lennard-Jones molecules in which the unlike parameters are give by these equations.

It is important to consider carefully the evidence for these equations, other than that provided by liquid mixtures themselves, and, where it is good, the limits of accuracy that may be put on parameters so calculated. The evidence[33] is:

(*1*) The second virial coefficient of a binary gas mixture is a quadratic function of the composition

$$B = y_1^2 B_{11} + 2y_1 y_2 B_{12} + y_2^2 B_{22} \qquad \text{(constant } T\text{)} \quad (7.29)$$

where B_{11} and B_{22} are the coefficients of the two pure gases and are functions solely of the temperature and of the forces between 1–1 and 2–2 pairs of molecules, respectively. B_{12} is an identical function of the 1–2 forces and one of our most direct sources of information about these. The second virial coefficient, B, has been measured for many gas mixtures and the results have been analysed to give B_{12}. These have been used to obtain ϵ_{12} and σ_{12}, in the same way that B_{11} gives ϵ_{11} and σ_{11}. The derived parameters confirm the Lorentz–Berthelot relations to within about 2 per cent for simple molecules[1]. A most thorough test of these relations has been made by Guggenheim and McGlashan[34] by using not the (12,6) potential but the principle of corresponding states which is closely related to a potential having only two parameters. They also confirm the relations, but there is again an uncertainty of several per cent, even with the simplest molecules, in the values of the cross parameters. However, Fender and Halsey[35] found from B_{12}

that the cross-energy for argon + krypton was significantly lower than the geometric mean, and apparently closer to the harmonic mean, which is 0·987 of the geometric. More recently, Brewer[35] has found 0·986 and Byrne, Jones and Staveley 0·994. This apparent discrepancy of 1 per cent is sufficiently large to produce appreciable changes in the calculated values of the thermodynamic properties of the liquid mixtures (Section 9.5).

Interactions between aliphatic fluorocarbons and hydrocarbons are much weaker than the Lorentz–Berthelot relations require[36]. One case, $CH_4 + CF_4$, for which B_{11}, B_{12} and B_{22} are known accurately, is discussed in Section 9.5, where the derived parameters are used to calculate the properties of the liquid mixture. Lambert and his colleagues[37] have shown that non-polar organic molecules, of the kind often studied in liquid mixtures, have virial coefficients that conform reasonably well to these relations, but they find, as is to be expected, that polar molecules do not conform.

There is a second way of measuring B_{12} that has, in a few cases, greatly extended the temperature range over which this coefficient may be determined[38]. The solubility of a pure solid of low volatility in a compressed gas may be written as a virial expansion in powers of the gas density. Its first term has the coefficient $(v_2^s - 2B_{12})$ where v_2^s is the molar volume of the solid. Measurement of such solubility can, therefore, give B_{12} at temperatures at which one of the components is a solid. This downward extension of the accessible range of temperature increases the accuracy with which ϵ_{12} and σ_{12} can be determined.

(2) The coefficient, D_{12}, which measures the rate of interdiffusion of two gases is almost independent of composition for spherical molecules and almost entirely determined by the 1–2 forces[1]. Unfortunately, there are again few accurate measurements that cover a wide enough range of temperature to give reliable values of ϵ_{12}. The tests that have been made[1,33,39] suggest, once again, that the Lorentz–Berthelot equations are good to about 2 per cent for simple molecules. The viscosities of gas mixtures have been more widely and accurately measured but are less sensitive to the 1–2 forces[1,38].

The only conclusion that can yet be drawn is that ϵ_{12} and σ_{12} are given by these equations with an accuracy of about 2 per cent. Unfortunately, the calculation of the excess properties of liquid mixtures demands a much greater accuracy. The properties of Lorentz–Berthelot mixtures are nevertheless well worth calculating, but it is apparently necessary, when comparing theory and experiment, to allow for departures of the order of a few per cent even in the most simple mixtures. It is probable that most of these departures will be such that ϵ_{12} falls below the geometric mean, and they are most likely when the substances are of different chemical type. Hydrocarbon + fluorocarbon is an extreme case of such a difference, but even for substances as similar as aliphatic and aromatic hydrocarbons the departures have substantial thermodynamic consequences. Indeed, London's theory of the dispersion forces leads us to expect these departures for mixtures in which the components have molecules of different size, polarizability and, above all, ionization potential[36, 40].

REFERENCES

[1] Hirschfelder, J. O., Curtiss, C. F. and Bird, R. B. *Molecular Theory of Gases and Liquids*, New York (Wiley) 1954; Hirschfelder, J. O. (ed.) 'Intermolecular Forces', *Adv. chem. Phys.* 12 (1967)

[2] Fitts, D. D. A. *Rev. phys. Chem.* 17 (1966) 59; Smith, E. B. *Rep. Prog. Chem.* 63 (1966) 13

[3] Hirschfelder, J. O. and Meath, W. J. *Adv. chem. Phys.* 12 (1967) 3

[4] Slater, J. C. and Kirkwood, J. G. *Phys. Rev.* 37 (1931) 682; Kirkwood, J. G. *Phys. Z.* 33 (1932) 57

[5] Dalgarno, A. *Adv. chem. Phys.* 12 (1967) 143

[6] Dalgarno, A., with Lynn, N. *Proc. phys. Soc. Lond.* A70 (1957) 802; with Kingston, A. E. 73 (1959) 455; 78 (1961) 607; *Proc. R. Soc.* A259 (1960) 424; Kingston, A. E. *Phys. Rev.* 135 (1964) A1018

[7] Barker, J. A. and Leonard, P. J. *Phys. Lett.* 13 (1964) 127

[8] Bell, R. J. *Proc. phys. Soc. Lond.* 86 (1965) 17

[9] de Boer, J. *Physica* 9 (1942) 363; Evett, A. A. and Margenau, H. *Phys. Rev.* 90 (1953) 1021; Karplus, M. *J. chem. Phys.* 41 (1964) 880

[10] Buckingham, A. D. *Q. Rev. chem. Soc.* 13 (1959) 183; *Adv. chem. Phys.* 12 (1967) 107

[11] Buckingham, A. D. and Longuet-Higgins, H. C. *Molec. Phys.* 14 (1968) 63

[12] Stogryn, D. E. and Stogryn, A. P. *Molec. Phys.* 11 (1966) 371

[13] Pimental, G. C. and McClellan, A. L. *The Hydrogen Bond*, San Francisco (Freeman) 1960

[14] *Discuss. Faraday Soc.* 40 (1965)

[15] Mason, E. A. and Monchick, L. *Adv. chem. Phys.* 12 (1967) 329; Mason, E. A. and Spurling, T. H. *The Virial Equation of State*, Oxford (Pergamon) 1968

[16] Bernstein, R. B. and Muckerman, J. T. *Adv. chem. Phys.* 12 (1967) 389

[17] Keller, J. B. and Zumino, B. *J. chem. Phys.* 30 (1959) 1351; Frisch, H. L. and Helfand, E. 32 (1960) 269; Jonah, D. A. and Rowlinson, J. S. *Trans. Faraday Soc.* 62 (1966) 1067; Schaber, A., to be published

[18] Corner, J. *Trans. Faraday Soc.* 44 (1948) 914; Dobbs, E. R. and Jones, G. O. *Rep. Prog. Phys.* 20 (1957) 516; Horton, G. K. *Am. J. Phys.* 36 (1968) 93

[19] Rowlinson, J. S. *Discuss. Faraday Soc.* 40 (1965) 19; Mason, E. A., Munn, R. J. and Smith, F. J. *ibid.* 27

[20] Michels, A., Levelt, J. M. and de Graaff, W. *Physica* 24 (1958) 659; Weir, R. D., Wynne Jones, I., Rowlinson, J. S. and Saville, G. *Trans. Faraday Soc.* 63 (1967) 1320

[21] Kihara, T. *Rev. mod. Phys.* 25 (1953) 831; *Adv. chem. Phys.* 1 (1958) 267; Barker, J. A., Fock, W. and Smith, F. *Physics Fluids* 7 (1964) 897; O'Connell, J.P. and Prausnitz, J. M. *J. phys. Chem.* 72 (1968) 632

[22] Rowlinson, J. S. *Molec. Phys.* 7 (1964) 477; 9 (1965) 197

[23] Sherwood, A. E. and Prausnitz, J. M. *J. chem. Phys.* 41 (1964) 413, 429

[24] Axilrod, B. M. and Teller, E. *J. chem. Phys.* 11 (1943) 299; 19 (1951) 724

[25] Bell, R. J. and Kingston, A. E. *Proc. phys. Soc. Lond.* 88 (1966) 901

[26] Rossi, J. C. and Danon, F. *Discuss. Faraday Soc.* 40 (1965) 97; Chell, G. G. and Zucker, I. J. *Proc. phys. Soc. Lond.* C1 (1968) 35

[27] Jansen, L. *Phys. Rev.* 135 (1964) A1292; with Lombardi, E. *Discuss. Faraday Soc.* 40 (1965) 78; Sherwood, A. E., De Rocco, A. G. and Mason, E. A. *J. chem. Phys.* 44 (1966) 2984; Williams, D. R., Schaad, L. J. and Murrell, J. N. 47 (1967) 4916; Graben, H. W., Present, R. D. and McCulloch, R. D. *Phys. Rev.* 144 (1966) 140; Swenberg, C. E. *Phys. Lett.* 24A (1967) 163

[28] Pople, J. A. *Proc. R. Soc.* A221 (1954) 498, 508; Buckingham, A. D. and Pople, J. A. *Trans. Faraday Soc.* 51 (1955) 1173

[29] Trappeniers,N.*Physica*17(1951)501;Balescu,R.22(1956)224;Rowlinson, J. S.*J. chem. Phys.* 20 (1952) 337; *Aust. J. Chem.* 7 (1954) 397; Hamann, S. D. and Lambert, J. A. *ibid.* 1, 18, 219; 8 (1955) 21; Thomaes, G. *J. Chim. phys.* 49 (1952) 323; McCoubrey, J. C. and Singh, N. M. *Trans. Faraday Soc.* 53 (1957) 877; De Rocco, A. G. *J. phys. Chem.* 62 (1958) 890; with Spurling, T. H. and Storvick, T. S. *J. chem. Phys.* 46 (1967) 599, 1498

[30] Amdur, I., Mason, E. A. and Harkness, A. L. *J. chem. Phys.* 22 (1954) 1071; 25 (1956) 632

[31] Lorentz, H. A. *Annln Phys.* 12 (1881) 127

[32] Berthelot, D. *C. r. hebd. Séanc. Acad. Sci., Paris* 126 (1898) 1703, 1857

[33] See also Prigogine, I. *The Molecular Theory of Solutions*, Ch. 2, Amsterdam (North-Holland) 1957

[34] Guggenheim, E. A. and McGlashan, M. L. *Proc. R. Soc.* A206 (1951) 448; Guggenheim, E. A. *Mixtures*, Ch. 8, Oxford Univ. Press, 1952

[35] Fender, B. E. F. and Halsey, G. D. *J. chem. Phys.* 36 (1962) 1881; Brewer, J. *Rep. AFOSR* (U.S.A.) 67–2795 (1967); Byrne, M. A., Jones, M. R. and Staveley, L. A. K. *Trans. Faraday Soc.* 64 (1968) 1747

[36] Garner, M. D. G. and McCoubrey, J. C. *Trans. Faraday Soc.* 55 (1959) 1524; Hudson, G. H. and McCoubrey, J. C. 56 (1960) 761

[37] Fox, J. H. P. and Lambert, J. D. *Proc. R. Soc.* A210 (1952) 557; Lambert, J. D., Murphy, S. J. and Sanday, A. P. A226 (1954) 394

[38] Rowlinson, J. S. and Richardson, M. J. *Adv. chem. Phys.* 2 (1959) 85

[39] Rowlinson, J. S. and Townley, J. R. *Trans. Faraday Soc.* 49 (1953) 20

[40] Reed, T. M. *J. phys. Chem.* 59 (1955) 428; 63 (1959) 1798; Kohler, F. *Mh. Chem.* 88 (1957) 857; Munn, R. J. *Trans. Faraday Soc.* 57 (1961) 187

8
THE STATISTICAL THERMODYNAMICS
OF FLUIDS

8.1 INTRODUCTION

This and the following Chapter are an account of some of the successes and failures of the statistical theories of liquids and mixtures. The best of these theories follow from the laws of classical mechanics and the fundamental theorems of statistical mechanics by means of a few well-defined approximations.

The usefulness of a theory is generally related to the precision with which these approximations can be stated. Those that are mathematically well-defined and those that have to be used only at late stages in the development are usually capable of successive refinement. Approximations that involve gross physical assumptions about the nature of the fluid states may lead to a good agreement between some part of the theory and experiment, but in the case of mixtures have been found to be less useful in the long run. If they are 'physical' rather than 'mathematical', then it is often more difficult to suggest systematic ways of improving the treatment. Moreover, such approximations lead more often to thermodynamic inconsistencies.

Here the development of the theory of liquids is set out in such a way that the less reasonable approximations are introduced at as late a stage as possible. The results of the first four Sections of this Chapter, and to some degree of the fifth, are based on the minimum of assumptions needed in any theory at the present day. These are almost unexceptionable and are used again in the next Chapter.

8.2 MOLECULAR DISTRIBUTION FUNCTIONS

The structure and properties of a fluid at equilibrium may be described by the molecular distribution functions[1-6]. These define the probability of the occurrence of a particular arrangement of molecules in an assembly of fixed number (N) and fixed volume (V). The first is the probability of finding a molecule in a small volume element*, $d\mathbf{r}_1$, at a position whose co-ordinates from any convenient origin are defined by the vector $\mathbf{r}_1$. This probability is

---

* See Notation, p. xi.

obviously proportional to $d\mathbf{r}_1$ and may be denoted $n^{(1)}(\mathbf{r}_1) \, d\mathbf{r}_1$. It is independent of $\mathbf{r}_1$ in an isotropic fluid and is given by

$$n^{(1)} \equiv n = N/V \qquad (8.1)$$

A pair distribution function, $n^{(2)}(\mathbf{r}_1, \mathbf{r}_2)$, defines the probability of finding simultaneously molecules at $\mathbf{r}_1$ and $\mathbf{r}_2$. This must satisfy the equation

$$\int n^{(2)}(\mathbf{r}_1, \mathbf{r}_2) \, d\mathbf{r}_2 = n^{(1)}(\mathbf{r}_1) \cdot (N - 1) = N(N - 1)/V \qquad (8.2)$$

This equation follows from the fact that the integral represents the chance of finding a molecule at $\mathbf{r}_1$ (that is, $n^{(1)}$) multiplied by the total number of molecules, $(N - 1)$, encountered in performing the integration over the whole of the volume of the fluid. Distribution functions of higher order may be defined similarly. Thus

$$n^{(h)}(\mathbf{r}_1 \ldots \mathbf{r}_h) \, d\mathbf{r}_1 \ldots d\mathbf{r}_h$$

is the probability of the simultaneous presence of h molecules in the h volume elements $d\mathbf{r}_1 \ldots d\mathbf{r}_h$. This function is related to $n^{(h+1)}$ by a generalization of (8.2)

$$\int n^{(h+1)} \, d\mathbf{r}_{h+1} = (N - h)n^{(h)} \qquad (8.3)$$

If the molecules are assumed to be distinguishable, then the probability of finding *given* molecules out of the whole assembly of N molecules in each of the h volume elements is

$$\frac{(N - h)!}{N!} \, n^{(h)} \, d\mathbf{r}_1 \ldots d\mathbf{r}_h$$

When h is unity, this probability is $(n^{(1)}/N) \, d\mathbf{r}_1$ or $(d\mathbf{r}_1/V)$ or simply, the ratio of the volume element to the total volume.

In a perfect gas in which the molecules are point particles without mutual interaction

$$n^{(h)} = N!/V^h(N - h)! \simeq (N/V)^h \qquad (8.4)$$

The second part of this equation holds only if h is small compared with N.

These functions may be more accurately named configurational distribution functions, since they define only the positions of a group of molecules and tell nothing of their linear momenta or of their rotational or vibrational states. It is sometimes useful to define total distribution functions, $f^{(h)}$, which include this further information. It is often legitimate to factorize $f^{(h)}$ into two functions, one of which is $n^{(h)}$ and the other purely a molecular property, i.e. it is independent of the geometry of the sites $\mathbf{r}_1 \ldots \mathbf{r}_h$. It is always possible to do so for an assembly of structureless particles between which there are conservative central forces.

The inert gases are the only physical examples of such an assembly, and this Section is restricted to them. Polyatomic molecules are discussed in Section 8.5 where it is shown that the factorization is possible for what is formally a class of molecules slightly wider than the inert gases, namely those with spherical potential energies in which the molecular rotations and vibrations are independent of their environment. The total distribution function, $f^{(h)}$, for an assembly of monatomic molecules defines both the positions $\mathbf{r}_1 \ldots \mathbf{r}_h$ and the momenta $\mathbf{p}_1 \ldots \mathbf{p}_h$ of the h molecules. Clearly

$$\int \ldots \int f^{(h)} \, d\mathbf{p}_1 \ldots d\mathbf{p}_h = n^{(h)} \tag{8.5}$$

$$\iint f^{(h+1)} \, d\mathbf{r}_{h+1} \, d\mathbf{p}_{h+1} = (N - h)f^{(h)} \tag{8.6}$$

A simple and convenient starting point for a discussion of the statistical mechanics of a fluid is the probability of a given configuration of all N molecules in the assembly. This is denoted $n^{(N)}$ and is proportional to $\exp(-\mathcal{U}/kT)$ where $\mathcal{U}$ is that part of the energy of the given configuration that arises from the intermolecular forces. This type of proportionality is more familiar when applied to the state of single molecules than to that of an assembly of N molecules. The probability that a single molecule is in an energy state ϵ_i in an assembly of independent molecules (the *micro-canonical ensemble*) is proportional to $\exp(-\epsilon_i/kT)$. This may be expressed

$$\frac{n_i}{N} = \left(\frac{1}{\psi}\right) e^{-\epsilon_i/kT} \tag{8.7}$$

where the left-hand side is the ratio of the number of molecules of energy ϵ_i to the total number in the assembly (or the probability that any molecule chosen at random has this energy), and ψ, the reciprocal of the constant of proportionality, is the *molecular partition function*. In an ensemble of assemblies, in which each assembly has N molecules (the *canonical ensemble*), it follows similarly that the probability of a configuration of energy $\mathcal{U}$ is

$$n^{(N)} = \left(\frac{1}{Q}\right) e^{-\mathcal{U}/kT} \tag{8.8}$$

where Q is again the reciprocal of the constant of proportionality. It is a function of the number, volume and temperature of the assembly. In a perfect gas, $n^{(N)}$ is given by the first part of (8.4) and $\mathcal{U}$ is zero for all configurations. Hence

$$Q = V^N/N! = (eV/N)^N \tag{8.9}$$

Stirling's approximation for a factorial has been used in the second part of this equation.

The distribution function $n^{(N)}$ is related to $n^{(N-1)}$ by (8.2) which is similarly related to $n^{(N-2)}$, etc. Hence by repeated integration the general distribution function is given by

$$n^{(h)} = \frac{1}{Q(N-h)!} \int \cdots \int e^{-\mathcal{U}/kT} \, d\mathbf{r}_{h+1} \cdots d\mathbf{r}_N \tag{8.10}$$

and, in particular

$$\frac{N}{V} = n^{(1)} = \frac{1}{Q(N-1)!} \int \cdots \int e^{-\mathcal{U}/kT} \, d\mathbf{r}_2 \cdots d\mathbf{r}_N \tag{8.11}$$

or

$$Q = \frac{1}{N!} \int \cdots \int e^{-\mathcal{U}/kT} \, d\mathbf{r}_1 \cdots d\mathbf{r}_N \tag{8.12}$$

This last equation may be integrated over all $d\mathbf{r}_1$ without any difficulty by referring all the vectors $\mathbf{r}_2 \cdots \mathbf{r}_N$ to molecule 1 as origin. The integration over $d\mathbf{r}_1$ thus gives simply the total volume, V, and so leads to (8.11). The integrations in (8.10)–(8.12) are taken over all configurations within the volume V that are accessible to the molecules. If $\mathcal{U}$ is put equal to zero in (8.12), then (8.9) is obtained again.

An alternative starting point to (8.8) is the corresponding equation for the total distribution function

$$f^{(N)} = \left(\frac{1}{Zh^{3N}}\right) e^{-\mathcal{H}/kT} \tag{8.13}$$

where $\mathcal{H}$ is the sum of $\mathcal{U}$ and the molecular kinetic energies (not a heat content) for a given distribution of molecular positions and momenta. It is convenient to define the constant of proportionality with the factor of $(1/h^{3N})$ where h is Planck's constant. A set of integrations similar to (8.10)–(8.12) leads to

$$Z = \frac{1}{h^{3N}N!} \int \cdots \int e^{-\mathcal{H}/kT} \, d\mathbf{r}_1 \cdots d\mathbf{r}_N \, d\mathbf{p}_1 \cdots d\mathbf{p}_N \tag{8.14}$$

The integration over the momenta may be made at once and leads to

$$Z = \left(\frac{2\pi m k T}{h^2}\right)^{3N/2} Q \qquad (8.15)$$

$$= (\psi^t/V)^N Q \qquad (8.16)$$

where ψ^t is the molecular translational partition function. The functions Z and Q are called, respectively, the *phase integral* (or partition function) and the *configuration integral* of the assembly.

The introduction of Planck's constant into (8.13) makes the classical translational partition function ψ^t into the limiting form of the quantal partition function at high temperatures. It also makes Z and ψ^t dimensionless quantities that may be properly called partition functions (or sums-over-states), but Q and (ψ^t/V) are not dimensionless. The factorization of (8.16) is not, therefore, the expression of one partition function as the product of two simpler ones, if such a function is defined as a sum-over-states, but is nevertheless the most common of the several possible ways of factorizing Z. The total and configurational thermodynamic functions defined empirically in Section 2.6 are, respectively, the thermodynamic properties associated with Z and Q.

The relation of Q to the configurational thermodynamic functions is obtained most simply through the configurational energy U'. This is the average value of the intermolecular energy in an assembly of fixed number, volume and temperature. If $\mathscr{U}$ is the intermolecular energy of any arbitrary configuration of the molecules and $n^{(N)}$ the probability of that configuration, then U', the average value of $\mathscr{U}$, is given by

$$U' = \overline{\mathscr{U}} = \frac{1}{N!} \int \ldots \int \mathscr{U} n^{(N)} \, d\mathbf{r}_1 \ldots d\mathbf{r}_N \qquad (8.17)$$

$$= \frac{1}{QN!} \int \ldots \int \mathscr{U} e^{-\mathscr{U}/kT} \, d\mathbf{r}_1 \ldots d\mathbf{r}_N \qquad (8.18)$$

The factor of $(1/N!)$ is a normalization factor to prevent the repeated counting of essentially the same configuration of the indistinguishable molecules, as $d\mathbf{r}_1$, etc. occupy all possible positions in the volume V. Eqn. (8.18) is the usual equation for obtaining the average value of any function such as $\mathscr{U}$ in a canonical ensemble. The configurational free energy, A', is related to U' by the equation of classical thermodynamics

$$(\partial/\partial T)_V(A'/T) = -U'/T^2 \qquad (8.19)$$

and so, by integration,

$$A' = -T \int \left[\frac{1}{T^2 N!} \int \ldots \int \mathcal{U} n^{(N)} \, d\mathbf{r}_1 \ldots d\mathbf{r}_N \right] dT \qquad (8.20)$$

$$= -kT \int \left[\frac{1}{QN!} \int \ldots \int \frac{\mathcal{U}}{kT^2} e^{-\mathcal{U}/kT} \, d\mathbf{r}_1 \ldots d\mathbf{r}_N \right] dT \qquad (8.21)$$

$$= -kT \int \left(\frac{\partial \ln Q}{\partial T} \right)_V dT \qquad (8.22)$$

$$= -kT \ln Q \qquad (8.23)$$

The constant of integration must be zero to satisfy the third law of thermodynamics, and it is shown below that A' cannot contain an additional term which is a function only of the volume if $(\partial A'/\partial V)_T$ is to approach $(-p)$ for a perfect gas as $\mathcal{U}$ approaches zero.

Eqn. (8.12), (8.18) and (8.23) are the basis of statistical theories of fluids. They relate the bulk properties A' and U' to the intermolecular energy $\mathcal{U}(\mathbf{r}_1 \ldots \mathbf{r}_N)$ of each molecular configuration. Eqn. (8.18) may be greatly simplified if the intermolecular energy is a sum of pair potentials, so that the contribution to $\mathcal{U}$ of a pair of molecules at $\mathbf{r}_1$ and $\mathbf{r}_2$ is an energy $u(r_{12})$ which is a function only of r_{12}, the scalar distance between $\mathbf{r}_1$ and $\mathbf{r}_2$. The energy may now be written

$$\mathcal{U} = \tfrac{1}{2} \sum_{i,j \neq} \sum u(r_{ij}) = \sum_{i>j} \sum u(r_{ij}) \qquad (8.24)$$

(both forms of summation are in common use), and the average configuration energy becomes

$$U' = \overline{\mathcal{U}} = \tfrac{1}{2} \iint u(r_{12}) n^{(2)}(\mathbf{r}_1, \mathbf{r}_2) \, d\mathbf{r}_1 \, d\mathbf{r}_2 \qquad (8.25)$$

The factor of $(\tfrac{1}{2})$ is again a normalizing factor to prevent counting twice the contribution from a given pair of volume elements—once when the vector $\mathbf{r}_1$ lies in the first and $\mathbf{r}_2$ in the second, and again when the positions are reversed. If molecule 1 is chosen as the origin of the co-ordinate system for $\mathbf{r}_2$, then the integrand is independent of the position of molecule 1. The integration over $d\mathbf{r}_1$ can, therefore, be made at once to give the volume V and

$$U' = \frac{V}{2} \int u(\mathbf{r}_2) n^{(2)}(0, \mathbf{r}_2) \, d\mathbf{r}_2 \qquad (8.26)$$

$$= \frac{V}{2} \int_0^\infty u(r) n^{(2)}(r) 4\pi r^2 \, dr \qquad (8.27)$$

where $n^{(2)}(r)$ is the probability of finding molecules simultaneously at two given points separated by a distance r. (This is not the same as the probability that any two given molecules should be distant r from each other.) The pair distribution function is, therefore, the most important of the distribution functions and it is often convenient to introduce a normalized pair function, or a *radial distribution function* $g(r)$, which approaches unity for large values of r. This is related to $n^{(2)}$ by

$$n^{(2)}(\mathbf{r}_1, \mathbf{r}_2) = n^{(1)}(\mathbf{r}_1)n^{(1)}(\mathbf{r}_2)g[\mathbf{r}_1, (\mathbf{r}_2 - \mathbf{r}_1)] \qquad (8.28)$$

which reduces in an isotropic fluid to

$$n^{(2)}(r) = n^2 g(r) \qquad (8.29)$$

The radial distribution function is unity for all values of r in a perfect gas.

The total free energy, A, is related to Z by an equation analogous to (8.23)

$$A = A_{\text{mol}} + A' = -kT \ln Z \qquad (8.30)$$

$$A_{\text{mol}} = -kT \ln (\psi^t/V)^N \qquad (8.31)$$

Henceforth the prime will be dropped from A, U, etc. as only configurational thermodynamic properties are needed for the determination of the equation of state, etc. of liquids and mixtures. The pressure is itself a configurational property, since (ψ^t/V) and so A_{mol} are independent of the volume. It may be related to the pair distribution function by an equation similar to (8.27) for an assembly of pair potentials. Consider[7] a fluid confined to a cube of side l, a corner of which is the origin of the co-ordinate system, and let

$$\mathbf{r}_i = \mathbf{t}_i l \qquad (8.32)$$

where $\mathbf{t}_i$ is a vector whose length is between 0 and 1

$$p = -\left(\frac{\partial A}{\partial V}\right)_T = \frac{kT}{Q}\left(\frac{\partial Q}{\partial V}\right)_T = \frac{kT}{3l^2 Q}\left(\frac{\partial Q}{\partial l}\right)_T \qquad (8.33)$$

where

$$Q = \frac{l^{3N}}{N!}\int\cdots\int \exp\left[-\tfrac{1}{2}\sum_{i,j\neq}\sum u(lt_{12})/kT\right]\mathrm{d}\mathbf{t}_1\ldots\mathrm{d}\mathbf{t}_N \qquad (8.34)$$

where t_{12} is the scalar distance between $\mathbf{t}_1$ and $\mathbf{t}_2$, and

$$\left(\frac{\partial Q}{\partial l}\right) =$$

$$\frac{3NQ}{l} - \frac{l^{3N}}{(N-2)!}\int\cdots\int\left[\frac{\mathrm{d}u(lt_{12})}{\mathrm{d}(lt_{12})}\cdot\frac{t_{12}}{2kT}\right]e^{-\mathscr{U}/kT}\mathrm{d}\mathbf{t}_1\ldots\mathrm{d}\mathbf{t}_N \qquad (8.35)$$

as there are $N(N-1)$ terms in the product of exponential terms in (8.34) and, on differentiation, each gives a term of the kind shown in (8.35). The introduction of $n^{(2)}$ from (8.10) and a change of the variables leads to

$$\left(\frac{\partial Q}{\partial l}\right) = \frac{3NQ}{l} - \frac{Q}{2l}\iint\left[\frac{\mathrm{d}u(r)}{\mathrm{d}r}\cdot\frac{r}{kT}\right]n^{(2)}(\mathbf{r}_1, \mathbf{r}_2)\,\mathrm{d}\mathbf{r}_1\,\mathrm{d}\mathbf{r}_2 \quad (8.36)$$

$$= \frac{3NQ}{l} - \frac{Ql^2}{2kT}\int_0^\infty r\frac{\mathrm{d}u(r)}{\mathrm{d}r}\,n^{(2)}(r)4\pi r^2\,\mathrm{d}r \quad (8.37)$$

Hence

$$p = \frac{NkT}{V} - \tfrac{1}{6}\int_0^\infty v(r)n^{(2)}(r)4\pi r^2\,\mathrm{d}r \quad (8.38)$$

where

$$v(r) = r(\mathrm{d}u(r)/\mathrm{d}r) \quad (8.39)$$

is the *intermolecular virial function*. It is related to a virial function, $\mathscr{V}$, of any arbitrary configuration by

$$\mathscr{V} = -\tfrac{1}{3}\sum_{i>j}\sum v(r_{ij}) \quad (8.40)$$

Hence, by (8.38), the average value in a canonical ensemble is

$$\overline{\mathscr{V}} = pV - NkT \quad (8.41)$$

The fluctuations of $\mathscr{U}$ and $\mathscr{V}$ about their mean values $\overline{\mathscr{U}}$ and $\overline{\mathscr{V}}$ are of importance in both the theory of liquids and of mixtures. The mean square of the fluctuations of, say, $\mathscr{U}$, is given by

$$\overline{(\mathscr{U} - \overline{\mathscr{U}})^2} = \overline{\mathscr{U}^2} - 2(\overline{\mathscr{U}\overline{\mathscr{U}}}) + (\overline{\mathscr{U}})^2 \quad (8.42)$$

$$= \overline{\mathscr{U}^2} - 2[(\overline{\mathscr{U} - \overline{\mathscr{U}}})\overline{\mathscr{U}} + (\overline{\mathscr{U}})^2] + (\overline{\mathscr{U}})^2 \quad (8.43)$$

$$= \overline{\mathscr{U}^2} - (\overline{\mathscr{U}})^2 \quad (8.44)$$

as the mean value of $(\mathscr{U} - \overline{\mathscr{U}})$ is, by definition, zero.

Similarly

$$\overline{(\mathscr{V} - \overline{\mathscr{V}})^2} = \overline{\mathscr{V}^2} - (\overline{\mathscr{V}})^2 \quad (8.45)$$

and the cross-term

$$\overline{(\mathscr{U} - \overline{\mathscr{U}})(\mathscr{V} - \overline{\mathscr{V}})} = \overline{\mathscr{U}\mathscr{V}} - \overline{\mathscr{U}}\overline{\mathscr{V}} \quad (8.46)$$

These averages are taken over the canonical ensemble, as in (8.18). Now from (8.12) and (8.18)

$$kT^2(\partial \ln Q/\partial T)_V = \overline{\mathscr{U}} \quad (8.47)$$

$$(kT^2)^2(\partial^2 \ln Q/\partial T^2)_V = \overline{\mathscr{U}^2} - 2kT\overline{\mathscr{U}} \quad (8.48)$$

These equations can be solved to give the right-hand side of (8.44), and so from the relation of Q to A, (8.23),

$$\overline{(\mathscr{U} - \overline{\mathscr{U}})^2} = kT(TC_V) \tag{8.49}$$

where C_V is the configurational heat capacity at constant volume.

The differentiation of Q with respect to volume has been made in (8.35)–(8.37)

$$kTV(\partial \ln Q/\partial V)_T = pV = NkT + \overline{\mathscr{V}} \tag{8.50}$$

Differentiation of the second part of this equation with respect to temperature (at constant volume) gives

$$V(\partial p/\partial T)_V = Nk + (\overline{\mathscr{U}\mathscr{V}} - \overline{\mathscr{U}}\overline{\mathscr{V}})/kT^2 \tag{8.51}$$

and so

$$\overline{(\mathscr{U} - \overline{\mathscr{U}})(\mathscr{V} - \overline{\mathscr{V}})} = kT(TV\gamma_V - NkT) \tag{8.52}$$

Thus two of the fluctuations, (8.44) and (8.46), can be expressed in terms of experimentally accessible functions. The third, (8.45), cannot be so expressed, for differentiation of the second part of (8.50) with respect to volume (at constant temperature) gives

$$p + V\left(\frac{\partial p}{\partial V}\right)_T = \frac{1}{kTV}[\overline{\mathscr{V}^2} - (\overline{\mathscr{V}})^2 - \overline{\mathscr{W}}kT] \tag{8.53}$$

where

$$\mathscr{W} = \tfrac{1}{9}\sum_{i>j}\sum w(r_{ij}) \tag{8.54}$$

$$w(r) = r(\mathrm{d}v(r)/\mathrm{d}r) = r(\mathrm{d}u(r)/\mathrm{d}r) + r^2(\mathrm{d}^2u(r)/\mathrm{d}r^2) \tag{8.55}$$

The functions $w(r)$ and $\mathscr{W}$ are related to the second derivative of the potential function $u(r)$ but not directly to any experimental quantity in the way that the first derivative is related to the pressure by (8.38). If, however, $u(r)$ is a Lennard-Jones (n, m) potential, then $u(r)$, $v(r)$ and $w(r)$ are all of the same functional form and related by the identity[8]

$$w(r) + (n + m)v(r) + nmu(r) = 0 \tag{8.56}$$

and so, summing over all molecules,

$$\mathscr{W} - [(n + m)/3]\mathscr{V} + (nm/9)\mathscr{U} = 0 \tag{8.57}$$

or

$$\overline{\mathscr{W}} = [(n + m)/3](pV - NkT) - (nm/9)U \tag{8.58}$$

Hence

$$\overline{(\mathscr{V} - \overline{\mathscr{V}})^2} =$$
$$kT\left[-\frac{nm}{9}U + \left(\frac{n + m + 3}{3}\right)pV - \left(\frac{n + m}{3}\right)NkT - \frac{V}{\beta_T}\right] \tag{8.59}$$

255

The size of these fluctuations may be judged from their values in one mole of liquid argon at its normal boiling point of 87·29 K. From *Tables 2.5* and *2.12*, and with the assumption of a (12,6) potential

$$\overline{(\mathscr{U} - \overline{\mathscr{U}})^2}/kT = 600 \text{ J mol}^{-1}$$

$$\overline{(\mathscr{U} - \overline{\mathscr{U}})(\mathscr{V} - \overline{\mathscr{V}})}/kT = 4350 \text{ J mol}^{-1}$$

$$\overline{(\mathscr{V} - \overline{\mathscr{V}})^2}/kT = 29\,500 \text{ J mol}^{-1}$$

Schwarz's inequality requires that the product of the first and third of these fluctuations is greater than the square of the second. These figures fail to satisfy the inequality—a failure which shows the inaccuracy of the (12,6) potential. This point is discussed in Chapter 7 where it is mentioned that an experimental knowledge of the isotopic separation factor between liquid and vapour provides an approximate value for the mean square fluctuation of $\mathscr{V}$.

The relatively large size of the last fluctuation plays an important part in the theory of mixtures of molecules of different sizes. At high temperatures this order of sizes is changed. The fluctuation in $\mathscr{U}$ increases to maximum at the critical point, the cross-term and the fluctuation in $\mathscr{V}$ fall.

These fluctuations may be written in terms of a sum of *molecular fluctuation integrals* for an assembly of pair potentials[8]

$$\overline{(\mathscr{U} - \overline{\mathscr{U}})^2} = \overline{\left[\sum_{i>j}\sum (u_{ij} - \bar{u})\right]^2} \tag{8.60}$$

where $\bar{u}$ is the average value of a pair potential in the assembly. That is,

$$U = \tfrac{1}{2}N(N - 1)\bar{u} \tag{8.61}$$

Now the terms on the right-hand side of (8.60) can be divided into three types; first $(u_{ij})^2$, second $(u_{ij})(u_{ik})$, and third $(u_{ij})(u_{kl})$, where i, j, k and l denote different molecules. The total number of terms is $N^2(N - 1)^2/4$, as there are $N(N - 1)/2$ pair potentials in an assembly of N molecules. These terms may be classified as

Type	No. of terms in sum
$(u_{ij})^2$	$\tfrac{1}{2}[N!/(N - 2)!]$
$(u_{ij})(u_{ik})$	$[N!/(N - 3)!]$
$(u_{ij})(u_{kl})$	$\tfrac{1}{4}[N!/(N - 4)!]$

(Only half these numbers of terms are physically distinct in the second and third types.) The average on the right-hand side of

(8.60) can now be written as

$$\overline{(\mathscr{U} - \overline{\mathscr{U}})^2} = \frac{1}{QN!} \int \cdots \int \left[\sum_i \sum_{j} (u_{ij} - \bar{u}) \right]^2 e^{-\mathscr{U}/kT} d\mathbf{r}_1 \ldots d\mathbf{r}_N \quad (8.62)$$

$$= -kT[A_{ff}^{(2)} + A_{ff}^{(3)} + A_{ff}^{(4)}] = -kTA_{ff} \quad (8.63)$$

where

$$A_{ff}^{(2)} = -\frac{1}{2kT} \sum_{i,j \neq} \overline{(u_{ij} - \bar{u})^2} \quad (8.64)$$

$$= -\frac{1}{2kT} \iint (u_{12} - \bar{u})^2 n^{(2)}(\mathbf{r}_1, \mathbf{r}_2) \, d\mathbf{r}_1 \, d\mathbf{r}_2 \quad (8.65)$$

$$A_{ff}^{(3)} = -\frac{1}{kT} \sum_{i,j,k \neq} \overline{(u_{ij} - \bar{u})(u_{ik} - \bar{u})} \quad (8.66)$$

$$= -\frac{1}{kT} \int \cdots \int (u_{12} - \bar{u})(u_{13} - \bar{u})$$
$$\times n^{(3)}(\mathbf{r}_1, \mathbf{r}_2, \mathbf{r}_3) \, d\mathbf{r}_1 \, d\mathbf{r}_2 \, d\mathbf{r}_3 \quad (8.67)$$

$$A_{ff}^{(4)} = -\frac{1}{4kT} \sum_{i,j,k,l \neq} \overline{(u_{ij} - \bar{u})(u_{kl} - \bar{u})} \quad (8.68)$$

$$= -\frac{1}{4kT} \int \cdots \int (u_{12} - \bar{u})(u_{34} - \bar{u})$$
$$\times n^{(4)}(\mathbf{r}_1, \mathbf{r}_2, \mathbf{r}_3, \mathbf{r}_4) \, d\mathbf{r}_1 \, d\mathbf{r}_2 \, d\mathbf{r}_3 \, d\mathbf{r}_4 \quad (8.69)$$

where $A_{ff}^{(2)}$, etc. are the molecular fluctuation integrals. (The reason for this choice of subscript notation is made clear in Section 9.3 and in the Appendix.) Similarly

$$\overline{(\mathscr{U} - \overline{\mathscr{U}})(\mathscr{V} - \overline{\mathscr{V}})} = -kT(A_{fk}^{(2)} + A_{fk}^{(3)} + A_{fk}^{(4)}) = -kTA_{fk} \quad (8.70)$$

$$\overline{(\mathscr{V} - \overline{\mathscr{V}})^2} = -kT(A_{kk}^{(2)} + A_{kk}^{(3)} + A_{kk}^{(4)}) = -kTA_{kk} \quad (8.71)$$

where

$$A_{fk}^{(2)} = \frac{1}{2kT} \sum_{i,j \neq} \tfrac{1}{3}\overline{(u_{ij} - \bar{u})(v_{ij} - \bar{v})} \quad (8.72)$$

$$= \frac{1}{6kT} \iint (u_{12} - \bar{u})(v_{12} - \bar{v})n^{(2)}(\mathbf{r}_1, \mathbf{r}_2) \, d\mathbf{r}_1 \, d\mathbf{r}_2 \quad (8.73)$$

$$A_{fk}^{(3)} = \frac{1}{kT} \sum_{i,j,k \neq} \tfrac{1}{3}\overline{(u_{ij} - \bar{u})(v_{ik} - \bar{v})} \quad (8.74)$$

$$= \frac{1}{3kT} \int \cdots \int (u_{12} - \bar{u})(v_{12} - \bar{v})n^{(3)}(\mathbf{r}_1, \mathbf{r}_2, \mathbf{r}_3) \, d\mathbf{r}_1 \, d\mathbf{r}_2 \, d\mathbf{r}_3 \quad (8.75)$$

$$A_{fk}^{(4)} = \frac{1}{4kT} \sum_{i,j,k,l \neq} \frac{1}{3} \overline{(u_{ij} - \bar{u})(v_{kl} - \bar{v})} \tag{8.76}$$

$$= \frac{1}{12kT} \int \cdots \int (u_{12} - \bar{u})(v_{34} - \bar{v})$$
$$\times n^{(4)}(\mathbf{r}_1, \mathbf{r}_2, \mathbf{r}_3, \mathbf{r}_4) \, d\mathbf{r}_1 \, d\mathbf{r}_2 \, d\mathbf{r}_3 \, d\mathbf{r}_4 \tag{8.77}$$

and

$$A_{kk}^{(2)} = - \frac{1}{2kT} \sum_{i,j \neq} \frac{1}{9} \overline{(v_{ij} - \bar{v})^2} \tag{8.78}$$

$$= - \frac{1}{18kT} \iint (v_{12} - \bar{v})^2 n^{(2)}(\mathbf{r}_1, \mathbf{r}_2) \, d\mathbf{r}_1 \, d\mathbf{r}_2 \tag{8.79}$$

$$A_{kk}^{(3)} = - \frac{1}{kT} \sum_{i,j,k \neq} \frac{1}{9} \overline{(v_{ij} - \bar{v})(v_{ik} - \bar{v})} \tag{8.80}$$

$$= - \frac{1}{9kT} \int \cdots \int (v_{12} - \bar{v})(v_{13} - \bar{v}) n^{(3)}(\mathbf{r}_1, \mathbf{r}_2, \mathbf{r}_3) \, d\mathbf{r}_1 \, d\mathbf{r}_2 \, d\mathbf{r}_3 \tag{8.81}$$

$$A_{kk}^{(4)} = - \frac{1}{4kT} \sum_{i,j,k,l \neq} \frac{1}{9} \overline{(v_{ij} - \bar{v})(v_{kl} - \bar{v})} \tag{8.82}$$

$$= - \frac{1}{36kT} \int \cdots \int (v_{12} - \bar{v})(v_{34} - \bar{v})$$
$$\times n^{(4)}(\mathbf{r}_1, \mathbf{r}_2, \mathbf{r}_3, \mathbf{r}_4) \, d\mathbf{r}_1 \, d\mathbf{r}_2 \, d\mathbf{r}_3 \, d\mathbf{r}_4 \tag{8.83}$$

These fluctuation integrals cannot be related to any experimental quantity or, in general, to each other. However, there is one useful relation between the pair fluctuation integrals for an assembly of Lennard-Jones $(n, n/2)$ molecules[8]

$$(nu_{ij} + v_{ij})^2 = -n\epsilon(nu_{ij} + 2v_{ij}) \tag{8.84}$$

Summing and taking average values gives

$$\sum_{i>j} (n^2 \overline{u_{ij}^2} + 2n\overline{u_{ij}v_{ij}} + \overline{v_{ij}^2}) = -n\epsilon \sum_{i>j} (n\overline{u_{ij}} + 2\overline{v_{ij}}) \tag{8.85}$$

or

$$n^2 A_{ff}^{(2)} - 6n A_{fk}^{(2)} + 9 A_{kk}^{(2)} = - \frac{n\epsilon}{kT} (n\overline{\mathscr{U}} - 6\overline{\mathscr{V}}) \tag{8.86}$$

as terms with $(\bar{u})^2$ are of the order of $(1/N)$ compared with the terms with $(\overline{u_{ij}^2})$, (8.61). The right-hand side of (8.86) is experimentally accessible and so provides a check on values of the pair fluctuation integrals given by any approximate theory of liquids. Further properties of these integrals are collected in the Appendix.

8.3 MOLECULAR CORRELATION FUNCTIONS

The functions introduced in the last Section are *distribution functions*, that is, they describe the probability of certain molecular distributions, in particular that of pairs of molecules. However, it is often more convenient to work instead with the closely related *correlation functions* which measure the departure of the distributions from their random values. These can again be defined for pairs, triplets and higher groups of molecules but, for simplicity, only the most important of them—the pair functions—are described here.

The *total correlation function*, $h(r)$, is the difference between the distribution function $g(r)$ and its random value of unity. That is, $h(r)$ is defined by

$$h(r) = g(r) - 1 \tag{8.87}$$

This function is called the total function to distinguish it from the *direct correlation function*, $c(r)$, which was introduced by Ornstein and Zernike[3,9] in 1914. They deduced, correctly, that $h(r)$ is generally of longer range than $u(r)$ and sought, therefore, a correlation function which they hoped would have a range comparable with that of $u(r)$. They defined $c(r)$ by the integral equation

$$h(r_{12}) = c(r_{12}) + n \int c(r_{13}) h(r_{23}) \, d\mathbf{r}_3 \tag{8.88}$$

total = direct + indirect correlation function

The physical meaning of this definition is seen most readily by repeatedly replacing $h(r)$ by $[c(r) + \text{integral}]$ within the integral of (8.88). This gives

$$h(r_{12}) = c(r_{12}) + n \int c(r_{13}) c(r_{32}) \, d\mathbf{r}_3$$

$$+ n^2 \iint c(r_{13}) c(r_{34}) c(r_{42}) \, d\mathbf{r}_3 \, d\mathbf{r}_4 + \ldots \tag{8.89}$$

Thus the total function, $h(r_{12})$, is decomposed into a correlation of 1 and 2, both directly, through $c(r_{12})$, and indirectly, through all possible chains of direct correlation within the fluid.

It is convenient also to define three other functions which are useful in the description of molecular correlations:

$$f(r) = \exp\left[-u(r)/kT\right] - 1 \tag{8.90}$$

$$y(r) = g(r) \exp\left[u(r)/kT\right] = [1 + h(r)][1 + f(r)]^{-1} \tag{8.91}$$

$$\psi(r) = -kT \ln g(r) = u(r) - kT \ln y(r) \tag{8.92}$$

In the dilute gas (that is, at the level of the second virial coefficient), it is readily shown that both $h(r)$ and $c(r)$ reduce to $f(r)$, that $y(r)$ is unity and that $\psi(r)$ is equal to $u(r)$. The first of these three functions is sometimes called *Mayer's f-function*, the last the *potential of average force*. The usefulness of the second function, $y(r)$, is that it remains a continuous function of r even when $u(r)$, and hence $g(r)$, are discontinuous.

The *pressure*, or *virial equation* (8.38), can be rewritten in terms of $y(r)$ and $f'(r)$, the derivative of $f(r)$

$$\frac{p}{nkT} = 1 + \tfrac{1}{6}n \int rf'(r)y(r) \, \mathbf{dr} \tag{8.93}$$

The total correlation function $h(r)$ is related to the compressibility by the simple equation*

$$kT\left(\frac{\partial n}{\partial p}\right)_T = 1 + n\int h(r) \, \mathbf{dr} \tag{8.94}$$

A similar equation for $c(r)$ can be obtained by integrating (8.88) over $\mathbf{dr_2}$

$$\int h(r) \, \mathbf{dr} = \int c(r) \, \mathbf{dr} + n\int c(r) \, \mathbf{dr} \int h(r) \, \mathbf{dr} \tag{8.95}$$

Substitution into (8.94) now gives

$$\frac{1}{kT}\left(\frac{\partial p}{\partial n}\right)_T = 1 - n\int c(r) \, \mathbf{dr} \tag{8.96}$$

The two forms of the *compressibility equation*, (8.94) and (8.96), are entirely equivalent and it is a matter of convenience which is used. Generally the second is preferred, since it yields, on integration, p as a function of n. The constant of integration is fixed by using the perfect-gas limit as a boundary condition. The pressure so obtained agrees with that from (8.93) if $c(r)$ and $y(r)$ are both exact and if $\mathscr{U}$ is a sum of pair potentials. There is a difference of pressure if either condition is broken, and this is a useful test of the consistency of any approximations to $c(r)$ and $y(r)$ that may be obtained from the theories discussed below.

The distribution and correlation functions, and hence the thermo-dynamic properties, can be written as integrals over sums of products of the functions f_{ij}. This is seen from (8.10)–(8.12) by replacing $\mathscr{U}$

---

* This is the only equation in this book that requires the use of the grand-canonical ensemble for its derivation, and so, for brevity, the enquiring reader is referred to a textbook on statistical mechanics.

by the sum of u_{ij} (8.24) and substituting f_{ij} for u_{ij} from (8.90)

$$\exp\left(-\mathcal{U}/kT\right) = \prod_{i>j}\prod \exp\left(-u_{ij}/kT\right) = \prod_{i>j}\prod \left(1+f_{ij}\right) \quad (8.97)$$

The right-hand side can be multiplied out to give sums of products of the f_{ij}, and it is now trivial, in expressions such as (8.10)–(8.12), to integrate over all molecules not represented in a particular product. A typical term in Q is $f_{12}f_{13}f_{23}$, and here the integration over $d\mathbf{r}_4 \ldots d\mathbf{r}_N$ and [by the argument below (8.12)] over $d\mathbf{r}_1$ can be made at once to give a factor of V^{N-2}. In this way Q, $g(r)$, $c(r)$, etc. can be written as expansions in powers of the number density, n.

The corresponding expansion of the pressure, that is the *virial equation of state* [not to be confused with (8.38)], and functions derived from it, are useful only in the dilute or moderately dense gas. The expansions do converge at the densities of liquids[10]. However, a knowledge of the structure of the expansions of both correlation and thermodynamic functions is useful in the theory of dense fluids, and so is summarized here. The combinatorial algebra that arises from the substitution of (8.97) in numerator and denominator of (8.10) is surprisingly formidable but can be found in the appropriate reviews[1–4,11].

The expansion of $n^{(2)}$, that is of g or h, is quoted below without derivation, and this one result is then used to generate the expansions of other functions, such as y and c. However, first it is necessary to define some terms and symbols.

Graph A graph is the pictorial representation of an integral whose integrand is a product of f_{ij} functions, each of which is represented by a bond. If i and j remain fixed during the integration, they are called *root points* and are denoted by open circles. If the positions of i and j are the variables of the integral, then they are called *field points* and are denoted by filled circles. Thus

$$\underset{1}{\circ}\!\!-\!\!\!-\!\!\underset{2}{\circ} \; = f_{12}$$

$$\overset{3}{\bullet} \diagup\diagdown \underset{1 \quad\; 2}{\circ \qquad \circ} \; = \int f_{13}f_{23}\,d\mathbf{r}_3$$

In the graphs that express h_{12}, y_{12} and c_{12}, the root points are molecules 1 and 2.

261

Articulation point

If a graph that is 'cut' at a field point falls into two or more parts, at least one of which contains no root points, then that field point is called an articulation point. Thus 3 is an articulation point in

All graphs with articulation points are excluded (by definition) from the sets defined below.

Connected graph

In a connected graph all field points are linked, directly or through others to all root points.

Bridge point

A bridge point (or node) is a field point through which all paths from root point 1 to root point 2 have to pass, e.g. 3 in

Chain

A graph with at least one bridge point, and hence with no direct f_{12} bond.

Bundle

A graph with independent (or parallel) routes from 1 to 2, e.g.

 and

Clearly it has no bridge points.

Elementary graph

A connected graph which is neither a chain nor a bundle, e.g.

An elementary graph cannot have a direct f_{12} bond; the addition of such a bond to an elementary graph turns it into a bundle.

262

Summation   Graphs are added to form sets, and in doing this
convention   each graph is first multiplied by n raised to a power
equal to the number of field points, and divided
by the symmetry number of the set of field points.

The starting point of the graphical expansions is the statement

$$h_{12} \equiv \text{all connected graphs} \qquad (8.98)$$

where it is understood, here and later, that 1 and 2 are the root
points and that graphs with articulation points are excluded. This
expansion is written explicitly

$$\qquad (8.99)$$

From (8.98) we have

$$y_{12} - 1 \equiv \text{all connected graphs without } f_{12} \text{ bonds} \qquad (8.100)$$

This is most readily seen to be true by showing that (8.100) implies
(8.99). The set of 'all connected graphs' can be obtained from
(8.100) by adding the following three sets:

$$\text{all connected graphs} \equiv f_{12} + (y_{12} - 1) + f_{12}(y_{12} - 1)$$
$$= (1 + f_{12})y_{12} - 1 \qquad (8.101)$$

which, by (8.91), is h_{12}. It is this absence of f_{12} bonds from y_{12} that
leads to its important property of continuity, even for potentials for
which f is discontinuous.

From (8.98) and the definitions above it follows that h_{12} comprises
f_{12} and all chains, bundles and elementary graphs. Hence, from
(8.89), c_{12} contains f_{12}, the bundles and elementary graphs, since
all higher terms in this equation have bridge points at molecule 3,
molecules 3 and 4, etc. Furthermore, these higher terms contain *all*
the chains, since each connected graph must appear once, and once

only, and so cannot be present both in c_{12} and in the higher terms, which have bridge points at all possible field points $3 \ldots N$. Hence

$$c_{12} \equiv \text{all connected graphs without bridge points} \qquad (8.102)$$

Therefore

$$h_{12} - c_{12} \equiv \text{all chains} \qquad (8.103)$$

Let e_{12} be the set of all elementary graphs. Then

$$[\exp (h_{12} - c_{12} + e_{12}) - 1]$$

is the set that includes all chains, all elementary graphs and all bundles of chains and elementary graphs. The factorial terms in the expansion of the exponential are the appropriate symmetry numbers of the graphs in these bundles. This set is, therefore, $(y_{12} - 1)$. That is

$$y_{12} = \exp (h_{12} - c_{12} + e_{12}) \qquad (8.104)$$

This equation can be solved for c to give the useful result

$$c_{12} = h_{12} - \ln y_{12} + e_{12} \qquad (8.105)$$

Hence the potential of average force is free from bundles since, from (8.92)

$$(u_{12} - \psi_{12})/kT = \ln y_{12} = (h_{12} - c_{12}) + e_{12}$$
$$\equiv \text{all chains and elementary graphs} \qquad (8.106)$$

If a further set is defined by

$$d_{12} \equiv \text{all connected graphs free from } f_{12} \text{ bonds}$$
$$\text{and without bridge points}$$
$$= (y_{12} - 1) - (h_{12} - c_{12}) \qquad (8.107)$$

then it follows from (8.102) that d is a sub-set of c. Furthermore, the whole of c can be obtained by adding to d all the graphs in fy, since this set and d are mutually exclusive and since all graphs in y that have bridge points lose them on inserting the f bond. Hence, from this argument, or directly from (8.105) and (8.107)

$$c_{12} = f_{12} y_{12} + d_{12} \qquad (8.108)$$

The direct correlation function was defined by (8.88)—an integral equation which relates c to h, and so to g and y. Eqn. (8.105) and (8.108) are two further relations between c and y, but their usefulness is diminished by the presence on the right-hand sides of the sets of graphs e_{12} and d_{12}. Nevertheless, they are exact and potentially useful consequences of the Ornstein–Zernike equation to which we return in Section 8.6.

These and the earlier equations obtained so far in this Chapter are the formal preliminaries to any discussion of the theory of fluids. They show that a complete knowledge of the thermodynamic properties of a fluid can be obtained from a knowledge of Q or, if the system has only pair potentials, of $h(r)$ or $c(r)$ as functions of N, V and T. The equations are not themselves a useful theory of fluids, since they do not enable us to determine these functions. It is true that (8.10) and (8.12) provide, in principle, a direct method of determining Q and all $n^{(h)}$, but it has been known for many years that this direct attack on the problem is prohibitively difficult. The explicit calculation of $h(r)$ and $c(r)$ is, therefore, deferred to Section 8.6, and the next two Sections are an account of some useful comparisons of theory and experiment which can be made without these calculations.

8.4 THE PRINCIPLE OF CORRESPONDING STATES

The difficulties of the direct calculation of the configuration integral for both pure substances and for mixtures have led many to search for ways of obtaining results of practical use from the integral by means of manipulations that fall far short of complete evaluation. The most simple and useful of these is the statistical derivation of the principle of corresponding states[12].

Consider N molecules each of two substances, 1 and 2, whose intermolecular potentials are related by the equations

$$u_{11}(r) = \epsilon_{11}F(\sigma_{11}/r) \tag{8.109}$$

$$u_{22}(r) = \epsilon_{22}F(\sigma_{22}/r) \tag{8.110}$$

where ϵ and σ are an energy and a distance and F denotes some function common to both species. (Lennard-Jones potentials with the same values of n and m for both substances are examples of potentials that are related by equations of this type.) Let the N molecules of the first substance be confined to a volume V at a temperature T, and those of the second to a volume $(V\sigma_{22}^3/\sigma_{11}^3)$ at a temperature $(T\epsilon_{22}/\epsilon_{11})$. If the two containing vessels have the same shape, then their linear dimensions are in the ratio $(\sigma_{11}/\sigma_{22})$. Hence for each configuration of the first assembly there is a corresponding configuration for the second, such that

$$\frac{\mathscr{U}_1[\ldots \mathbf{r}_i \ldots]}{kT} = \frac{\mathscr{U}_2[\ldots \mathbf{r}_i(\sigma_{22}/\sigma_{11}) \ldots]}{k(T\epsilon_{22}/\epsilon_{11})} \tag{8.111}$$

and so, from (8.12)

$$Q_1(V, T) = (\sigma_{22}/\sigma_{11})^{-3N} Q_2(V\sigma_{22}^3/\sigma_{11}^3, T\epsilon_{22}/\epsilon_{11}) \tag{8.112}$$

Thus the configuration integral Q_1 is calculable from a knowledge of Q_2 as a function of V and T. This equation may be written a little more neatly by introducing dimensionless ratios of the characteristic energies, f, and of the characteristic distances, g. The potential of either substance may then be written in the common form

$$u_{\alpha\alpha}(r) = f_{\alpha\alpha}u_{00}(r/g_{\alpha\alpha}) \tag{8.113}$$

where

$$f_{\alpha\alpha} = \epsilon_{\alpha\alpha}/\epsilon_{00}, \qquad g_{\alpha\alpha} = \sigma_{\alpha\alpha}/\sigma_{00} \tag{8.114}$$

and u_{00} is a common reference potential from which u_{11}, u_{22}, etc. may be obtained by choosing the appropriate scale factors f_{11} and g_{11}, etc. The useful name of *conformal substances* has been proposed for a group whose potentials are all related to each other and to a *reference substance* (subscript zero) by (8.113). The neater form of (8.112) is now

$$Q_1(V, T) = g_{11}^{3N}Q_0(V/g_{11}^3, T/f_{11}) \tag{8.115}$$

and so for the configurational free energy

$$A_1(V, T) = f_{11}A_0(V/g_{11}^3, T/f_{11}) - 3NkT \ln g_{11} \tag{8.116}$$

Differentiation with respect to the volume gives for a single phase

$$p_1(V, T) = (f_{11}/g_{11}^3)p_0(V/g_{11}^3, T/f_{11}) \tag{8.117}$$

If the equation of state of the reference substance is

$$\varphi_0(p, V, T) = 0 \tag{8.118}$$

then that for substance 1 is

$$\varphi_0(pg_{11}^3/f_{11}, V/g_{11}^3, T/f_{11}) = \varphi_1(p, V, T) = 0 \tag{8.119}$$

This is an expression of the *principle of corresponding states*.

If the state of the reference substance is represented by a (p, V, T) surface, as in *Figure 1.1*, then the states of all other conformal substances are represented by geometrically similar surfaces in which the axes of pressure, volume and temperature are multiplied by (f/g^3), g^3 and f, respectively. It follows that all singular points on the surface, such as the solid, liquid and gas at the triple point and the fluid at the critical point, have values of p, V, and T in the ratio of these scale factors. In particular

$$p_1^c = (f_{11}/g_{11}^3)p_0^c, \qquad v_1^c = g_{11}^3v_0^c, \qquad T_1^c = f_{11}T_0^c \tag{8.120}$$

so that (8.119) may be expressed in terms of the critical constants

$$\varphi_1\left[\left(\frac{p}{p_1^c}\right), \left(\frac{v}{v_1^c}\right), \left(\frac{T}{T_1^c}\right)\right] = \varphi_0\left[\left(\frac{p}{p_0^c}\right), \left(\frac{v}{v_0^c}\right), \left(\frac{T}{T_0^c}\right)\right] = 0 \tag{8.121}$$

and

$$(pv/RT)_1^c = (pv/RT)_0^c \qquad (8.122)$$

These equations put the principle of corresponding states into the usual empirical form that has been used since the time of van der Waals. The simple dimensional analysis on which its statistical derivation is based needed only three assumptions: first, the phase integral can be factorized into a molecular and a configurational part; secondly, the latter may be treated by the methods of classical statistical mechanics; and thirdly, that the substances are conformal.

The choice of the critical constants as the characteristic parameters with which to reduce p, V and T to dimensionless ratios is an arbitrary one. There is no theoretical reason for preferring them to those of any other singular point, but there are two practical reasons. First, the empirical principle of corresponding states has been widely used for many years, particularly by engineers, and has invariably been based upon these scale factors. Secondly, small departures from (8.113) produce disproportionately large effects on the physical properties of the solid state. There are many sets of substances whose potentials are almost conformal and whose fluids obey (8.121) moderately well, but for which the properties of the solid states show little or no regularity. The solid state is particularly sensitive to small departures of the potential from spherical symmetry. The effect of these on the fluid states is discussed in the next Section. The only practical disadvantage in the use of the critical constants is the difficulty of measuring V^c accurately. However, there are only two independent molecular parameters, f and g, and so it is possible to determine these from T^c and $(T^c/p^c)^{1/3}$, respectively.

The inert gases are the only substances whose molecules are spherical monatomic particles, and it is to these that one looks first for an example of a conformal set of substances. There are six inert gases, but only three of these, argon, krypton and xenon, can be used for a proper test of (8.121). Liquid helium and, to a lesser extent, liquid neon cannot be treated adequately by classical mechanics owing to the lightness of their molecules (see Chapter 1). Radon probably resembles the three gases below it, but too little is known of its properties for a searching test of the principle.

The reduced properties of argon, krypton and xenon are summarized in *Table 8.1*, in which ratios that should be the same for all three substances are shown in heavy type. The table is similar to one first published by Guggenheim[12] in 1945, but some of the more recent results on which it is based have improved the agreement with the principle of corresponding states.

Table 8.1. The reduced properties of argon, krypton and xenon

	1 T^c K	*2* p^c bar	*3* v^c cm³ mol⁻¹	*4* $(pv/RT)^c$
Argon	150·7	49·0	74·6	**0·291**
Krypton	209·4	55·0	92·2	**0·291**
Xenon	289·8	58·8	118·8	**0·290**

	5 T^b K	*6* $T\dagger$ K	*7* T^b/T^c	*8* $T\dagger/T^c$
Argon	87·3	86·9	0·579	**0·577**
Krypton	119·9	121·0	0·573	**0·578**
Xenon	165·1	167·9	0·570	**0·580**

	9 Δh_e J mol⁻¹	*10* Δs_e (T^b)	*11* Δs_e $(T\dagger)$ J mol⁻¹ K⁻¹	*12* $(c_p)^l$ (T^t) J mol⁻¹ K⁻¹
Argon	6520	74·7	**75·0**	**29·7**
Krypton	9030	75·3	**74·6**	**32·0**
Xenon	12 640	76·6	**75·3**	**32·0**

	13 T^t K	*14* T^t/T^c	*15* p^t bar	*16* p^t/p^c
Argon	83·8	**0·556**	0·689	**0·0141**
Krypton	116·0	**0·554**	0·730	**0·0133**
Xenon	161·3	**0·557**	0·815	**0·0139**

	17 $(v^l/v^s)^t$	*18* Δh_f J mol⁻¹	*19* Δs_f J mol⁻¹ K⁻¹
Argon	**1·15**	1176	**14·0**
Krypton	**1·15**	1636	**14·1**
Xenon	**1·15**	2298	**14·2**

$T\dagger$ is the temperature at which the vapour pressure is equal to $(p^c/50)$. Δh_e and Δh_f are the latent heat of evaporation at the normal boiling point and the latent heat of fusion.
Sources: Argon: *Tables 2.5* and *2.12*, and sources quoted by Guggenheim[12].

Krypton: Critical constants, Kobe and Lynn; boiling point and triple point, Meihuizen, Crommelin and Mathias[13]; latent heats and heat capacity, Clusius and his colleagues[13]; other properties from sources quoted by Guggenheim[12].

Xenon: Critical constants, Kobe and Lynn; boiling point, triple point, latent heat and heat capacity, Clusius and his colleagues[13]; other properties from sources quoted by Guggenheim[12].

The first four columns are the critical constants. The ratio $(pv/RT)^c$ is the same for each substance, within an experimental error of about 1 per cent in v^c.

The 5th column is the normal boiling point, which is not a corresponding state, as each substance has a different critical pressure. The 6th column is, therefore, the boiling point at a fixed fraction,

$(\frac{1}{50})$ of the critical pressure. The 7th and 8th columns show that the normal boiling point is not a constant fraction of the critical temperature but that the reduced boiling point at a given reduced pressure is sensibly constant.

The 9th column is the latent heat of evaporation at the normal boiling point. The 10th shows that the entropy of evaporation at this point (Trouton's constant) is not the same for each substance, but at a given reduced temperature (or pressure) it is a constant (11th column). The configurational heat capacity at constant pressure of the liquid at the triple point is about 30 J mol^{-1} K^{-1} (column 12). It is shown in the next Section that this is one of the properties of the liquid state most sensitive to a lack of conformation in the potentials. Columns 14 and 16 indicate that the reduced triple-point temperatures and pressures are constant. The latter is again a very sensitive test of the principle, as vapour pressure changes rapidly with temperature. The last three columns show that the reduced volume and entropy changes on fusion are also constants.

These three liquids, and liquid argon in particular, may therefore be used as a standard of normal behaviour with which other liquids may be compared. *Table 8.2* is a summary of the reduced properties of liquid argon. Guggenheim[12] has shown that the densities of the saturated gas and liquid phases may be well represented by

$$\frac{v^c}{v^g} = 1 + \frac{3}{4}\left(1 - \frac{T}{T^c}\right) - \frac{7}{4}\left(1 - \frac{T}{T^c}\right)^{1/3} \qquad (8.123)$$

$$\frac{v^c}{v^l} = 1 + \frac{3}{4}\left(1 - \frac{T}{T^c}\right) + \frac{7}{4}\left(1 - \frac{T}{T^c}\right)^{1/3} \qquad (8.124)$$

The second of these equations reproduces the volumes of *Table 8.2* to 1 per cent and the coefficients of thermal expansion to 3 per cent (after correcting for the difference between α_σ and α_p).

This excellent conformation of the three inert gases to the principle of corresponding states implies that their potentials are of a common form (8.113), although it does not exclude the presence of suitably conformal three-body potentials. It does not determine this pair form, but it was shown in the previous Chapter that a Lennard-Jones (12,6) potential is probably reasonably correct as an effective potential for the liquid. If this is used, then there must be a fixed ratio between ϵ and kT^c and between σ^3 and (v^c/N). The best values of these ratios appear to be

$$kT^c = 1 \cdot 25\epsilon, \qquad v^c = 3 \cdot 14 N\sigma^3, \qquad p^c = 0 \cdot 116(\epsilon/\sigma^3)$$

These values are used throughout this book for estimating ϵ and σ, as, for example, in the discussion of *random mixtures* of Lennard-Jones molecules in Chapter 9.

Table 8.2. The reduced properties of liquid argon

T/T^c	p/p^c	v/v^c	$(\alpha_p T^c)$	$(\beta_T p^c)$	$(\gamma_V T^c/p^c)$
(0·55)	—	(0·377)	(0·66)	(0·0098)	(67)
0·556^t	0·0141	0·378	0·66	0·0100	66
0·60	0·0297	0·390	0·69	0·0119	58
0·65	0·0563	0·404	0·75	0·0150	50
0·70	0·101	0·419	0·83	0·0183	44
0·75	0·166	0·437	0·93	0·024	39
0·80	0·258	0·458	1·20	0·036	33
0·85	0·381	0·490	—	—	27
0·90	0·539	0·532	—	—	21
0·95	0·742	0·600	—	—	15
1·00	1·000	1·000	∞	∞	5·5

T/T^c	$\Delta h_e/RT^c$	h'/RT^c	u'/RT^c	c_p'/R	c_V'/R
(0·55)	(5·288)	(−4·76)	(−4·76)	(3·54)	(0·84)
0·556^t	5·270	−4·74	−4·74	3·54	0·84
0·60	5·122	−4·58	−4·58	3·59	0·8
0·65	4·93	−4·38	−4·38	3·70	0·8
0·70	4·68	−4·16	−4·17	3·9	0·7
0·75	4·4	−3·91	−3·93	4·3	0·6
0·80	4·0	−3·65	−3·68	4·8	0·6
0·85	3·6	−3·37	−3·42	5·6	0·6
0·90	3·1	—	—	7·1	0·6
0·95	—	—	—	—	0·7
1·00	0·0	—	—	∞	∞ ?

The reduced temperature of 0·55 is below the triple point. Extrapolated values are given for ease of interpolation.

8.5 Liquids with Non-Central Forces

If the molecules in a fluid are not spherical structureless particles, then the phase integral, (8.14), is to be taken not only over all the positions and translational momenta but also over the conjugate co-ordinates that describe the rotational and vibrational states.

The phase integral cannot now be reduced to a product of molecular partition functions and the configurational integral unless $\mathcal{U}$ is independent of the orientations and rotational energy, and of the internal vibrational states of the molecules. This is never exactly true, and is a good approximation only for a few very simple molecules such as methane.

It is more realistic to assume that $\mathcal{U}$ is a function of the relative orientations but independent of the rotational momenta and of the internal vibrational states. It is now possible to integrate at once over the translational and rotational momenta, and to form the quantal sum-over-states for the vibrational levels. This is straightforward and leads to

$$Z = (\psi^t/V)^N(\psi^r)^N(\psi^s)^N Q \qquad (8.125)$$

$$Q = \left(\frac{1}{4\pi}\right)^N \frac{1}{N!}\int \cdots \int e^{-\mathscr{U}/kT}\mathrm{d}\mathbf{r}_1 \ldots \mathrm{d}\mathbf{r}_N\, \mathrm{d}\omega_1 \ldots \mathrm{d}\omega_N \qquad (8.126)$$

where ψ^t, ψ^r and ψ^s are the molecular partition functions for translational, rotational and vibrational motion. The integration over the angular co-ordinates of each molecule is denoted $\mathrm{d}\omega$, where

$$\int \mathrm{d}\omega = 4\pi \qquad (8.127)$$

The configurational free energy is again given by $(-kT \ln Q)$.

Thus, if the further assumption is made that $\mathscr{U}$ is independent of the orientations, then an assembly of polyatomic molecules has the same configuration integral as an assembly of monatomic molecules. However, this is never true and the object of the work described in this Section is calculation of the change made in Q, and so in A, by the introduction of non-central potentials into $\mathscr{U}$. Again, as in the derivation of the principle of corresponding states, the complete evaluation of Q is avoided, and an expression is sought for the ratio between Q of an assembly of non-central and Q of one of central forces.

This may be obtained by a perturbation method[14] if the non-central forces are not too strong. Let the non-central part of the pair potential, u, of an assembly of axially symmetric molecules be represented by an expansion of spherical harmonics as in (7.7)

$$u = u_0 + u_1 \qquad (8.128)$$

$$u_0(r_{ij}) = X^{000}(r_{ij}) \qquad (8.129)$$

$$u_1(r_{ij}, \theta_i, \varphi_i, \theta_j, \varphi_j) = \sum_{l_i>0}\sum_{l_j>0}\sum_m X^{l_i l_j m}(r_{ij}) S_{l_i m}(\theta_i^{ij}, \varphi_i^{ij}) S_{l_j m}(\theta_j^{ji}, \varphi_j^{ji}) \qquad (8.130)$$

where the suffixes to the angles indicate the axes from which they are measured. Hence

$$\mathscr{U} = \mathscr{U}_0 + \mathscr{U}_1 \qquad (8.131)$$

$$\mathscr{U}_0 = \sum\sum_{i>j} u_0(r_{ij}), \qquad \mathscr{U}_1 = \sum\sum_{i>j} u_1(r_{ij}, \theta_i, \varphi_i, \theta_j, \varphi_j) \qquad (8.132)$$

These equations for $\mathscr{U}$ may be substituted in the configuration integral, (8.126), and the factor $\exp(-\mathscr{U}_1/kT)$ expanded in powers of $\mathscr{U}_1$. The integral of $\mathscr{U}_1$ over all angles is zero, so that the first

271

non-vanishing term in the expansion is of the order of $(kT)^{-2}$

$$Q = \frac{1}{N!} \int \ldots \int e^{-\mathcal{U}_0/kT} d\mathbf{r}_1 \ldots d\mathbf{r}_N$$

$$+ \left(\frac{1}{4\pi}\right)^N \frac{1}{N!} \frac{1}{2(kT)^2} \int \ldots \int \mathcal{U}_1^2 e^{-\mathcal{U}_0/kT} d\mathbf{r}_1 \ldots d\mathbf{r}_N d\omega_1 \ldots d\omega_N$$

(8.133)

$$= Q_0 + Q_2$$

or

$$A = A_0 + A_2 = A_0 - kT(Q_2/Q_0) \tag{8.134}$$

$$A_2 = -\left(\frac{1}{4\pi}\right)^N \frac{1}{Q_0 N! \, 2kT} \int \ldots \int \mathcal{U}_1^2 e^{-\mathcal{U}_0/kT} d\mathbf{r}_1 \ldots d\mathbf{r}_N d\omega_1 \ldots d\omega_N$$

(8.135)

Thus A_2 is necessarily negative and approaches zero at high temperatures. $\mathcal{U}_1^2$ is formed of products of the type $(u_1)_{ij}^2$, $(u_1)_{ij}(u_1)_{ik}$ and $(u_1)_{ij}(u_1)_{kl}$. The number of terms of each type is given above in Section 8.2. The last may be ignored, since the integral vanishes on integrating over the co-ordinates of four different molecules, and so, making the trivial integrations over the angles

$$A_2 = -\left(\frac{1}{4\pi}\right)^2 \frac{1}{Q_0(N-2)! \, 4kT} \int \ldots \int e^{-\mathcal{U}_0/kT}$$

$$\times \left[\int\int (u_1)_{12}^2 \, d\omega_1 \, d\omega_2\right] d\mathbf{r}_1 \ldots d\mathbf{r}_N$$

$$- \left(\frac{1}{4\pi}\right)^3 \frac{1}{Q_0(N-3)! \, 2kT} \int \ldots \int e^{-\mathcal{U}_0/kT}$$

$$\times \left[\int \ldots \int (u_1)_{12}(u_1)_{13} \, d\omega_1 \, d\omega_2 \, d\omega_3\right] d\mathbf{r}_1 \ldots d\mathbf{r}_N \tag{8.136}$$

From (8.130)

$$\int\int (u_1)_{12}^2 \, d\omega_1 \, d\omega_2 = (4\pi)^2 \sum_{l_i>0} \sum_{l_j>0} \sum_m [X^{l_j l_j m}(r_{ij})]^2 \tag{8.137}$$

as

$$\int S_{l,m}(\theta_1^{12}, \varphi_1^{12}) S_{l,-m}(\theta_1^{12}, \varphi_1^{12}) \, d\omega_1$$

$$= \int S_{l,m}(\theta_2^{21}, \varphi_2^{21}) S_{l,-m}(\theta_2^{21}, \varphi_2^{21}) \, d\omega_2 = 4\pi \tag{8.138}$$

and all other terms vanish. Again from (8.130)

$$\int \ldots \int (u_1)_{12}(u_1)_{13} \, d\omega_1 \, d\omega_2 \, d\omega_3$$

$$= (4\pi)^3 \sum_{l>0} [X^{l00}(r_{12})][X^{l00}(r_{13})] P_l(\cos \theta_{213}) \quad (8.139)$$

where θ_{213} is the angle subtended by molecules 2 and 3 at molecule 1. This equation follows from

$$\int S_{l0}(\theta_1^{12}, \, \varphi_1^{12}) S_{l0}(\theta_1^{13}, \, \varphi_1^{13}) \, d\omega_1 = P_l(\cos \theta_{213}) \quad (8.140)$$

and the vanishing of all the other terms. These results are now put into (8.136) and the distribution functions (8.10) are used to give

$$A_2 = -\frac{1}{2kT} \left[\tfrac{1}{2} \iint n^{(2)}(\mathbf{r}_1, \mathbf{r}_2) \sum_{l_1>0} \sum_{l_2>0} \sum_m [X^{l_1 l_2 m}(r_{12})]^2 \, d\mathbf{r}_1 \, d\mathbf{r}_2 \right.$$

$$+ \int \ldots \int n^{(3)}(\mathbf{r}_1, \mathbf{r}_2, \mathbf{r}_3) \sum_{l>0} [X^{l00}(r_{12})] [X^{l00}(r_{13})]$$

$$\left. \times P_l(\cos \theta_{213}) \, d\mathbf{r}_1 \, d\mathbf{r}_2 \, d\mathbf{r}_3 \right] \quad (8.141)$$

This is therefore the first term in the expansion of the free energy about that of the central-force assembly. It was derived first by Pople[14] who observed that, if the distribution functions were independent of temperature, then

$$A_2 = \tfrac{1}{2}U_2 = TS_2 = -\tfrac{1}{2}T(C_V)_2 < 0 \quad (8.142)$$

Thus the presence of non-central forces leads to a lowering of the free energy, energy and entropy, and to an increase in the heat capacity. However, this last set of equations is of little quantitative use, as the distribution functions are, in general, unknown functions of volume and temperature. Only for a slightly imperfect gas can an explicit expression be obtained for (8.141).

A more useful application of (8.141) is to assemblies in which the non-central forces are such that there are no terms of the kind $X^{l00}(r)$ in the pair potential. Such assemblies include all those in which there are classical electrostatic interactions between unpolarizable and otherwise spherical molecules. The multipole expansion, (7.10)–(7.13), shows that there are no terms of this type in a non-ionic fluid. Consider, for example, an assembly of Lennard-Jones (12,6) molecules each of which has a point dipole at its centre. Then

$$X^{000}(r) = \lambda r^{-12} - \nu r^{-6} \quad (8.143)$$

$$X^{110}(r) = 2X^{111}(r) = 2\mu^2/3r^3 \quad (8.144)$$

273

where μ is the dipole moment. Hence, from the first term of (8.141)

$$A_2 = -\frac{1}{4kT} \iint n^{(2)}(\mathbf{r}_1, \mathbf{r}_2) \left(\frac{2\mu^4}{3r_{12}^6}\right) d\mathbf{r}_1 \, d\mathbf{r}_2 \qquad (8.145)$$

$$= \frac{V}{2} \int_0^\infty n^{(2)}(r) \left(\frac{-\mu^4}{3r^6 kT}\right) 4\pi r^2 \, dr \qquad (8.146)$$

This is the change in the free energy produced by small dipoles in an otherwise central-force assembly. It is also the change that would be produced by adding to each term $(u_0)_{ij}$ of the central-force assembly, $(-\mu^4/3r_{ij}^6 kT)$, a spherical but temperature-dependent energy. That is, $(A_0 + A_2)$ is also the free energy of a hypothetical assembly in which the pair potential is a function of the temperature. This follows at once by considering the isothermal perturbation of A that would follow from the addition of such a temperature-dependent energy to each pair potential

$$dA = -kT \, d(\ln Q) = \frac{1}{Q_0 N!} \int \cdots \int d\mathscr{U} e^{-\mathscr{U}_0/kT} \, d\mathbf{r}_1 \ldots d\mathbf{r}_N \quad (8.147)$$

$$= \frac{1}{Q_0 N!} \int \cdots \int \sum_{i>j} \sum \left(\frac{-\mu^4}{3r_{ij}^6 kT}\right) e^{-\mathscr{U}_0/kT} \, d\mathbf{r}_1 \ldots d\mathbf{r}_N \quad (8.148)$$

$$= \frac{1}{Q_0 2(N-2)!} \int \cdots \int \left(\frac{-\mu^4}{3r_{12}^6 kT}\right) e^{-\mathscr{U}_0/kT} \, d\mathbf{r}_1 \ldots d\mathbf{r}_N \quad (8.149)$$

$$= -\frac{1}{4kT} \iint n^{(2)}(\mathbf{r}_1, \mathbf{r}_2) \left(\frac{2\mu^4}{3r_{12}^6}\right) d\mathbf{r}_1 \, d\mathbf{r}_2 \qquad (8.150)$$

which is identical with (8.145). The third of these equations follows from the second, as there are $N(N-1)/2$ identical terms in the integrand of (8.148). Thus the polar assembly has the same free energy as a hypothetical central-force assembly for which

$$u(r) = \lambda r^{-12} - \left(\nu + \frac{\mu^4}{3kT}\right) r^{-6} \qquad (8.151)$$

$$= 4\epsilon_0 \left\{ \left(\frac{\sigma_0}{r}\right)^{12} - \left(\frac{\sigma_0}{r}\right)^6 [1 + 2\chi(T)] \right\} \qquad (8.152)$$

where

$$\chi(T) = \mu^4/24\epsilon_0 \sigma_0^6 kT \qquad (8.153)$$

The free energy can be put into an experimentally accessible form by writing for a (12,6) potential

$$-4\epsilon(\sigma/r)^6 = 2u(r) + \tfrac{1}{6}v(r) \qquad (8.154)$$

where $v(r)$ is the intermolecular virial function (8.39). So, from (8.25), (8.27), (8.38) and (8.40)

$$A_2 = \chi(T)[4\overline{\mathscr{U}} - \overline{\mathscr{V}}] \tag{8.155}$$
$$= \chi(T)[4U - pV + NkT] \tag{8.156}$$

The potential (8.151) is conformal with the (12,6) potential (8.143) and differs from it only in having maximum depth greater by a factor of $(1 + 4\chi)$ and a collision diameter smaller by a factor of $(1 - \chi/3)$. So, by the principle of corresponding states, (8.116), the free energy may be put into the form

$$A[V, T] = (1 + 4\chi)A_0[V(1 + \chi), T(1 - 4\chi)] + \chi NkT \tag{8.157}$$

and

$$\varphi[p, V, T] = \varphi_0[p(1 - 5\chi), V(1 + \chi), T(1 - 4\chi)] = 0 \tag{8.158}$$
$$(pv/RT)^c = (pv/RT)_0^c \tag{8.159}$$

A Taylor expansion of (8.157) gives (8.156), and it is only to this first term that (8.157) is accurate.

It is possible to avoid the calculation of $n^{(2)}$ in (8.146) only because of the fact that the square of the dipole energy depends on r^{-6} and so is conformal with part of the Lennard-Jones potential. This identity leads at once to (8.151)–(8.153) and to the entirely equivalent equation (8.154). In fact, (8.157)–(8.159) were originally derived by a different method[15], applicable only to such special cases, before the derivation of the general equation (8.141).

This special treatment of dipolar molecules cannot be extended satisfactorily to cover polarizable molecules, since the coefficients that describe the angular part of induced interactions are of the type $X^{l00}(r)$, such as, for example, the induced dipole energy (7.16).

It is difficult to find simple polar molecules whose potentials can be represented satisfactorily by a spherical (12,6) potential and a weak point dipole. The closest are perhaps hydrogen chloride, bromide and iodide. Unfortunately, little precise work has been done on these liquids, and their critical volumes are very uncertain. However, it is found that the departure of the reduced vapour pressure of hydrogen chloride from that of *Table 8.2* is about 80 per cent greater than this treatment requires[15]. This discrepancy is presumably due to other non-central forces, such as a variation with orientation of the London and of the repulsive forces. An ellipticity equal to that of the nitrogen molecule (see below) is sufficient to account for it.

The variations of the London and of the repulsive forces with orientation are clearly necessary features of any model for an assembly of polyatomic molecules. Consider first the most general case, a potential formed from a set of coefficients of (7.7)

$$X^{l_1 l_2 m}(r) = \lambda'_{l_1 l_2 m} r^{-n} - \nu'_{l_1 l_2 m} r^{-m} \qquad (8.160)$$

where enough coefficients λ' and ν' are chosen to represent any desired shape. This potential is to be used in (8.141), and to make progress it is necessary first to assume that all λ' and ν' vanish if either l_1 or l_2 is equal to zero. (The term with both equal to zero (λ, ν) is the spherical part of the potential.) This assumption is unfortunate, as it eliminates the most natural choice of terms for the representation of ellipticity, (7.25). However, it is necessary if the triplet term is to be eliminated from (8.141). Now put

$$\lambda'_{l_1 l_2 m}/\lambda = \xi_{l_1 l_2 m} + (n/3)\eta_{l_1 l_2 m} \qquad (8.161)$$

$$\nu'_{l_1 l_2 m}/\nu = \xi_{l_1 l_2 m} + (m/3)\eta_{l_1 l_2 m} \qquad (8.162)$$

where the sets of pure numbers ξ and η are more convenient parameters than λ' and ν'. Substitution in (8.160) gives

$$X^{l_1 l_2 m}(r) = \xi_{l_1 l_2 m} u(r) - \tfrac{1}{3}\eta_{l_1 l_2 m} v(r) \qquad (8.163)$$

where $v(r)$ is again the intermolecular virial function. Substitution in (8.141) now gives

$$A_2 = -\frac{1}{4kT} \int\int n^{(2)}(\mathbf{r}_1, \mathbf{r}_2) \sum_{l_1 > 0} \sum_{l_2 > 0} \sum_m$$
$$\times [\xi_{l_1 l_2 m} u - \tfrac{1}{3}\eta_{l_1 l_2 m} v]^2 \, d\mathbf{r}_1 \, d\mathbf{r}_2 \qquad (8.164)$$

$$= \tfrac{1}{2} \sum_{l_1 > 0} \sum_{l_2 > 0} \sum_m [(\xi_{l_1 l_2 m})^2 A_{ff}^{(2)}$$
$$+ 2(\xi_{l_1 l_2 m})(\eta_{l_1 l_2 m}) A_{fk}^{(2)} + (\eta_{l_1 l_2 m})^2 A_{kk}^{(2)}] \qquad (8.165)$$

where $A_{ff}^{(2)}$, etc. are the molecular fluctuation integrals of Section 8.2. An experimentally accessible function for A_2 can be obtained only after making a further assumption. If the dependence on orientation of the repulsive part of the potential is neglected, then all λ' of (8.160) are zero. Hence, from (8.161)

$$\eta_{l_1 l_2 m} = -\left(\frac{3}{n}\right)\xi_{l_1 l_2 m} \qquad (8.166)$$

and

$$A_2 = \frac{1}{2n^2}\left(n^2 A_{ff}^{(2)} - 6n A_{fk}^{(2)} + 9 A_{kk}^{(2)}\right) \sum_{l_1 > 0} \sum_{l_2 > 0} \sum_m (\xi_{l_1 l_2 m})^2 \qquad (8.167)$$

This particular combination of pair-fluctuation integrals is an experimentally accessible function for the particular case of a

Lennard-Jones $(n, n/2)$ assembly. From (8.86) with $n = 12$

$$A_2 = (2\overline{\mathscr{U}} - \overline{\mathscr{V}}) \frac{\epsilon}{4kT} \sum_{l_1>0} \sum_{l_2>0} \sum_{m} (\xi_{l_1 l_2 m})^2 \qquad (8.168)$$

$$= (2U - pV + NkT) \frac{\epsilon}{4kT} \sum_{l_1>0} \sum_{l_2>0} \sum_{m} (\xi_{l_1 l_2 m})^2 \qquad (8.169)$$

This is a simple and accessible expression for the perturbation free energy A_2, which may be used to examine the effect of non-central forces on the thermodynamic properties of the assembly. It was originally derived by a different route[15], in which the temperature-dependent parameter $\delta(T)$ was used for the constants in (8.169)

$$\delta(T) = \frac{\epsilon}{4kT} \sum_{l_1>0} \sum_{l_2>0} \sum_{m} (\xi_{l_1 l_2 m})^2 \qquad (8.170)$$

The essential simplifications that are necessary in order to arrive at (8.169) are three: first, the neglect of potentials which lead to the triplet term in (8.141); secondly, that of the variation with orientation of the repulsive forces $(\lambda' = 0)$; and thirdly, the assumption of a $(n, n/2)$ potential for the central forces. This ensures that all terms X are proportional to $r^{-n/2}$ and so X^2 are to r^{-n}. The addition of these terms to the $(n, n/2)$ potential leads to a hypothetical potential that is conformal with the original unperturbed potential but is a function of temperature.

By the same arguments as were used above for the dipole energy, this hypothetical potential has the form $(n = 12)$

$$u(r) = 4\epsilon_0 \{ (\sigma_0/r)^{12}[1 - 2\delta(T)] - (\sigma_0/r)^6 \} \qquad (8.171)$$

Such a perturbed potential has a depth increased by a factor of $(1 + 2\delta)$ and a collision diameter diminished by the factor $(1 - \delta/3)$. Hence the alternative form of (8.169) is

$$A[V, T] = (1 + 2\delta)A_0[V(1 + \delta), T(1 - 2\delta)] + \delta NkT \qquad (8.172)$$

and

$$\varphi[p, V, T] = \varphi_0[p(1 - 3\delta), V(1 + \delta), T(1 - 2\delta)] = 0 \qquad (8.173)$$

$$(pv/RT)^c = (pv/RT)_0^c \qquad (8.174)$$

It is seen that the critical ratio is the same as that of the central-force assembly for both of the perturbation potentials so far considered. Byers Brown[16] has shown that this is so for any potential which leads to expressions for A_2 which, like (8.155) and (8.168), are linear in $\overline{\mathscr{U}}$ and $\overline{\mathscr{V}}$. A_2 is not linear in these averages if the repulsive parameters λ' are retained in (8.165), and it may then be shown that the critical ratio is no longer the same as that of the unperturbed assembly. Unfortunately, the free energy cannot be properly evaluated for such a model because of our ignorance of the fluctuation integrals. Nevertheless, the greatly simplified model that is needed in order to arrive at (8.169) is not so unrealistic that a comparison with experiment becomes worthless. It has the one important feature that would seem to be needed by all realistic models, namely, that the orientation which leads to the minimum value of the energy is also that which permits the closest approach of the centres of the molecules. The physical consequence of this is the increase of the temperature scale by a factor of $(1 + 2\delta)$ and a decrease of the volume scale by a factor of $(1 - \delta)$ in (8.172) and (8.173).

These equations can be compared with the experimental values of the following properties:

(1) Vapour pressure

If the reduced vapour pressure of a (12,6) assembly is given by

$$\ln (p/p^c) = c(1 - T^c/T) \qquad (8.175)$$

then the reduced vapour pressure of the assembly with non-central forces is lower at a given reduced temperature by an amount[15]

$$\Delta[\ln (p/p^c)] = -\delta(T^c)\left[\left(1 - \frac{T}{T^c}\right)\left(2c - \frac{3T}{T^c}\right)\left(\frac{T^c}{T}\right)^2\right] \qquad (8.176)$$

where, from *Table 8.2*, c is 5·3650. *Figure 8.1* shows that this equation predicts the correct form of the deviation for the vapour pressures of many simple substances. The inaccuracies at low vapour pressures are due principally to the failure of the simple equation (8.175) to represent accurately that of argon.

(2) The reduced density of the liquid

The slope of the rectilinear diameter is a measure of the reduced densities of the liquid phase—the steeper the slope, the greater the reduced density. These slopes cannot be measured very accurately, but it has been shown that those of all non-spherical molecules are greater than that of argon[15]. This increased liquid density is the most direct consequence of the decrease of the effective collision diameters by factors of $(1 - \delta/3)$.

(3) Trouton's constant

If the gas and liquid densities and the vapour pressure are correctly described by this theory, then the entropy of evaporation must also be correct. However, it is useful to treat the latter as an

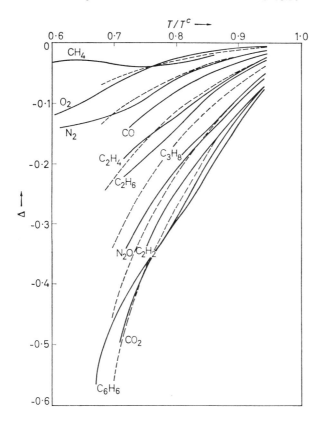

Figure 8.1. The deviations of the natural logarithms of the reduced vapour pressures of 11 liquids from eqn. (8.175).
———— experimental deviations
– – – – values of Δ calculated from (8.176) with $\delta(T^c) = 0.01, 0.02,$
0.04, 0.06, 0.08 and 0.10

independent source of information about the non-central forces, as it is known experimentally for many liquids whose vapour pressures have not been measured accurately up to the critical point.

It was shown in the last Section that a comparison of entropies of evaporation is properly made at a given reduced pressure, not an absolute one such as 1 atm. However, the entropy of evaporation at 1 atm is the quantity most commonly measured, and so it is worth putting the theory into a form where it gives directly the deviations of this entropy. From the Clapeyron–Clausius equation and (8.175)

$$s_0^g - s_0^l = R(cT^c/T^b) \qquad (8.177)$$

This reproduces the Trouton's constants of the inert gases best with the parameter c put equal to 5·23. This is 3 per cent lower than the mean value used to fit the reduced vapour pressure from the triple to the critical points. The entropy of evaporation of other substances is obtained from (8.175) and (8.177) and is larger[15] than that above by

$$\Delta(s_0^g - s_0^l) = R\,\delta(T^c)[4c(T^c/T^b)^2 - (2c + 3)(T^c/T^b)] \qquad (8.178)$$

Values of $\delta(T^c)$ calculated from this equation are shown in Table 8.3.

Table 8.3. The values of the parameter $\delta(T^c)$ of (8.170) calculated from five properties of the liquids

Substance	Vapour pressure	Rectilinear diameter	Trouton's constant	c_v	c_p
N_2	0·02	0·02	0·00	0·01	0·01
O_2	0·01	0·01	0·00	0·00₅	0·00₅
CO	0·02₅	0·03	0·01	—	0·01₅
CO_2	0·10	0·09	—	—	—
N_2O	0·08	0·06	0·06	—	—
CH_4	0·00₅	—	0·00	0·00	0·00
C_2H_6	0·05	—	0·03	—	0·02
C_2H_4	0·04	0·05	0·03	—	0·02
C_2H_2	0·09	0·06	0·09	—	—
C_3H_8	0·08	0·03	0·04	—	0·03
C_3H_6	0·08	0·11	0·04	—	—
n-C_4H_{10}	0·11	—	0·06	—	—
c-C_6H_{12}	0·10	0·06	0·05	—	—
C_6H_6	0·10	—	0·07	0·04	0·05
CF_4	—	—	0·07	—	—
CCl_4	0·09	0·05	0·06	—	0·04
SF_6	0·10	0·10	0·06	—	—
UF_6	0·14	—	0·11	—	—
c-C_6F_{12}	—	—	0·13	—	—

The experimental results are taken from the Tables of Chapter 2, from sources quoted in reference 15, from API 44 and from NBS 500.

(4) Configurational heat capacities at constant volume and constant pressure

The configurational heat capacities are larger than those of the central-force assembly. The differences are found by differentiation of A_2 and G_2, both of which are given by (8.169). The full expressions are very long, as the differences required for a comparison with experiment are not those at a given (V, T) or (p, T) but at a given value of the reduced temperature and the appropriate orthobaric liquid volume and pressure. The expressions can be simplified without any great loss of accuracy by assuming that the vapour pressure is negligible and that $(\partial^2 p/\partial T^2)_V$ is zero. This gives

$$(c_V)^\theta = (c_V)_0^\theta + R\,\delta(T^c)$$
$$\times \left[-\frac{4u}{RT} + \frac{4c_v}{R} - \frac{2T}{R}\left(\frac{\partial c_v}{\partial T}\right)_\sigma (1-\theta) - \frac{2v}{R}\left(\frac{\partial p}{\partial T}\right)_V\right]_0 \quad (8.179)$$

$$(c_p)^\theta = (c_p)_0^\theta + R\,\delta(T^c)\left[-\frac{4u}{RT} + \frac{4c_p}{R} - \frac{2T}{R}\left(\frac{\partial c_p}{\partial T}\right)_\sigma (1-\theta)\right]_0$$

$$(8.180)$$

where θ denotes a common value of (T/T^c) for each substance. The

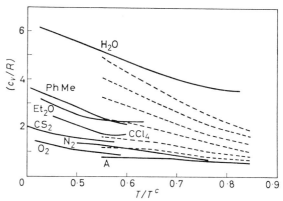

Figure 8.2. Configurational heat capacities at constant volume of 8 liquids
———— experimental results
– – – – calculated heat capacities for values of $\delta(T^c)$ of 0·01, 0·02, 0·04, 0·06, 0·08 and 0·10

deviation of c_p is very much greater than that of c_v, as $p(\partial V/\partial T)_p$ is negligible for a liquid of low vapour pressure compared to $V(\partial p/\partial T)_V$. *Figures 8.2* and *8.3* show that these deviation functions compare well with experiment.

(5) Critical ratios

The constancy of these is not confirmed by experiment. Increasingly non-central forces lead to a fall in $(pv/RT)^c$ from 0·291 for the inert gases to 0·242 for ammonia. Most simple organic molecules are between 0·27 and 0·28.

(6) The properties of the gases[15]

This treatment has been used to interpret the deviations from the principle of corresponding states of the second virial coefficient,

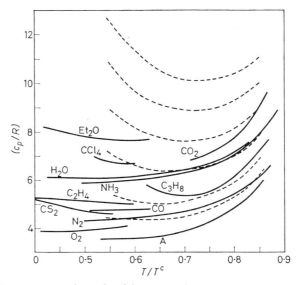

Figure 8.3. Configurational heat capacities at constant pressure of 11 liquids. Conventions as in *Figure 8.2*

of the ratio (pv/RT) as a function of reduced density and temperature, and of the isothermal Joule–Thomson coefficients.

The values of $\delta(T^c)$ found from these comparisons with experiment are shown in *Table 8.3*. Its consistency is quite satisfactory, that is, the value of $\delta(T^c)$ is generally about the same for any one substance irrespective of the thermodynamic property used to measure it. In many measurements, in particular those of the slope of the rectilinear diameter, the experimental error is of the order of several hundredths of a unit of $\delta(T^c)$.

The substance with the smallest deviation is methane. This is undoubtedly a simple molecule with weak non-central forces, but it is possible that the very small deviations are due in part to the *quantum corrections*. Methane is a very light molecule and its behaviour may not be adequately described by classical mechanics.

It is known from the properties of helium and hydrogen that the quantum corrections give rise to deviations that are of the opposite sign to those due to non-central forces. That is, the effect of the quantum corrections is to reduce the apparent value of $\delta(T^c)$, and even in extreme cases to make the apparent value negative. Such corrections may account in part for the very low value of $\delta(T^c)$ of methane.

The hydrocarbons above methane have values of $\delta(T^c)$ that increase in a very reasonable way with their molecular complexity. Acetylene is notably the most asymmetric of the C_2 hydrocarbons. This arises, no doubt, from its strong quadrupole moment due to the partial positive charges on its acidic hydrogen atoms. Similarly, carbon dioxide is more asymmetric than nitrous oxide owing to its strong quadrupole moment with partial negative charges on the oxygen atoms.

The last five molecules in this table have a high degree of symmetry but nevertheless have very large values of $\delta(T^c)$. In a brief discussion in Section 7.2 it was suggested that these globular molecules differ from the inert gases principally in having steeper attractive and repulsive potentials. There is, as yet, no satisfactory calculation of the perturbation of the free energy by a change in the indices of a Lennard-Jones potential, but it has been shown[15] that it is probable that such change leads to a free-energy difference whose dependence on volume and temperature is similar to that of (8.169), and so gives rise to similar deviations from the principle of corresponding states.

The treatment used in this Section follows directly from a perturbation calculation of the free energy for a simple but not too unrealistic form of the intermolecular potential. Its success suggests that the properties of liquids (and of gases at moderate densities) are not very sensitive to the precise form of the non-central forces. At higher densities the reduced thermodynamic properties are more affected by the individual forms of the potential. This lack of sensitivity at moderate densities has led to the development of empirical correlations[17-19] of the reduced properties in which one of the parameters corresponds to $\delta(T^c)$ of this Section. Pitzer and his colleagues[18] introduce an *acentric factor*, ω, which is defined by means of the reduced vapour pressure and numerically related to $\delta(T^c)$ by

$$\omega = 2 \cdot 40 \delta(T^c) \tag{8.181}$$

Riedel[17] has similarly a parameter α_k which is the logarithmic slope of the vapour-pressure equation at the critical point. It is related to $\delta(T^c)$ by

$$\alpha_k = 5 \cdot 808 + 11 \cdot 8 \delta(T^c) \tag{8.182}$$

where $5 \cdot 808$ is the slope for the inert gases. Hirschfelder and his colleagues[19] have extended their empirical treatment to high densities and so need more than one parameter to describe the non-central forces.

8.6 THE DETERMINATION OF THE PAIR DISTRIBUTION FUNCTION

The results of the last two Sections have been obtained without explicit evaluation of the distribution function, $g(r)$, of the direct correlation function, $c(r)$, or of the configuration integral, Q. The comparisons of theory and experiment have, therefore, been the calculation of the properties of one liquid from those of another. This Section describes the experimental and theoretical methods that can be used to determine directly $g(r)$, $c(r)$ and Q.

There are two experimental methods, in one of which the 'experiments' are conducted in a computer, and in the other, more conventionally, in the laboratory. If the pair potential can be specified precisely such as, for example, for the model potentials of Chapter 7, then $g(r)$, etc. can be obtained directly by the simulation of a model assembly on a computer. An assembly is 'created' in which a small number of particles, usually from 30 to 500, is placed in a cubic enclosure. The pair potential is specified and each particle is assigned a random position and velocity. The evolution of the assembly is followed by solving numerically the equations of motion, and it is found that after a relatively small number of collisions the particles have a distribution function $f^{(N)}$ which is at equilibrium with respect to both position and velocity. To avoid surface effects, the convention is adopted that any particle which leaves the enclosure through any particular wall is deemed to re-enter it simultaneously with the same velocity through the opposite wall.

The properties of the assembly at equilibrium are readily calculated from the information used by the computer in solving the equations of motion. Thus $g(r)$ can be found from the mean number of particles at distances between r and $r + dr$ from some specified particle. This count is made not only over the cubic enclosure but also over the 'images' by which it is deemed to be surrounded. Thermodynamic properties such as U, T and p are found by computing mean values of the potential energy, kinetic energy and the mean momentum carried across a plane per unit time.

Extensive calculations of this kind have been made for hard spheres and for Lennard-Jones (12,6) molecules by Alder and his colleagues, and by others who have had access to a large computer. An alternative method of obtaining the same final results has been used principally by Wood and his colleagues. They calculate integrals such as Q by Monte Carlo procedures, and so obtain the thermodynamic properties. Both methods are discussed at length in recent reviews[20,21].

The results for hard spheres are summarized in *Figure 8.4*, the most remarkable feature of which is the phase change at a density of about $\frac{2}{3}$ that of the regular close-packed array. The computer results are unambiguous evidence for the existence of a transition,

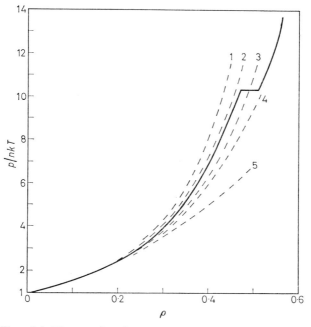

Figure 8.4. The equation of state of an assembly of hard spheres. The reduced density, ρ, is unity when the spheres occupy all space. The maximum attainable density is that of a regular close-packed structure, $\rho = 0.7405$. The full lines ($=$ machine calculations) show the transition to the solid state near $\rho = 0.5$. The five calculated curves are 1 $(HNC)_p$, 2 $(PY)_c$, 3 $(PY)_p$, 4 $(HNC)_c$, and 5 the compressibility solution of Kirkwood's integral equation. The last resembles the Born–Green equation at the densities at which both have solutions.

but it is more difficult to be sure that it is of first order, as drawn in the Figure. However, the evidence from both the molecular dynamics calculations of Alder and the Monte Carlo calculations of Wood is strongly in favour of the transition being of first order and leads to the following values for the limiting pressure and density at which the fluid phase is stable

$$p/nkT = 10.3 \qquad pb_0/NkT = 19 \qquad (8.183)$$

where $b_0 = \frac{2}{3}\pi N\sigma^3$

σ = diameter of the hard sphere

At higher densities the assembly has the crystalline structure of a close-packed lattice, and so the transition is analogous to the melting of real substances.

The calculations for a Lennard-Jones fluid are much less satisfactory. A first-order transition is again found at high densities and again corresponds to the melting of the assembly. At low temperatures there is a vapour-pressure line which ends at a critical point at about $kT^c/\epsilon = 1\cdot35$. However, the pressures, temperatures and orthobaric volumes along this line are still uncertain. Whereas U and p can be obtained directly from the computer results by taking simple averages, the calculation of S, G and μ requires an integration of p with respect to density from the limit of the dilute gas along a path in the homogeneous fluid to the state of the orthobaric liquid. This demands an accuracy that is not yet attainable, and so we lack a proper knowledge of the vapour pressure of a Lennard-Jones fluid. At low temperatures the position is a little better, since the orthobaric volume and configurational energy can be obtained[22] to a good approximation by putting $p_\sigma = 0$.

These computer experiments are valuable because they give, in principle, the distribution functions, phase diagram and thermodynamic properties of an assembly of specified pair potentials. For real molecular assemblies we are still uncertain of the precise pair and multi-body potentials, but we can obtain $g(r)$, $c(r)$ and the thermodynamic properties (Chapter 2) by direct measurement in the laboratory.

The equilibrium distribution and correlation functions are determined experimentally by the scattering (or diffraction) of a monochromatic beam of x-rays or neutrons[4,5,23]. The scattered intensity at an angle θ to the incident beam, of radiation of wavelength λ, is a function of a reciprocal length s, defined by

$$s = (4\pi/\lambda) \sin (\theta/2) \qquad (8.184)$$

If $(1/s)$ is comparable with the range of $u(r)$, then the pattern of scattered radiation is determined by the total correlation function, $h(r)$. The intensity at 'angle' s, after subtraction of the single-atom scattering, is proportional to $H(s)$, a Fourier transform of $h(r)$ defined by the pair of equations

$$s\, H(s) = \frac{2n}{\sqrt{2\pi}} \int_0^\infty r\, h(r) \sin (rs)\, \mathrm{d}r \qquad (8.185)$$

$$r\, h(r) = \frac{2}{n\sqrt{2\pi}} \int_0^\infty s\, H(s) \sin (rs)\, \mathrm{d}s \qquad (8.186)$$

Thus an experimental determination of $H(s)$ leads directly to a knowledge of $h(r)$. The scattering at zero angle, which is almost inaccessible to experiment, is related to the compressibility of the fluid. This is seen by dividing (8.185) by s and taking the limit of $s = 0$. From (8.94) we then have

$$(2\pi)^{3/2}H(0) = n\int h(r) \, d\mathbf{r} = kT\left(\frac{\partial n}{\partial p}\right)_T - 1 \qquad (8.187)$$

The determination of $c(r)$ from the intensity $H(s)$ is not so direct but follows from a Fourier transform of the Ornstein–Zernike equation (8.88). Define a function $C(s)$, which is related to $c(r)$ in the same way that $H(s)$ is related to $h(r)$, by (8.185) and (8.186). The variable $d\mathbf{r}_3$ of (8.88) can be written in bipolar coordinates

$$\int d\mathbf{r}_3 = \frac{2\pi}{r_{12}} \int_0^\infty r_{13} \, dr_{13} \int_{|r_{12}-r_{13}|}^{(r_{12}+r_{13})} r_{23} \, dr_{23} \qquad (8.188)$$

Substitute now the transform (8.186) for $r_{23} \, h(r_{23})$ in (8.88) and integrate first over dr_{23}, using the result

$$\int_{|r_{12}-r_{13}|}^{(r_{12}+r_{13})} s \sin (r_{23}s) \, dr_{23} = 2 \sin (r_{12}s) \sin (r_{13}s) \qquad (8.189)$$

The Ornstein–Zernike equation can now be written

$$r_{12}h(r_{12}) - r_{12}c(r_{12})$$

$$= 4\sqrt{2\pi} \int_0^\infty H(s) \sin (r_{12}s) \, ds \int_0^\infty r_{13}c(r_{13}) \sin (r_{13}s) \, dr_{13} \qquad (8.190)$$

$$= \frac{4\pi}{n} \int_0^\infty sC(s) \, H(s) \sin (r_{12}s) \, ds \qquad (8.191)$$

Hence by using (8.186) and the corresponding equation for $r \, c(r)$ on the left-hand side of (8.191), and remembering that the Ornstein–Zernike equation is valid for all r_{12}, we obtain its solution in the form

$$H(s) - C(s) = (2\pi)^{3/2}C(s) \, H(s) \qquad (8.192)$$

or

$$C(s) = H(s)[1 + (2\pi)^{3/2}H(s)]^{-1} \qquad (8.193)$$

Since $C(s)$ is defined as a transform of $c(r)$, by analogy with (8.185), this solution provides a route for the experimental determination of $c(r)$ from $H(s)$, namely

$$c(r) = \frac{2}{n\sqrt{2\pi}} \int_0^\infty \frac{s \, H(s)}{1 + (2\pi)^{3/2}H(s)} \cdot \frac{\sin (rs)}{r} \, ds \qquad (8.194)$$

This equation has been used by Pings[23], and some of his results for argon are shown in *Figure 8.5*.

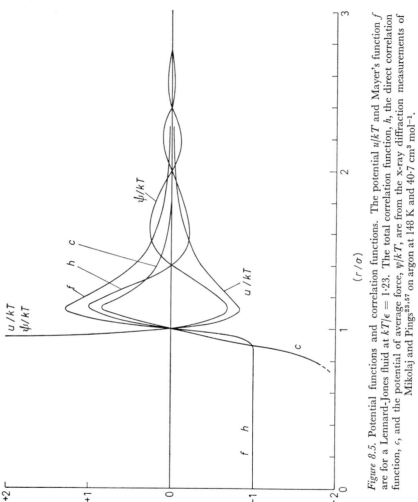

Figure 8.5. Potential functions and correlation functions. The potential u/kT and Mayer's function f are for a Lennard-Jones fluid at $kT/\epsilon = 1\cdot23$. The total correlation function, h, the direct correlation function, c, and the potential of average force, ψ/kT, are from the x-ray diffraction measurements of Mikolaj and Pings[23,57] on argon at 148 K and 40·7 cm³ mol⁻¹.

In principle, it is possible to obtain the thermodynamic properties from the experimental values of $h(r)$ and $c(r)$ by using the results of Sections 8.2 and 8.3, but in practice this route is of little value, since the accuracy that would be required in the scattering experiments is beyond anything yet attainable. The situation is at its worst in the liquid at low pressures and temperatures. Here $p \simeq 0$ and yet the integrand of, say, (8.93) has both positive and negative regions whose separate integrals would each give a pressure of several kilobars. Great experimental accuracy in $h(r)$, and hence in $y(r)$, is needed if the differences of these large pressures are to have any significance.

Any links between the pair potentials on the one hand and $h(r)$, $c(r)$ and Q on the other that are to be reliable enough for the calculation of thermodynamic properties must, therefore, be based upon some theory that is derived, with as little approximation as possible, from the exact equations of Sections 8.2 and 8.3. Such theoretical links can be divided into three main groups. It is convenient to associate the first with the calculation of the total functions, $h(r)$, $g(r)$ or $n^{(2)}(r)$ which are interrelated by (8.87) and (8.29); the second with that of the direct function, $c(r)$; and the third with that of the configuration integral, Q. These three main routes are now considered in turn.

The first is based on a family of integral equations that relate $n^{(2)}$ to $n^{(3)}$, $n^{(3)}$ to $n^{(4)}$, etc. These may be obtained by differentiating (8.10) with respect to the vector $\mathbf{r}_1$. For the pair function

$$\frac{\partial n^{(2)}(\mathbf{r}_1, \mathbf{r}_2)}{\partial \mathbf{r}_1} = \frac{-1}{kTQ(N-2)!} \int \cdots \int \left(\frac{\partial \mathcal{U}}{\partial \mathbf{r}_1}\right) e^{-\mathcal{U}/kT} \, d\mathbf{r}_3 \ldots d\mathbf{r}_N$$

Now $\hspace{10cm}$ (8.195)

$$\left(\frac{\partial \mathcal{U}}{\partial \mathbf{r}_1}\right) = \frac{\partial u_{12}}{\partial \mathbf{r}_1} + \sum_{i=3}^{N} \frac{\partial u_{1i}}{\partial \mathbf{r}_1} \hspace{3cm} (8.196)$$

and so the integrand of (8.195) is formed of two types of term. The first is the product of the exponential term and a function only of the positions of the first two molecules. This may be integrated at once over $d\mathbf{r}_3 \ldots d\mathbf{r}_N$ to give the pair function (8.10). The second type are $(N-2)$ identical terms, the first of which is a product of the exponential term and a function of the positions of the first three molecules. The integration over $d\mathbf{r}_4 \ldots d\mathbf{r}_N$ leads, therefore, to the triplet function. Thus

$$kT\left(\frac{\partial n^{(2)}(\mathbf{r}_1, \mathbf{r}_2)}{\partial \mathbf{r}_1}\right) + n^{(2)}(\mathbf{r}_1, \mathbf{r}_2)\left(\frac{\partial u_{12}}{\partial \mathbf{r}_1}\right)$$
$$+ \int n^{(3)}(\mathbf{r}_1, \mathbf{r}_2, \mathbf{r}_3) \left(\frac{\partial u_{13}}{\partial \mathbf{r}_1}\right) d\mathbf{r}_3 = 0 \quad (8.197)$$

This equation may be generalized for any function $n^{(\lambda)}$ by starting with the appropriate equation (8.10). Thus there is a family of integro-differential equations, the first of which, (8.197), gives $n^{(2)}$ in terms of $n^{(3)}$, the next gives $n^{(3)}$ in terms of $n^{(4)}$, and so on up to $n^{(N)}$. There is no hope of solving these equations save by the most drastic termination of the series. This is done by putting into the first equation an approximate value of $n^{(3)}$ and solving for $n^{(2)}$. The approximation is

$$n^{(3)}(\mathbf{r}_1, \mathbf{r}_2, \mathbf{r}_3)n^3/n^{(2)}(\mathbf{r}_1, \mathbf{r}_2)n^{(2)}(\mathbf{r}_1, \mathbf{r}_3)n^{(2)}(\mathbf{r}_2, \mathbf{r}_3) = 1 \qquad (8.198)$$

This is the *superposition approximation* of Kirkwood[24] and, if put into words, states that the probability of the simultaneous presence of molecules at $\mathbf{r}_1$, $\mathbf{r}_2$ and $\mathbf{r}_3$ is the product of the independent occurrence of pairs at $\mathbf{r}_1$ and $\mathbf{r}_2$, at $\mathbf{r}_1$ and $\mathbf{r}_3$, and at $\mathbf{r}_2$ and $\mathbf{r}_3$. The equation is clearly not exact but its substitution into (8.197) gives one of which there is, at least, some hope of its solution. An integral equation for $n^{(2)}$ is obtained after integration by parts and may be written[1,4]

$$kT \ln \left[\frac{n^{(2)}(r)}{n^2} \right] + u(r) = kT \ln y(r)$$

$$= \frac{\pi}{n^3} \int_0^\infty \int_{-s}^s (s^2 - t^2)\left(\frac{t+r}{rs}\right)[n^{(2)}(t+r) - n^2] \, dt \, n^{(2)}(s)v(s) \, ds \qquad (8.199)$$

where s and t are dummy variables and $n^{(2)}(-r)$, $u(-r)$ and $v(-r)$ are formally defined to be equal to $n^{(2)}(r)$, $u(r)$ and $v(r)$. This is the form of the integral equation of Born and Green. Kirkwood started from a slightly different but entirely equivalent set of integro-differential equations. These were also exact but the first of the set becomes an integral equation for $n^{(2)}$ that is not quite the same as (8.199) on using the superposition approximation.

Most of the attempts to solve (8.199), or the similar equation of Kirkwood, have used an expansion of $n^{(2)}$ in powers of the density. This leads to a virial equation for the pressure on substitution in (8.38). It is found that the superposition approximation gives correctly the known functions for the second and third virial coefficients but not the fourth and higher[25]. This is clearly a consequence of the inadequacy of (8.198) when dealing with the simultaneous interaction of all molecules in a cluster of four or more. The approximation is exact for independent pairs and triplets, and even for a pair of triplets that have one or two molecules in common. It is not correct for larger clusters and so is unlikely to be adequate in the liquid[26].

Numerical solution of the integral equation is needed to obtain the pressure even for so simple a model as the hard-sphere fluid. The result is quantitatively poor, as is shown in *Figure 8.4*, although it is of historical interest that Kirkwood's solution[27] of this equation was the first indication that such a fluid had a phase transition, and the inspiration of the later experimental work on computers by Alder and by Wood.

It is possible to improve the original superposition approximation (8.198) but only at the cost of considerable complication. Thus Fisher[4] has suggested applying the closure to $n^{(4)}$, not $n^{(3)}$, and so obtains a pair of integro-differential equations that have to be solved simultaneously for $n^{(2)}$ and $n^{(3)}$. Little or no progress has been made in this direction. Rice and Young[28] observe that (8.198) has an expansion in terms of triply-rooted graphs[11,26]—an expansion of which unity is merely the first term. By inserting on the right-hand side of (8.198) the first correction term, which is proportional to n, they obtain an integral equation which is correct to the fourth virial coefficient and shows some improvement at higher densities for the Lennard-Jones fluid. A more powerful technique is that of Cole and Moreton[29] who use a functional Taylor expansion to generate a much larger set of graphs which can be used to replace the right-hand side of (8.198). Again the fourth virial coefficient is now exact and there is an improvement in the fifth. However, these approximations are tedious to apply, and most recent work has been with the structurally more simple equations that arise in the study of the direct correlation function, $c(r)$.

The latter is defined by the Ornstein–Zernike equation, (8.88). This is an integral equation for c but it has an explicit solution in terms of h, namely (8.194) and (8.185). Clearly if there were a second equation between c and h, then a simultaneous solution could be made to give both functions. The graphical expansions of Section 8.3 provide such equations but only with the penalty of the introduction of other unknown functions, such as the sets of graphs e_{12} and d_{12} of (8.105) and (8.108), respectively. The former, e_{12}, is the set of elementary graphs and the smallest which cannot be expressed explicitly as a closed function of f_{12} and y_{12}. A worthwhile approximation is, therefore, to assume that this set of graphs can be neglected and to write in place of (8.105)

$$c_{12} = h_{12} - \ln y_{12} \qquad (8.200)$$

This approximation is named the *hyper-netted chain* (HNC) approximation[30], after the nature of the graphs retained on the right-hand side of (8.200). Clearly this and the Ornstein–Zernike equation (8.88) form a pair of simultaneous equations for c and y, since h and

y are related by

$$h_{12} = (1 + f_{12}) y_{12} - 1 \qquad (8.201)$$

Substitution of (8.200) into (8.88) yields the HNC integral equation for y

$$\ln y_{12} = n \int [(1 + f_{13}) y_{13} - 1 - \ln y_{13}][(1 + f_{23}) y_{23} - 1] \, d\mathbf{r}_3 \qquad (8.202)$$

which is simpler in form than the Born–Green equation (8.199) but also has no known explicit solution even for so simple a model as a hard-sphere potential.

The set of elementary graphs e_{12} is a sub-set of the set d_{12} defined by (8.107). Hence to put $d_{12} = 0$ appears to be a grosser approximation than that of the HNC theory. It has nevertheless a simple physical interpretation, since if $d_{12} = 0$, then, from (8.108)

$$c_{12} = f_{12} y_{12} \qquad (8.203)$$

or the range of $c(r)$ is no greater than that of $f(r)$, and hence of $u(r)$. This approximation, therefore, takes literally the original idea of Ornstein and Zernike that the direct correlation function is essentially one of short range. It can be shown[31] that (8.203) is, in fact, the only self-consistent way of requiring that the range of $c(r)$ shall not exceed that of $f(r)$. The results (*Figure 8.5*) show that $c(r)$ does indeed bear a strong resemblance to the general shape of $f(r)$, at least at large separations.

This approximation was first proposed, on quite different grounds, by Percus and Yevick[32] and is now known by the initials of their names, PY. The specification of $c(r)$ in terms of the omitted graphs, $d(r)$, was first made by Stell[3,33].

The integral equation obtained by the substitution of (8.203) in the Ornstein–Zernike equation is simpler even than (8.202), namely

$$y_{12} - 1 = n \int [f_{13} y_{13}][(1 + f_{23}) y_{23} - 1] \, d\mathbf{r}_3 \qquad (8.204)$$

It can be solved explicitly for an assembly of hard spheres[34], and the resulting expression for y_{12} between 0 and σ suffices for the calculation of p both from the *pressure equation* (8.93) and the *compressibility equation* (8.96). The results are

$$\left(\frac{p}{nkT} \right)_p = \frac{1 + 2\rho + 3\rho^2}{(1 - \rho)^2} \qquad (8.205)$$

$$\left(\frac{p}{nkT} \right)_c = \frac{1 + \rho + \rho^2}{(1 - \rho)^3} \qquad (8.206)$$

292

where ρ is a reduced density which is the ratio of the true volume of the N molecules to the volume V. That is, $\rho = nb_0/4N$, where b_0 is defined by (8.183).

Figure 8.4 shows that these equations are close to the experimental (i.e. computer) results for the fluid state and, although mutually inconsistent, are not wildly so. They are superior in accuracy and consistency to those obtained by solving numerically[35] the HNC equation (8.202). However, neither approximation shows the transition to the solid phase, and (8.205) and (8.206) suggest that p becomes infinite only as ρ approaches unity. This is a physically impossibly high density, since ρ cannot exceed the reduced density of a regular close-packed array of spheres, namely $\pi\sqrt{2}/6 = 0\cdot7405$.

However, these results lack physical meaning on quite different grounds before the limit $\rho = 1$ is reached. It is found that, if $\rho > 0\cdot8$, then the solution of (8.204) leads to negative values of y_{12} at certain separations r_{12}. Since g_{12} is a probability, it must be positive, and so negative solutions for y_{12} are inadmissible. The solution of (8.204) that leads to (8.205) and (8.206) is a cubic in r_{12} for $r_{12} < \sigma$, and it is known[34] that this is the only solution of this form. However, Temperley[36] observed that there are other solutions that have additional terms containing functions of the form $\cos(a_i r)$ where the coefficients a_i are reciprocal distances. These oscillatory solutions resemble the form of a distribution function of a solid, but Hutchinson[37] has shown that unfortunately they are also physically unacceptable, since they imply negative intensity of scattered radiation for certain values of the parameter s (8.184).

It follows that there is no solution of the PY equation that is physically acceptable beyond about $\rho = 0\cdot8$, and also that this equation does not describe the transition to the solid. Perhaps this is not surprising for an equation which implies a spherically symmetrical distribution of molecules around any chosen molecule.

Many attempts have been made to improve the HNC and PY approximations. Consistency between the pressure and compressibility equations can be achieved by a suitable choice of the function d_{12} and leads to a considerable improvement in the higher coefficients of the virial expansion[31,38]. More powerful methods have been devised by developing sets of coupled integral equations which reduce to HNC and PY on truncation at the first equation. By taking a pair of equations we obtain the approximations known as HNC2 and PY2. There is no unique way of developing such equations, and so there is more than one approximation that can be called PY2. Wertheim[39] uses what might be described as a superposition approximation for the elimination of a direct triplet function, c_3, whilst Percus[40] and Verlet[41] use a functional Taylor expansion. A detailed account of these methods is given in the original papers, in which it is seen that both require explicit consideration of triplet correlation functions. Both have their disadvantages. Wertheim's method is restricted to states of the fluid which can be approached from zero density along an isotherm which does not cut the vapour-pressure line, and so is inapplicable to the orthobaric liquid. Verlet's method is free from this disadvantage but is committed to an inherent lack of symmetry between molecules 1 and 2 in c_{12}, which is displeasing and would be troublesome in a mixture.

Table 8.4. The critical constants of a Lennard-Jones (12,6) fluid, according to three different approximations (Verlet and Levesque[41])

Approximation	kT^c/ϵ	$v^c/N\sigma^3$	$(pv/RT)^c$
$(HNC)_p$	1·25	3·4	0·30
$(HNC)_c$	1·32	3·6	0·36
$(PY)_p$	1·25	3·8	0·38
$(PY)_c$	1·39	3·6	0·30
$(PY2)_p$	1·36	2·8	0·31
$(PY2)_c$	1·33	3·0	0·34

Figure 8.4 shows that the PY approximation is superior to HNC for hard spheres. PY2 (Verlet) is superior to both. However, although these results are encouraging, it is dangerous to assume that what is accurate for this assembly is necessarily equally so for more realistic models.

The PY equation (8.204) cannot be solved analytically for the Lennard-Jones potential, but numerical solutions have been obtained by Broyles and his colleagues[42] and, more recently, by Verlet and Levesque[41] and Throop and Bearman[43]. Verlet and Levesque have given a detailed comparison of the performance of HNC, PY and PY2 in fitting Verlet's own Monte Carlo calculations for the critical constants of a Lennard-Jones fluid. The results are summarized in *Table 8.4*.

Watts[44] has made an independent study of the PY and HNC equations for a Lennard-Jones potential. He uses a modified form of the Ornstein–Zernike equation which is due to Baxter[45], into which he inserts the characteristic approximations (8.200) and (8.203). This modified equation is less susceptible to errors arising from the truncation of the range of $h(r)$ and $c(r)$ that is necessary in the integrations, and so his results are probably more accurate than those of Verlet and Levesque. For a Lennard-Jones potential he obtains the results shown in *Table 8.5*. He finds that, at temperatures below T^c, there are densities at which neither equation has a solution. The boundary of this area on a (p, n) graph is tangential to one isotherm only—the critical isotherm. However, he observes that the compressibility is infinite at this critical point only for the $(PY)_e$ version and not for $(PY)_p$, $(HNC)_e$ or $(HNC)_p$. Similar results have been obtained by Young and Rice[28] for the solution of Kirkwood's integral equation for a fluid with a square-well potential. Clearly these results and the discrepancies between *Tables 8.4* and *8.5* indicate that we have still much to learn about the behaviour of these theories in the region of the critical point and the orthobaric liquid.

Table 8.5. The critical constants of a Lennard-Jones fluid, according to two different approximations (Watts[44])

Approximation	kT^c/ϵ	$v^c/N\sigma^3$	$(pv/RT)^c$
$(HNC)_e$	1·41	3·6	—
$(PY)_e$	1·32	3·6	0·34

The best Monte Carlo result[41] with which these figures can be compared gives $kT^c/\epsilon = 1\cdot35$, which agrees well with the PY and the PY2 results but is significantly higher than the figure of $1\cdot25$ which is the result of the attempts to fit a Lennard-Jones potential to argon (see Section 8.4). Similarly, the calculated values of $(pv/RT)^c$ all lie at 0·3 or above, whilst the experimental values for the inert gases are certainly below 0·3 (*Table 8.1*). Both disagreements are further evidence that argon is not truly a Lennard-Jones fluid. It apparently behaves as one at high densities[22] but not at the critical density and below.

It is clear that these approximations, and particularly PY2, go a long way towards providing a quantitatively accurate theory of the liquid state for a realistic model potential. However, much remains to be done with this approach before we know accurately both the 'experimental' properties of the orthobaric liquid for a specified model potential (preferably Lennard-Jones) and the values of these properties that are predicted by the integral equations. An alternative approach is discussed in the next Section.

The third of the theoretical routes for the calculation of the thermodynamic functions goes not through $h(r)$ or $c(r)$ but straight to the configurational integral Q, from which the free energy is obtained by using (8.23).

The integrand of Q is the Boltzmann factor, $\exp(-\mathscr{U}/kT)$, and one method of obtaining Q is to expand this in cluster integrals, by using the expansion (8.97). This leads to the virial equation of state which is useful for gases but not for liquids. An approximation for Q that is suitable at high densities is to assume that each molecule spends most of its time confined by a shell of its nearest neighbours. If this is so, then it is possible to replace the $3N$-fold integral (8.12) by an N-fold product of triple integrals. The latter each represent the configuration integral of a single molecule moving in the 'cell' to which it is supposed to be confined by its neighbours. These cells are formed into a three-dimensional lattice, so that the sum of their volumes is equal to the total volume of the fluid.

This physical approximation generates the so-called lattice theories of liquids. These have been elaborated greatly beyond the crude model outlined here, and allowance has been made for vacant cells, for a non-spherical distribution of neighbours around each cell and for the correlation of the motion of molecules in neighbouring cells. Nevertheless, it remains an unsatisfactory approach which overemphasizes the similarities of the solid and liquid states. Its achievements up to 1963 were well summarized in a book by Barker[46]; it is probably true to say that there has been no significant advance since then. The advent of the Percus–Yevick and hypernetted chain approximations has now reduced greatly the interest taken in lattice theories.

8.7 PERTURBATION THEORIES

The results discussed in the last Section show that we now have a good understanding of the behaviour of a fluid of hard spheres but that we know less of the behaviour of a Lennard-Jones fluid and cannot yet interpret quantitatively that of a real dense fluid in which the true pair potential is more complicated than the Lennard-Jones and in which there are three-body forces. In these circumstances, we turn to perturbation methods in order to extend our quantitative knowledge of the more complex systems. We assume that a complicated potential can be written as the sum of a simple potential (e.g. a hard sphere) for which we know $g(r)$ etc., and a weak perturbing potential. The effects of the latter are found by averaging the perturbation over the known distribution function of the simple or unperturbed assembly.

Such a method has been used already in Section 8.5 in order to obtain the properties of a fluid with non-central forces from the presumed-known properties of a fluid with central forces. However, in this Section we consider more drastic versions of the same method in which, for example, the whole of the attractive part of the potential becomes the perturbation.

The oldest treatment of this kind is that of van der Waals. His equation can be written

$$p\beta/n = (1 - 4\rho)^{-1} - an\beta \qquad (8.207)$$

where

$$\beta = 1/kT \qquad \rho = nb_0/4N \qquad (8.208)$$

The reduced density, ρ, is the same as used above in (8.205)–(8.206) in the discussion of the PY equations, and the parameter a is a molecular constant which represents the mean attractive potential. The first term on the right of (8.207) is the guess made by van der Waals at the equation of state of an assembly of hard spheres, and the second represents the reduction of pressure brought about by an attractive potential of a strength a which is everywhere small compared with the expansion parameter β. It is true that $(1 - 4\rho)^{-1}$ is a poor representation of the equation of state of a three-dimensional assembly of hard spheres, but this is an error which does not affect the form of the equation.

Kac, Uhlenbeck and Hemmer[47] have shown that the second term in (8.207) is rigorously correct for a pair potential of infinite range but zero depth, if the limit by which it is defined is taken so that U (8.27) remains finite and non-zero. The integral for U is then proportional to an.

More generally[48], for attractive potentials of non-zero depth there exists a perturbation expansion in powers of β, which can be written

$$\frac{A}{NkT} = \frac{A_0}{NkT} + \tfrac{1}{2}n\beta \int u_1(r)g_0(r) \, d\mathbf{r} + O(\beta^2) \qquad (8.209)$$

where $u_1(r)$ is the attractive part of the potential and $g_0(r)$ the distribution function for hard spheres. The term of order β^2 involves integrations over the three- and four-body distribution functions. The derivation of this equation is similar to that of (8.135) from (8.128) except that it is now necessary to retain only the first-order term in the expansion.

This perturbation treatment suggests that the structure of a simple liquid is determined primarily by the repulsive forces between the hard cores of the molecules, and assigns to the attractive forces the less specific rôle of providing a mean internal field (or internal pressure) which holds the liquid at a high density without the need for the application of a high external pressure. The quantitative success of the more sophisticated perturbation techniques discussed below suggests that this simplification is broadly true. It may be the key to the difficult problem of devising a quantitatively accurate theory of liquids at low temperatures and high densities, and has led already to a substantial improvement in the accuracy of the theory of mixtures which is discussed in the next Chapter.

A natural development of the van der Waals equation, (8.207), is the replacement of the first term on the right-hand side by the experimentally observed isotherm for hard spheres shown in *Figure 8.4*. This has solid and fluid branches and a first-order transition between them. The equation of state so obtained should, therefore, describe the melting transition of a fluid of which the pair potential is that of a hard sphere surrounded by an attractive potential of infinite range and zero depth. As an approximation, the equation can be applied to the melting of a substance such as argon, an application which was made by Longuet-Higgins and Widom[49]. They determined the two arbitrary parameters, a and b_0, by requiring the triple-point temperature and pressure to agree with those observed. The values of all other properties of gas, liquid and solid at this point were then determined from the equation of state. They obtained good agreement for the entropy and volume changes on fusion, and for the configurational energy of the solid. The slope of the melting line is given correctly at the triple point (as it must be if Δs and Δv are both correct), but the predicted melting pressure falls, at high temperatures, below that observed experimentally. This point is discussed below.

In the perturbation treatments so far described the potential $u_1(r)$ has been wholly attractive and has been averaged over the distribution function of an assembly of hard spheres. However, realistic potentials and real molecules have repulsive branches that are not infinitely steep, and so a further class of perturbations must be considered. All realistic potentials are steep and can usually be characterized by a single parameter of steepness. Thus a class of Lennard-Jones potentials can be described as $(n, \frac{1}{2}n)$, where the parameter of steepness, n, is conventionally taken to be 12. A perturbation expansion can be made in powers of n^{-1} around the free energy of a hard-sphere fluid. That is, we write[50]

$$A_n = A_0 + n^{-1}(\partial A/\partial n^{-1})_0 + O(n^{-2}) \qquad (8.210)$$

where n is the parameter of steepness (not the density). The value of (8.210) lies in the fact that the derivative is an accessible thermodynamic property of the hard-sphere fluid, namely

$$(\partial A/\partial n^{-1})_0 = 3(pV - NkT)_0[\ln x + F(x)] \qquad (8.211)$$
$$x = \epsilon/kT$$

where ϵ is an energy characteristic of the potential and $F(x)$ a readily calculable function which depends upon the exact shape of the potential[50]. Thus for the simple case of soft spheres

$$u(r) = \epsilon(r/\sigma^*)^{-n} \tag{8.212}$$

[compare 7.24] $F(x)$ reduces to Euler's constant $\gamma = 0.57722$. The combination of (8.210) and (8.211) can be written in a neater form by introducing a reduced length, g, a function of temperature, defined by

$$g = x^{1/n}[1 + n^{-1}F(x)] \tag{8.213}$$

when we have

$$A_n(V, T) = A_0(V/g^3, T) - 3NkT \ln g \tag{8.214}$$

(compare 8.116 and 8.157).

Thus the fluid with the soft potential $(n^{-1} \neq 0)$ behaves as if it were one of hard spheres whose diameters are, by (8.213), explicit functions of the temperature.

The pressure of the fluid, p, and the melting pressure, p^M, follow at once from (8.214) [compare 8.117–8.119]:

$$p_n(V, T) = g^{-3}p_0(V/g^3, T) \tag{8.215}$$

$$p_n^M(T) = g^{-3} p_0^M(T) \tag{8.216}$$

The melting line calculated from (8.216) will be accurate only if the temperature is high enough for it to be reasonable to treat the true potential as a perturbation of a hard sphere. Thus, if $F(x)$ is calculated for a Lennard-Jones potential, then (8.216) can be expected to give the limiting behaviour at high pressures and temperatures but to be quite unrealistic at low. This is shown in *Figure 8.6* in which the calculated line is based on the 'effective' Lennard-Jones parameters for argon set out at the end of Section 8.4, and is therefore free from any dependence on specially adjusted parameters. It is seen that this approach is complementary to that of Longuet-Higgins and Widom. Theirs is an approximation which is valid only at low pressures, since they assume that the repulsive potential is infinitely steep. The true melting pressure rises with temperature more rapidly than the linear logarithmic dependence required for a fluid of hard spheres.

If the potential has the simple form of (8.212), then the intermolecular potential and virial (8.39) are related exactly by

$$v(r) = -n^{-1}u(r) \tag{8.217}$$

and so the configurational energy and the slope of the melting line are given exactly for an assembly of soft spheres with index n by

$$U_n = \frac{3}{n}\,(pV - NkT)_n \qquad \frac{\mathrm{d} \ln p_n^M}{\mathrm{d} \ln T} = 1 + \frac{3}{n} \tag{8.218}$$

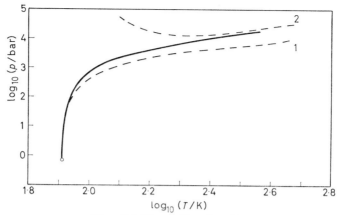

Figure 8.6. The melting line of argon
———— experimental curve
– – – – calculated by the perturbation treatments of (1) Longuet-Higgins and Widom[49] (valid at low pressures) and (2) Rowlinson[50] (valid at high temperatures)

Figures 8.4 and *8.6* bring out clearly the point made above that it is the repulsive forces which determine the gross features of both solid and liquid. Melting is a phenomenon which occurs at all temperatures in a fluid of hard spheres, provided that the pressure is sufficiently high. The attractive forces in liquid argon provide an internal pressure [conventionally measured by $T(\partial p/\partial T)_V$] of about 2 kbar which maintain it at a high density. If the external pressure is above about 3 kbar, then the attractive forces are unimportant and the melting line is given by (8.216); if it is below 2 kbar, then the attractive forces are important and produce the rapid change of logarithmic slope near that pressure that can be seen in *Figure 8.6*. Below 1 kbar the melting temperature is almost independent of external pressure, since this is negligible compared with the internal pressure.

The two models that lead to the calculated lines in *Figure 8.6* agree that there can be no solid–fluid critical point. If real molecules have sufficiently hard cores and if the hard-sphere fluid has a transition, then real molecules must have a transition at all finite temperatures. What is not quite clear is the restriction implied by the word 'sufficiently' in the last sentence. The results above show that what holds for $n^{-1} = 0$ holds also for the terms linear in n^{-1}. The higher terms of (8.210), like those of (8.209), unfortunately involve integrations over the three- and four-body distribution functions and so are not directly accessible.

The next step is the combination of the perturbation treatment of the attractive forces (8.209) with that for the repulsive forces (8.210). This was made first by McQuarrie and Katz[51] who took a Lennard-Jones (12,6) potential, treated the term in r^{-12} as a perturbation of a hard sphere and the $-r^{-6}$ term as the attractive perturbation, $u_1(r)$, in (8.209). This combination proves to be more effective than treating the whole Lennard-Jones potential as a perturbation of a hard sphere. In particular, it removes the singularity visible at low temperatures in the top curve of *Figure 8.6* and leads to the prediction of a liquid–vapour line and a critical point, as well as of a melting line.

Further improvements have been made by Barker and Henderson[52]. First, they take (8.209) to the second term by replacing its

Table 8.6. The critical constants of a Lennard-Jones (12,6) fluid according to a perturbation treatment (Barker and Henderson[52])

kT^c/ϵ	$v^c/N\sigma^3$	$(pv/RT)^c$
1·35	3·3	0·34

three- and four-body distribution functions by the second moment of the pair function. They then make an approximate replacement of the second moment by the compressibility. Their second improvement is that of taking the whole of $u(r)$ beyond the collision diameter as the perturbation in (8.209), and not the r^{-6} term alone, as was done by McQuarrie and Katz. This apparently trivial change is numerically important, since $|u_1(r)|$ is now smaller and so the convergence of (8.209) is improved. The critical constants they obtain for a Lennard-Jones fluid are shown in *Table 8.6*.

These results agree well with the best of those in *Table 8.4* and *8.5* and with the Monte Carlo value of $kT^c/\epsilon = 1·35$ for a (12,6) fluid. Moreover, Barker and Henderson find good agreement with the Monte Carlo isotherm of Verlet[41] at $kT/\epsilon = 1·35$ (the critical isotherm) and tolerable agreement on the liquid side of the two-phase region for isotherms[22, 41] at reduced temperatures of 1·00 and 0·72. No direct comparison can be made between their theoretical vapour-pressure curve and that for a (12,6) fluid, since the latter is not yet known. If, however, liquid argon is, *faute de mieux*, again taken as a fluid with an effective (12,6) potential, then the agreement with the vapour-pressure curve of *Table 2.5* is almost within computational error except close to the critical point.

It appears that this is a perturbation technique which converges sufficiently rapidly for the terms up to β^2 to be an adequate approximation to A even at temperatures as low as the triple point. This approach should be contrasted with the expansion of A in powers of the reduced density, ρ, which is known to diverge at liquid densities and in which five or six terms are needed to reach densities of the order of $\frac{1}{3}$ that of the normal liquid. Thus, if we consider our problem to be the determination of A over the whole area of a graph in which it is represented as a function of β and ρ, then we can start by assuming we know A along both axes. If $\rho = 0$, we have the limit of the perfect gas; if $\beta = 0$, we have the limiting behaviour at infinite temperature which we know from the experimental results for hard spheres and the first term of the perturbation expansion in inverse powers of the steepness of the potential. We can attempt to leave these axes by expansion of A either in powers of the density, ρ, or of the reciprocal temperature, β. The former is not convergent at high densities and its practical use is confined to the dilute and moderately dense gas. The latter is apparently highly convergent and two terms suffice to cover all fluid states. The only unsatisfactory feature of this approach is the need to appeal to the computer experiments to obtain the melting transition of hard spheres on the axis $\beta = 0$. Even the best of the HNC and PY approximations can represent only the fluid branch of this isotherm.

The testing of these perturbation treatments has usually been done by making comparisons with the computer results for model potentials because of our ignorance of the importance of three-body forces in real dense fluids. These forces certainly should not be neglected if the theories are to be used for quantitative comparisons with the properties of liquids near their triple points, although, as we have seen, argon appears to behave as a fluid with a (12,6) pair potential in the liquid state.

Two questions arise. The first is: how do the formal equations that relate p, U, etc. to $h(r)$, $c(r)$, etc. change if $\mathcal{U}$, the total configurational energy, can no longer be written as a sum of pair potentials, (8.24)? If we have instead

$$\mathcal{U} = \sum_{i<j}\sum u_{ij} + \sum_{i<j<k}\sum\sum u_{ijk} \tag{8.219}$$

then we find that eqn. (8.1)–(8.23) are unchanged but (8.25) becomes

$$U = \tfrac{1}{2}\int u_{12} n^{(2)}(\mathbf{r}_1, \mathbf{r}_2)\, \mathrm{d}\mathbf{r}_1\, \mathrm{d}\mathbf{r}_2 + \tfrac{1}{6}\int u_{123}\, n^{(3)}(\mathbf{r}_1, \mathbf{r}_2, \mathbf{r}_3)\, \mathrm{d}\mathbf{r}_1\, \mathrm{d}\mathbf{r}_2\, \mathrm{d}\mathbf{r}_3$$

$$\tag{8.220}$$

Similarly, from the virial theorem, we replace (8.38) by

$$pV = NkT - \tfrac{1}{6} \int v_{12} n^{(2)}(\mathbf{r}_1, \mathbf{r}_2) \, d\mathbf{r}_1 \, d\mathbf{r}_2$$

$$- \tfrac{1}{18} \int v_{123} n^{(3)}(\mathbf{r}_1, \mathbf{r}_2, \mathbf{r}_3) \, d\mathbf{r}_1 \, d\mathbf{r}_2 \, d\mathbf{r}_3 \quad (8.221)$$

where v_{123} is the virial of the three-body energy

$$v_{123} = \left(r_{12} \frac{\partial}{\partial r_{12}} + r_{13} \frac{\partial}{\partial r_{13}} + r_{23} \frac{\partial}{\partial r_{23}} \right) u_{123} \quad (8.222)$$

If u_{123} has the simple form of the triple–dipole potential of Axilrod and Teller (7.21), then (8.222) takes the simple form

$$v_{123} = -9u_{123} \quad (8.223)$$

The compressibility equations, (8.94) and (8.96), are formally unchanged by the introduction of the triplet potential, although $h(r)$ and $c(r)$ become functionals of u_{123}.

These equations answer the first question posed above, and we see that the introduction of a triplet potential requires that we know $n^{(3)}$ as well as $n^{(2)}$ if we are to calculate U and p from (8.220) and (8.221). However, this knowledge can, in a sense, be dispensed with if we work through the compressibility equations and if we can obtain an expression for the two-body correlation functions in the presence of three-body forces.

The second question, therefore, is: how do we modify the HNC, PY, etc. theories in the presence of the triplet potential? One way of achieving this is to use again the graphical expansions for these functions that were set out in Section 8.3. The topological terms of that Section are not entirely applicable to the new graphs generated by the triplet potential, but the necessary extensions of definition have been worked out by Friedman and by Baxter[53].

The hyper-netted chain theory (8.200) excludes from the exact expansion of $c(r)$, (8.105), all those graphs that come within the elementary set $e(r)$. In the absence of a triplet potential, the simplest member of this set [the penultimate graph of those drawn in (8.99)] has two field points and is, therefore, multiplied by n^2. However, Rushbrooke and Silbert[54] observed that in the presence of a triplet potential there is a term of lower order, that is, linear in the density. A simple extension of the HNC approximation in the presence of the triplet forces is, therefore, the inclusion in $c(r)$ of this leading term, but the omission of all higher terms whether they be two-body or three-body. The leading term is

$$e_{12}^{\text{triplet}} = n \int f_{123}(1 + f_{13})(1 + f_{23}) \, d\mathbf{r}_3 \qquad (8.224)$$

where

$$f_{123} = \exp\left(-u_{123}/kT\right) - 1 \qquad (8.225)$$

A similar extension[55] can be made for the PY equation, since the arguments above apply to the set of graphs d_{12} as well as to e_{12}. The leading term is again (8.224) and it can be shown that the graphs present in y can now be constructed from f bonds and $[(1 + f)e^{\text{triplet}}]$ bonds.

The numerical implications of these changes have still to be worked out. They do, however, have one simple consequence which accords with our scanty knowledge of triplet forces. The addition of (8.224) to the HNC or PY approximation for $c(r)$ is equivalent to replacing pair potential u_{12} by an effective pair potential u_{12}^*, given by

$$u_{12}^* = u_{12} - kT \, e_{12}^{\text{triplet}} \qquad (8.226)$$

Since it appears (Chapter 7) that the mean contribution of u_{123} in the dense fluid is positive, then e^{triplet} is probably negative and the effective potential in the dense fluid has a shallower minimum than the true pair potential determined from the properties of the dilute gas[54-56]. This result agrees with everything we know about intermolecular forces in liquids and with attempts at direct measurements by Mikolaj and Pings[23,57] of the variation of the effective depth of u with density from the x-ray diffraction pattern of gaseous argon. They find a linear variation of the effective depth with density but the slope appears to be unreasonably high. Levesque and Verlet[58] suggest that this experimental technique is not yet sufficiently accurate for detecting three-body forces.

It remains to be seen if the inclusion of only the first-order term (8.224) is an adequate way of treating the triplet potentials, but it looks promising in view of the small size of u_{123}.

REFERENCES

[1] de Boer, J. *Rep. Prog. Phys.* 12 (1948–9) 305; Cole, G. H. A. 19 (1956) 1; Rowlinson, J. S. 28 (1965) 169

[2] Hill, T. L. *Statistical Mechanics*, Ch. 6, New York (McGraw-Hill) 1956

[3] Frisch, H. L. and Lebowitz, J. L. (ed.) *The Equilibrium Theory of Classical Fluids*, New York (W. A. Benjamin) 1964

[4] Fisher, I. Z. *Statistical Theory of Liquids* (trans. Switz, T. M., with supplement by Rice, S. A. and Gray, P.), Chicago Univ. Press, 1964

REFERENCES

[5] Egelstaff, P. A. *An Introduction to the Liquid State*, London (Academic Press) 1967

[6] Temperley, H. N. V., Rowlinson, J. S. and Rushbrooke, G. S. (ed.) *The Physics of Simple Liquids*, Amsterdam (North-Holland) 1968

[7] Green, H. S. *Proc. R. Soc.* A189 (1947) 103

[8] Byers Brown, W. *Phil. Trans.* A250 (1957) 221

[9] Ornstein, L. S. and Zernike, F. *Proc. Sect. Sci. K. ned. Akad. Wet.* 17 (1914) 793

[10] Groeneveld, J. *Phys. Lett.* 3 (1962) 50; Penrose, O. *J. math. Phys.* 4 (1963) 1312; Lebowitz, J. L. and Penrose, O. 5 (1964) 841; Baer, S. and Lebowitz, J. L. *J. chem. Phys.* 40 (1964) 3474; Ruelle, D. *Rev. mod. Phys.* 36 (1964) 580; Penrose, O., in *Statistical Mechanics* (ed. Bak, T.) (W. A. Benjamin) New York, 1967 p. 101, Groeneveld, J., *ibid.* p. 110; Ree, F. H., to be published

[11] Mayer, J. E. *Handbuch der Physik* (ed. Flügge, S.), Vol. 12, Ch. 2, Berlin (Springer) 1958; Salpeter, E. E. *Annls Phys.* 5 (1958) 183; Uhlenbeck, G. E. and Ford, G. W. *Studies in Statistical Mechanics* (ed. de Boer, J. and Uhlenbeck, G. E.), Vol. 1, Part B, Amsterdam (North-Holland) 1962

[12] de Boer, J. and Michels, A. *Physica* 5 (1938) 945; Pitzer, K. S. *J. chem. Phys.* 7 (1939) 583; Guggenheim, E. A. 13 (1945) 253

[13] Meihuizen, J. J. and Crommelin, C. A. *Physica* 4 (1937) 1; Mathias, E., Crommelin, C. A. and Meihuizen, J. J. *ibid.* 1200; Clusius, K. *Z. phys. Chem.* B31 (1936) 459; with Riccoboni, L. B38 (1937) 81; with Weigand, K. B42 (1939) 111; with Kruis, A. and Konnertz, F. *Annln Phys.* 33 (1938) 642

[14] Pople, J. A. *Proc. R. Soc.* A221 (1954) 498, 508

[15] Cook, D. and Rowlinson, J. S. *Proc. R. Soc.* A219 (1953) 405; Rowlinson, J. S. *Trans. Faraday Soc.* 50 (1954) 647; 51 (1955) 1317; *Aust. J. Chem.* 7 (1954) 397

[16] Byers Brown, W. *Thermodynamic and Transport Properties of Fluids*, p. 205, London (Instn mech. Engrs) 1958

[17] Riedel, L. *Chemie-Ingr-Tech.* 26 (1954) 83, 259, 679; 27 (1955) 209, 475; 28 (1956) 557

[18] Pitzer, K. S. *J. Am. chem. Soc.* 77 (1955) 3427; with Lippmann, D. Z., Curl, R. F., Huggins, C. M. and Petersen, D. E. *ibid.* 3433; with Hultgren, G. O. 80 (1958) 4793; Curl, R. F. and Pitzer, K. S., ref. 16 p. 1; *Indust. Engng Chem.* 50 (1958) 265; Danon, F. and Pitzer, K. S. *J. chem. Phys.* 36 (1962) 425

[19] Hirschfelder, J. O., Buehler, R. J., McGee, H. A. and Sutton, J. R. *Indust. Engng Chem.* 50 (1958) 375, 386

[20] Fluendy, M. A. D. and Smith, E. B. *Q. Rev. chem. Soc.* 16 (1962) 241

[21] Alder, B. J. and Hoover, W. G., ref. 6 Ch. 4; Wood, W. W. *ibid.* Ch. 5; see also Alder, B. J. and Wainwright, T. E. *Phys. Rev.* 127 (1962) 359; *J. chem. Phys.* 27 (1957) 1208; 31 (1959) 459; 33 (1960) 1439; Hoover, W. G. and Ree, F. H. 47 (1967) 4873; Wood, W. W. and Jacobson, J. D. 27 (1957) 1207; with Parker, F. R. *Nuovo Cim.* 9 (1958) Suppl. 1, 133

[22] McDonald, I. R. and Singer, K. *Discuss. Faraday Soc.* 43 (1967) 40; *J. chem. Phys.* 47 (1967) 4766

THE STATISTICAL THERMODYNAMICS OF FLUIDS

[23] Pings, C. J., ref. 6 Ch. 10

[24] Kirkwood, J. G. *J. chem. Phys.* 3 (1935) 300; with Boggs, E. M. 10 (1942) 394

[25] Rushbrooke, G. S. and Scoins, H. I. *Phil. Mag.* 42 (1951) 582; *Proc. R. Soc.* A216 (1953) 203; Nijboer, B. R. A. and van Hove, L. *Phys. Rev.* 85 (1952) 777

[26] Abe, R. *Prog. theor. Phys.*, *Osaka* 21 (1959) 421; Rowlinson, J. S. *Molec. Phys.* 6 (1963) 517; Powell, M. J. D. 7 (1964) 591

[27] Kirkwood, J. G., with Maun, E. K. and Alder, B. J. *J. chem. Phys.* 18 (1950) 1040; with Lewinson, V. A. and Alder, B. J. 20 (1952) 929; Zwanzig, R. W., Kirkwood, J. G., Stripp, K. F. and Oppenheim, I. 21 (1953) 1268; 22 (1954) 1625

[28] Rice, S. A. and Young, D. A. *Discuss. Faraday Soc.* 43 (1967) 16; Young D. A. and Rice, S. A. *J. chem. Phys.* 47 (1967) 4228, 5061

[29] Cole, G. H. A. and Moreton, A. *Molec. Phys.* 13 (1967) 501

[30] van Leeuwen, J. M. J., Groeneveld, J. and de Boer, J. *Physica* 25 (1959) 792; Rushbrooke, G. S. 26 (1960) 259; Verlet, L. and Levesque, D. 28 (1962) 1124; Meeron, E. *J. math. Phys.* 1 (1960) 192; Morita, T. and Hiroike, K. *Prog. theor. Phys.*, *Osaka* 23 (1960) 385; Verlet, L. *Nuovo Cim.* 18 (1960) 77

[31] Rowlinson, J. S. *Molec. Phys.* 9 (1965) 217; 10 (1966) 533; *Discuss. Faraday Soc.* 43 (1967) 243; Lado, F. *J. chem. Phys.* 47 (1967) 4828

[32] Percus, J. K. and Yevick, G. J. *Phys. Rev.* 110 (1958) 1

[33] Stell, G. *Physica* 29 (1963) 517

[34] Thiele, E. *J. chem. Phys.* 39 (1963) 474; Wertheim, M. S. *Phys. Rev. Lett.* 10 (1963) 321; *J. math. Phys.* 5 (1964) 643

[35] Klein, M. *J. chem. Phys.* 39 (1963) 1388; *Physics Fluids* 7 (1964) 391

[36] Temperley, H. N. V. *Proc. phys. Soc. Lond.* 84 (1964) 339

[37] Hutchinson, P. *Molec. Phys.* 13 (1967) 495

[38] Hurst, C. *Phys. Lett.* 14 (1965) 192; *Proc. phys. Soc. Lond.* 88 (1966) 533; Henderson, D. 87 (1966) 592

[39] Wertheim, M. S. *J. math. Phys.* 8 (1967) 927

[40] Percus, J. K. *Phys. Rev. Lett.* 8 (1962) 462

[41] Verlet, L. *Physica* 30 (1964) 95; 31 (1965) 959; *Phys. Rev.* 159 (1967) 98; Levesque, D. *Physica* 32 (1966) 1985; Verlet, L. and Levesque, D. 36 (1967) 254

[42] Broyles, A. A., Chung, S. U. and Sahlin, H. L. *J. chem. Phys.* 37 (1962) 2462; Khan, A. A. and Broyles, A. A. 43 (1965) 43; *Phys. Rev.* 134 (1964) A367

[43] Throop, G. J. and Bearman, R. J. *J. chem. Phys.* 42 (1965) 2408; *Physica* 32 (1966) 1298

[44] Watts, R. O. *J. chem. Phys.* 48 (1968) 50; 50 (1969) 984

[45] Baxter, R. J. *Phys. Rev.* 154 (1967) 170; *J. chem. Phys.* 47 (1967) 4855

[46] Barker, J. A. *Lattice Theories of the Liquid State*, Oxford (Pergamon) 1963

[47] Kac, M. *Physics Fluids* 2 (1959) 8; with Uhlenbeck, G. E. and Hemmer, P. C. *J. math. Phys.* 4 (1963) 216; Uhlenbeck, G. E., Hemmer, P. C. and Kac, M. *ibid.* 229; Hemmer, P. C., Kac, M. and Uhlenbeck, G. E. 5 (1964) 60

REFERENCES

48 Zwanzig, R. W. *J. chem. Phys.* 22 (1954) 1420

49 Longuet-Higgins, H. C. and Widom, B. *Molec. Phys.* 8 (1964) 549

50 Rowlinson, J. S. *Molec. Phys.* 7 (1964) 349; 8 (1964) 107

51 McQuarrie, D. A. and Katz, J. L. *J. chem. Phys.* 44 (1966) 2393

52 Barker, J. A. and Henderson, D. *Discuss. Faraday Soc.* 43 (1967) 50; *J. chem. Phys.* 47 (1967) 2856, 4714; *Molec. Phys.* 14 (1968) 587; *J. chem. Educ.* 45 (1968) 2; *Symposium on Thermophysical Properties*, New York (Am. Soc. mech. Engrs) 1968 p. 30

53 Friedman, H. L. *Ionic Solution Theory*, Ch. 2, New York (Wiley) 1962; Rushbrooke, G. S., ref. 6; Baxter, R. J. *Annls Phys.* 46 (1968) 509

54 Rushbrooke, G. S. and Silbert, M. *Molec. Phys.* 12 (1967) 505

55 Rowlinson, J. S. *Molec. Phys.* 12 (1967) 513

56 Graben, H. W. *Phys. Rev. Lett.* 20 (1968) 529

57 Mikolaj, P. G. and Pings, C. J. *Phys. Rev. Lett.* 15 (1965) 849; 16 (1966) 4; *J. chem. Phys.* 46 (1967) 1401, 1412; Pings, C. J. *Molec. Phys.* 12 (1967) 501; *Discuss. Faraday Soc.* 43 (1967) 89

58 Levesque, D. and Verlet, L. *Phys. Rev. Lett.* 20 (1968) 905; Verlet, L. *Phys. Rev.* 165 (1968) 201

9

THE STATISTICAL THERMODYNAMICS
OF MIXTURES

9.1 INTRODUCTION

The extension of the statistical theory of fluids to fluid mixtures is not as straightforward as might be expected. Moreover, when extensions have been made, the results have not always been in a form in which they could be compared with experiment. The properties of mixtures set out in Chapters 4 and 5 are the excess thermodynamic properties, that is, the differences between those of the real and those of an ideal mixture at the same temperature and pressure. The theoretical calculation of excess functions was, for many years, a branch of statistical mechanics that had little connection with the methods and theories of the last Chapter. However, there has been now a reconciliation, and calculations of excess functions and of the properties of mixtures of high vapour pressure follow from theories that use the same methods and language as those of the theory of pure liquids. The treatment of mixtures in this Chapter is, therefore, not in historical order but keeps as closely as possible to the methods of the last.

9.2 RANDOM MIXTURES

The starting point of theories of mixtures is the configuration integral, Q. This is given by an obvious generalization of (8.12) to an assembly of N_α molecules of species α, N_β of species β, etc., all of which are in this Section assumed to be spherically symmetrical

$$Q = \frac{1}{\prod_\alpha N_\alpha!} \int \ldots \int e^{-\mathscr{U}/kT} \, d\mathbf{r}_1 \ldots d\mathbf{r}_N \qquad (9.1)$$

where

$$\sum_\alpha N_\alpha = N \qquad (9.2)$$

The configuration energy, $\mathscr{U}$, now depends not only on the positions of the N molecules but also on what may be called their assignment by species to these positions. That is, the value of $\mathscr{U}$ is altered if the chemical species of a pair of molecules at two given positions $\mathbf{r}_i$ and $\mathbf{r}_j$ is changed from, say, α at i and β at j to, say, γ at i and β at j, or to γ at i and δ at j. In a pure liquid $\mathscr{U}$ is a function only of the positions $\mathbf{r}_i$ and not of the assignment of the indistinguishable molecules to these N positions.

The direct evaluation of Q is, of course, even more difficult for a mixture than for a pure substance. Fortunately, it need not be attempted, since the calculation of the excess thermodynamic functions requires only the elucidation of the relation between Q of the mixture and Q of the pure substance, and not the complete evaluation of either. Even this limited objective can only be achieved for certain forms of the intermolecular potential and after the introduction of new approximations.

It was seen in the last Chapter that the most fruitful manipulations of Q were those that led to the principle of corresponding states and to the calculation of small deviations from it. It is natural to seek first the analogous results for a mixture. However, the dimensional arguments of Section 8.4 cannot be used directly because of the dependence of $\mathcal{U}$ on the assignment of the molecules to the N positions of each configuration. The energy is independent of the assignment only if all types of molecules have the same potential, as, for example, in an isotopic mixture. The species are there distributed at random over all assignments and a comparison of the configuration integral of the mixture with that of one of the pure isotopic components shows that the mixture is ideal. The ideal free energy and entropy of mixing are obtained at once from

$$A(V, T) - A_0(V, T) = -kT \ln (Q/Q_0) = kT \ln (\prod_\alpha N_\alpha!/N!)$$

(9.3)

by using Stirling's approximation for the factorials. Here A is the configurational free energy of the mixture and A_0 that of an equal amount of one of the pure components. This equation holds only for a mixture that obeys the laws of classical mechanics. Isotopic mixtures are not ideal at low temperatures, as was shown in Section 5.6.

This result suggests that the simplification of Q is most easily achieved for a non-ideal mixture by replacing $\mathcal{U}$ in (9.1) by its average over all assignments of molecules to the N positions of each configuration. This approximation defines a *random mixture*. The average over assignments is made separately for every possible configuration of the N molecules in the volume V—the configurations are not restricted, for example, to those of a lattice. The concept of a random mixture is important, since this is a type to which the principle of corresponding states may be extended and, as the approximation is mathematically well defined, it has served as a starting point for more sophisticated attempts to evaluate Q.

Prigogine and his colleagues[1,2], Scott[3], Byers Brown[4,5] and Kirkwood and his colleagues[6,7] have all formulated the theory of random mixtures and have suggested methods of improvement. The treatments are essentially the same in content. This account follows closely the full exposition of Byers Brown[4].

The true value of $\mathscr{U}$ is

$$\mathscr{U} = \sum_{i>j}\sum u(r_{ij}) \tag{9.4}$$

where i and j denote a pair of molecules of any species.

The average value of $\mathscr{U}$ over all assignments is

$$\langle\mathscr{U}\rangle = \sum_{i>j}\sum \langle u(r_{ij})\rangle \tag{9.5}$$

where the average of u is found from the probability that position $\mathbf{r}_i$ is occupied by a molecule of species α and position $\mathbf{r}_j$ by one of species β, and a summation over all species. There are N positions and so the probability that position i is occupied by a molecule of species α is (N_α/N) or x_α, if the distribution is random. The probability of a molecule of species β at position j is similarly x_β. Hence

$$\langle u(r_{ij})\rangle = \sum_\alpha \sum_\beta x_\alpha x_\beta u_{\alpha\beta}(r_{ij}), \qquad \langle\mathscr{U}\rangle = \sum_{i>j}\sum \sum_\alpha \sum_\beta x_\alpha x_\beta u_{\alpha\beta}(r_{ij}) \tag{9.6}$$

It is convenient to introduce a hypothetical pure substance whose intermolecular potential is the average over all assignments, $\langle u(r)\rangle$, and to call it the *equivalent substance* for composition x. The substitution of (9.6) into (9.1) shows that the random mixture is equivalent to an ideal isotopic mixture of molecules of the equivalent substance for that composition. That is

$$A(V, T, x) = A_x(V, T) + NkT \sum_\alpha x_\alpha \ln x_\alpha \tag{9.7}$$

$$A_x(V, T) = -kT \ln Q_x$$
$$= -kT \ln\left[\frac{1}{N!}\int \cdots \int e^{-\langle\mathscr{U}\rangle/kT} \, d\mathbf{r}_1 \ldots d\mathbf{r}_N\right] \tag{9.8}$$

where A_x is the configurational free energy of an equal number of molecules of the equivalent substance. The latter changes with x and a further simplification of (9.7) and (9.8) can be made only after the introduction of a restriction on the form of the intermolecular potential. Without such a restriction, $\langle u(r)\rangle$ of (9.6) need not be conformal with the $u_{\alpha\beta}(r)$ of which it is composed, and so the thermodynamic properties of the equivalent substance could not be calculated from (9.8) by the principle of corresponding states. It has been proved rigorously that this extension of the principle of corresponding states to mixtures can be made only for Lennard-Jones potentials, with no restriction on the indices n and m except that they should each be the same for all interactions[4,8]. This condition is more restrictive than the corresponding requirement for pure substances, (8.113), although the Lennard-Jones potential is, of course, a particular case of this equation. The averaging of $u(r)$ over all assignments for a Lennard-Jones potential gives

$$\langle u(r) \rangle = \langle \lambda \rangle r^{-n} - \langle \nu \rangle r^{-m} \tag{9.9}$$

$$\langle \lambda \rangle = \sum_\alpha \sum_\beta x_\alpha x_\beta \lambda_{\alpha\beta}, \qquad \langle \nu \rangle = \sum_\alpha \sum_\beta x_\alpha x_\beta \nu_{\alpha\beta} \tag{9.10}$$

Now the Lennard-Jones potential is conformal with that of a reference species and related to it by

$$u_{\alpha\beta}(r) = f_{\alpha\beta} u_{00}(r/g_{\alpha\beta}) \qquad \text{(cf. 8.113)} \tag{9.11}$$

where f and g have the meanings given in Section 8.4. In terms of the parameters λ and ν

$$f_{\alpha\beta} = \left(\frac{\nu_{\alpha\beta}}{\nu_{00}}\right)^{\frac{n}{n-m}} \left(\frac{\lambda_{\alpha\beta}}{\lambda_{00}}\right)^{\frac{-m}{n-m}} \tag{9.12}$$

$$g_{\alpha\beta} = \left(\frac{\nu_{\alpha\beta}}{\nu_{00}}\right)^{\frac{-1}{n-m}} \left(\frac{\lambda_{\alpha\beta}}{\lambda_{00}}\right)^{\frac{1}{n-m}} \tag{9.13}$$

and so f_x and g_x, the ratios for the equivalent substances, are given by

$$f_x = (\sum_\alpha \sum_\beta x_\alpha x_\beta f_{\alpha\beta} g_{\alpha\beta}^m)^{\frac{n}{n-m}} (\sum_\alpha \sum_\beta x_\alpha x_\beta f_{\alpha\beta} g_{\alpha\beta}^n)^{\frac{-m}{n-m}} \tag{9.14}$$

$$g_x = (\sum_\alpha \sum_\beta x_\alpha x_\beta f_{\alpha\beta} g_{\alpha\beta}^m)^{\frac{-1}{n-m}} (\sum_\alpha \sum_\beta x_\alpha x_\beta f_{\alpha\beta} g_{\alpha\beta}^n)^{\frac{1}{n-m}} \tag{9.15}$$

It follows at once from (8.116) and the corresponding equation for G that

$$A_x(V, T) = f_x A_0(V/g_x^3, T/f_x) - 3NkT \ln g_x \tag{9.16}$$

$$G_x(p, T) = f_x G_0(pg_x^3/f_x, T/f_x) - 3NkT \ln g_x \tag{9.17}$$

Differentiation of (9.16) with respect to volume gives for a system of one phase

$$p(V, T, x) = p_x(V, T) = (f_x/g_x^3) p_0(V/g_x^3, T/f_x) \tag{9.18}$$

Subtraction of the Gibbs free energy of the components from (9.17) gives

$$G^E(p, T, x) = f_x G_0(pg_x^3/f_x, T/f_x)$$
$$- \sum_\alpha x_\alpha f_{\alpha\alpha} G_0(pg_{\alpha\alpha}^3/f_{\alpha\alpha}, T/f_{\alpha\alpha}) - 3NkT \sum_\alpha x_\alpha \ln (g_x/g_{\alpha\alpha}) \tag{9.19}$$

Other excess functions are obtainable by differentiation. These equations are the generalization of the principle of corresponding states to random mixtures and the calculations of the excess functions of these. The gas–liquid critical points of the mixtures cannot be obtained simply from (9.18) and the critical constants of the pure reference substance, as the former are determined by the breakdown of material stability and the latter of mechanical stability (see Section 9.6).

The excess free energy is given exactly (for this model) by (9.19) but is not in a form where the effects of the parameters f and g are apparent. Prigogine and his colleagues[1,2] have described graphical methods for calculating the change in G on moving from, say, (p, T) to (p', T'). These facilitate the calculation of G^E and are the best way of making numerical comparisons with experiment. The meaning of (9.19) is made more clear, however, by expanding G in powers of $(p - p')$ and $(T - T')$. The coefficients of this Taylor expansion are the thermodynamic properties of the reference species. It is convenient to assume that the second derivatives, $(\partial V/\partial p)_T$, $(\partial V/\partial T)_p$ and C_p are constants. The results of Chapter 2 show that this is a reasonable, if crude, assumption for liquids at low temperatures. The use of this Taylor series in (9.19) and in its differentiated forms gives at zero pressure

$$G^E = (U - TC_p)_0 f^E + (TC_p)_0 \ln^E f - NkT \ln^E h \quad (9.20)$$

$$H^E = (U - TC_p)_0 f^E \quad (9.21)$$

$$TS^E = -(TC_p)_0 \ln^E f + NkT \ln^E h \quad (9.22)$$

$$V^E = (V - VT\alpha_p)_0 h^E + (VT\alpha_p)_0 (h/f)^E \quad (9.23)$$

where

$$f^E = f_x - \sum_\alpha x_\alpha f_{\alpha\alpha}, \qquad \ln^E f = \ln f_x - \sum_\alpha x_\alpha \ln f_{\alpha\alpha}, \quad \text{etc.}$$
$$(9.24)$$

and where a volume ratio, h, has been used to replace g^3, the cube of the linear scale factor in the potentials.

The thermodynamic functions on the right-hand side of these equations are evaluated for the reference substance at the same pressure and temperature as the mixture. These equations are further simplified if all the molecules are the same size (all $h_{\alpha\beta}$ equal). The excess functions can then conveniently be written as the sum of two terms, one of which is directly proportional to f^E and

312

the other of a higher order in the differences between the f parameters

$$f^E = \sum_{\alpha > \beta}\sum x_\alpha x_\beta (2f_{\alpha\beta} - f_{\alpha\alpha} - f_{\beta\beta}), \quad \text{etc.} \tag{9.25}$$

$$G^E = (U)_0 f^E + (TC_p)_0[\ln^E f - f^E] \tag{9.26}$$

$$H^E = (U - TC_p)_0 f^E \tag{9.27}$$

$$TS^E = (-TC_p)_0 f^E - (TC_p)_0[\ln^E f - f^E] \tag{9.28}$$

$$V^E = (-VT\alpha_p)_0 f^E + (VT\alpha_p)_0[(1/f)^E + f^E] \tag{9.29}$$

The terms in square brackets are all of the order of the square of the differences in f. Thus, to the first order of the energy differences between molecules of equal size, G^E, H^E, TS^E and V^E are all proportional to each other and, because of the uniformly negative coefficients of f^E, are either all negative or all positive. These first-order terms were obtained by Longuet-Higgins[9] several years before the full study of random mixtures. His method was a perturbation one for the calculation of Q_x from Q_0, and is exact to the first-order terms. These may be obtained for any conformal potentials of the type (9.11) and are not restricted to Lennard-Jones potentials as are the more complete equations above. (Neither his treatment nor that above is restricted to zero pressure but excess functions can only be discussed usefully in liquids for which energies of the order of pV are quite negligible and are omitted from (9.20)–(9.29). Such terms must, of course, be retained in G^E if it is to be used to give V^E by differentiation.)

There are many simple mixtures in which the higher-order terms in (9.26)–(9.29) may not be omitted. The most important are the *Lorentz–Berthelot mixtures* (Section 7.3) for which $f_{\alpha\beta}$ are the geometric means of $f_{\alpha\alpha}$ and $f_{\beta\beta}$. In such an equimolar binary mixture of molecules of equal size

$$f_{12}^2 = f_{11}f_{22}, \quad f_{x=1/2} = \tfrac{1}{4}(f_{11}^{1/2} + f_{22}^{1/2})^2 \tag{9.30}$$

and f^E, $\ln^E f$ and $(1/f)^E$ are all of second order in the difference $(f_{22} - f_{11})$, and, to this order

$$f^E = -\ln^E f = \tfrac{1}{3}(1/f)^E < 0 \tag{9.31}$$

Hence in such mixtures

$$G^E > H^E > 0 > TS^E, \quad V^E < 0 \tag{9.32}$$

Thus Lorentz–Berthelot mixtures of molecules of equal size do not have all excess functions of the same sign but have positive heats and free energies, and negative entropies and volumes. The behaviour predicted by (9.30)–(9.32) covers an important class of mixtures and has been confirmed experimentally in suitably chosen cases. The first theoretical model to show this behaviour was a simple lattice model, that is, an extension of the treatment of Lennard-Jones and Devonshire to binary mixtures. Prigogine and his colleagues[10] made extensive calculations with this model which have now been superseded by those based on the theory of random mixtures. One of the biggest disadvantages of the lattice model is its inability to treat mixtures of molecules of different sizes, and it is interesting, therefore, to examine next random mixtures of Lorentz–Berthelot molecules of unequal size.

The complete expression for the excess free energy of a Lorentz–Berthelot mixture is obtained by making a Taylor expansion of G_x (9.17) to the second order of the differences $\delta f_x = (f_x - 1)$ and $\delta h_x = (h_x - 1)$. Here a reference substance is chosen for which $f_{00} = h_{00} = 1$. This expansion may be written

$$G_x = G_0 + G_f(\delta f_x) + G_h(\delta h_x) + \tfrac{1}{2}G_{ff}(\delta f_x)^2$$
$$+ G_{fh}(\delta f_x)(\delta h_x) + \tfrac{1}{2}G_{hh}(\delta h_x)^2 + \ldots \quad (9.33)$$

where G_f, etc. are properties of the reference substance that are obtained by differentiation with respect to, say, $f_{\alpha\alpha}$ and $h_{\alpha\alpha}$ of an equation for G_α that is obtained by substituting $f_{\alpha\alpha}$ for f_x, etc. in (9.17). These thermodynamic functions are collected in the Appendix (A.3–A.10). The differences δf_x and δh_x are found by differentiating (9.14) and (9.15), with $g^3 = h$. Substitution in (9.33) gives

$$G_x = G_0 + G_f(\Delta f) + G_h(\Delta h) + \tfrac{1}{2}G_{ff}(\Delta f)^2$$
$$+ G_{fh}(\Delta fh) + G_{fh}(\Delta f)(\Delta h)$$
$$+ \tfrac{1}{2}Z_{hh}(\Delta h^2) + \tfrac{1}{2}[G_{hh} - Z_{hh}](\Delta h)^2 \quad (9.34)$$

where

$$(\Delta f) = \sum_\alpha \sum_\beta x_\alpha x_\beta \, \delta f_{\alpha\beta}, \quad (\Delta fh) = \sum_\alpha \sum_\beta x_\alpha x_\beta \, \delta f_{\alpha\beta} \, \delta h_{\alpha\beta}, \quad \text{etc.} \quad (9.35)$$

$$Z_{hh} = -\frac{nm}{9}G_f + \left(\frac{n+m-3}{3}\right)G_h \quad (9.36)$$

The first-order terms in (Δf) and (Δh) are again those obtained first by Longuet-Higgins[9]. The excess free energy is found by subtraction of $\sum_\alpha x_\alpha G_\alpha$ from (9.34). It is written most simply by introducing the differences*

$$e_{\alpha\beta} = 2f_{\alpha\beta} - f_{\alpha\alpha} - f_{\beta\beta}, \quad s_{\alpha\beta} = 2h_{\alpha\beta} - h_{\alpha\alpha} - h_{\beta\beta} \quad (9.37)$$
$$\theta_{\alpha\beta} = f_{\alpha\alpha} - f_{\beta\beta}, \quad \varphi_{\alpha\beta} = h_{\alpha\alpha} - h_{\beta\beta} \quad (9.38)$$

* These may be translated into the notation of Prigogine[2], $e = 2\theta$, $\theta = \delta$, $\varphi = 3\rho$. He uses no symbol for the difference s.

by restricting the mixture to two components, by defining the reference substance by the equations

$$f_{00} = \tfrac{1}{2}(f_{11} + f_{22}) = 1, \qquad h_{00} = \tfrac{1}{2}(h_{11} + h_{22}) = 1 \quad (9.39)$$

and by omitting terms of second order in e_{12} and s_{12}. This omission is often a useful approximation, as there are no first-order terms in θ and φ. Hence if e and s are of the same order as θ and φ, then their first-order terms are dominant, and if they are of the order of θ^2 and φ^2 (as in a Lorentz–Berthelot mixture), then their squares are negligible. With these simplifications

$$G^E/x_1 x_2 = G_f e_{12} + G_h s_{12} - \tfrac{1}{2} G_{ff} \theta_{12}^2$$
$$- (G_{fh} - \tfrac{1}{2} G_h) \theta_{12} \varphi_{12} - \tfrac{1}{2}(G_{hh} - \tfrac{1}{2} Z_{hh}) \varphi_{12}^2 \quad (9.40)$$

The equations for a Lorentz–Berthelot mixture are worth writing out in full. Here

$$e_{12} = -\tfrac{1}{4} \theta_{12}^2, \qquad s_{12} = -\tfrac{1}{6} \varphi_{12}^2 \quad (9.41)$$

and so

$$G^E/x_1 x_2 = G_{\theta\theta} \theta_{12}^2 + G_{\theta\phi} \theta_{12} \varphi_{12} + G_{\phi\phi} \varphi_{12}^2 \quad (9.42)$$

where, at zero pressure,

$$G_{\theta\theta} = -\tfrac{1}{4} U + \tfrac{1}{2} T C_p \quad (9.43)$$

$$G_{\theta\varphi} = -\tfrac{1}{2} Nk T \quad (9.44)$$

$$G_{\varphi\varphi} = -\frac{nm}{36} U - \left(\frac{n + m + 1}{12}\right) Nk T \quad (9.45)$$

and by differentiation

$$TS_{\theta\theta} = -\tfrac{1}{4} T C_p - \tfrac{1}{2} T^2 (\partial C_p/\partial T)_p \quad (9.46)$$

$$TS_{\theta\varphi} = \tfrac{1}{2} Nk T \quad (9.47)$$

$$TS_{\varphi\varphi} = \frac{nm}{36} T C_p + \left(\frac{n + m + 1}{12}\right) Nk T \quad (9.48)$$

$$V_{\theta\theta} = -\tfrac{3}{4} V T \alpha_p - \tfrac{1}{2} V T^2 \alpha_p^2 - \tfrac{1}{2} V T^2 (\partial \alpha_p/\partial T)_p \quad (9.49)$$

$$V_{\theta\varphi} = \tfrac{1}{2} V + V T \alpha_p \quad (9.50)$$

$$V_{\varphi\varphi} = \frac{nm}{36} V T \alpha_p + \left(\frac{n + m - 5}{12}\right) V \quad (9.51)$$

These equations for a random mixture of Lorentz–Berthelot molecules are those of Byers Brown[4] (eqn. 11.21–11.28), of Scott[3] (eqn. 30A–33A, after the introduction of (9.41) above) for what he calls a *single-liquid approximation,* of Prigogine, Bellemans and

315

THE STATISTICAL THERMODYNAMICS OF MIXTURES

Englert-Chwoles[1] (eqn. 4.31 and 4.32 for $G_{\theta\theta}$ and $V_{\theta\theta}$ only), and of Prigogine[2] (eqn. 9.54–9.57), after the introduction of (9.41), for what he calls the *crude approximation*. (There is, however, an omission of a factor of 3 from part of Prigogine's equation for the excess volume. He has the first term of (9.50) above as $V/6$ and the second term of (9.51) as $(n + m - 5)V/36$.)

The configurational thermodynamic functions in (9.43)–(9.51) have been calculated for 1 mole of liquid argon and liquid methane at their normal boiling points, and of liquid carbon tetrachloride at

Table 9.1. The coefficients of (9.42)-(9.51) for a random mixture of Lorentz–Berthelot molecules

		θ^2	$\theta\varphi$	φ^2
Argon at 87·3 K (normal boiling point)	g^E/x_1x_2RT	+3·80	−0·50	+14·5
	h^E/x_1x_2RT	+2·60	0	+23·2
	s^E/x_1x_2R	−1·20	+0·50	+ 8·7
	v^E/x_1x_2v	−0·51	+0·89	+1·87
Methane at 111·7 K (normal boiling point)	g^E/x_1x_2RT	+3·80	−0·50	+14·4
	h^E/x_1x_2RT	+2·40	0	+23·3
	s^E/x_1x_2R	−1·40	+0·50	+ 8·9
	v^E/x_1x_2v	−0·53	+0·87	+1·83
Carbon tetrachloride at 20°C	g^E/x_1x_2RT	+6·8	−0·50	+25·2
	h^E/x_1x_2RT	+5·1	0	+40·5
	s^E/x_1x_2R	−1·7	+0·50	+15·3
	v^E/x_1x_2v	−0·44	+0·86	+1·79

20°C. All the functions needed are tabulated in Chapter 2 except for the configurational energy of carbon tetrachloride which was obtained from Timmermans. A (12,6) potential has been used for the coefficients of φ^2. The results are shown in *Table 9.1*.

The simplified equations for molecules of equal sizes predicted positive excess heats and free energies and negative excess entropies and volumes for Lorentz–Berthelot mixtures. The more complete equations predict these signs within certain ranges of the parameters θ and φ.

This may be shown graphically by plotting the equations $G^E = 0$, etc. as functions of the parameters. They are simple binary quadratic equations in θ and φ that have real roots if the square of the coefficient of $\theta\varphi$ is larger than four times the product of the coefficients of θ^2 and φ^2. This is true for S^E and V^E, for both of which this product is negative, but not for G^E and H^E. The former can, therefore, have either sign and the latter are always positive.

316

The boundaries separating values of θ and φ for which S^E and V^E are positive and negative are shown in *Figure 9.1*, by using the figures for argon in *Table 9.1* as those of the reference substance. The sizes of these parameters are limited by the requirement that G^E in the equimolar mixture should be less than $\frac{1}{2}NkT$ for the mixture to be materially stable. This limits θ and φ to an *ellipse of miscibility*[3,4] as shown. The boundary of this ellipse is of little practical

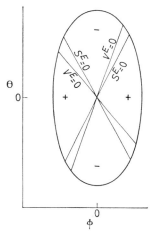

Figure 9.1. The signs of the excess entropy and volume in a random mixture of Lorentz–Berthelot molecules, as functions of θ and φ. The ellipse is the boundary of miscibility

importance, as there are no cases known of immiscibility in mixtures that are believed to conform to the Lorentz–Berthelot equations. Furthermore, it will be shown below (Section 9.4) that it is doubtful if a real mixture which conforms to the Lorentz–Berthelot equations would have the predicted large positive values of V^E along and near the axis $\theta = 0$.

The chemical potential of any component in a mixture with arbitrary values of the parameters is formed by differentiating (9.17) with respect to composition and adding the terms for an ideal mixture. The differentiation is best performed by the method described for a multicomponent mixture in Section 4.2. The result is[4]

$$m\mu_1 = G_x + mRT \ln x_1 + 2\bar{\mathcal{U}} \sum_\alpha x_\alpha (f_{1\alpha}^* - f)/f + 2\bar{\mathcal{V}} \sum_\alpha x_\alpha k_{1\alpha}^*/f$$
$$(9.52)$$

where there are m moles in the mixture and the starred parameters are defined by

$$f_{\alpha\beta}^* \epsilon_{00} = u_{\alpha\beta}(r_x^*) \qquad (9.53)$$

$$k_{\alpha\beta}^* \epsilon_{00} = (3/nm) v_{\alpha\beta}(r_x^*) \qquad (9.54)$$

$$f = \sum_\alpha \sum_\beta x_\alpha x_\beta f_{\alpha\beta}^* \qquad (9.55)$$

where r_x^* is the separation of two molecules at the minimum of energy in the equivalent substance for composition x, and $v(r)$ is again the molecular virial function, (8.39). To the first order of the differences $(h_{\alpha\beta} - h_x)$

$$f_{\alpha\beta}^* = f_{\alpha\beta}, \qquad k_{\alpha\beta}^* = f_{\alpha\beta}(h_{\alpha\beta} - h_x)/h_x \qquad (9.56)$$

so that $k_{\alpha\beta}^*$ vanish in mixtures of molecules of equal size. These starred parameters occur naturally in this equation for the chemical potential and again in the next Section in the theory of ordering, or of deviations from randomness.

9.3 ORDER IN MIXTURES

There are two ways in which the theory of random mixtures is unsatisfactory. First, the initial assumption, that of a random assignment of molecules to the N positions of each configuration, clearly cannot describe the situation in a real liquid where the molecules differ from each other in energy and size and so introduce some order into the assignment. Secondly, it is restricted to spherical Lennard-Jones molecules. The first of these limitations is examined and partially removed in this Section. However, the removal is by no means complete and it is shown in the next Section that both the theory of random mixtures and the more sophisticated treatments of this Section contain a basic flaw when applied to mixtures of molecules of different sizes. The treatment outlined below does, however, deal satisfactorily with the relatively small degree of order introduced by differences of energy. The study of such ordering in systems confined to lattices has a long history in theoretical physics.

Throughout this Chapter the words *order* and *ordering* are used in the sense of departure from the situation implied by (9.5) and (9.6), and should not be taken in any other sense.

The second limitation, to molecules of spherical shape, is deferred to Section 9.7.

The amount of order is small if the molecular energies and sizes are close. It is known that there is no effect on the thermodynamic properties of the mixture to the first order of the differences in the parameters. This follows, for example, from a comparison of (9.40) with the exact expansion of G^E in powers of these differences—the theory of *conformal solutions*[9,11,12]. If the differences e and s (9.37) are large, then first-order terms are dominant in all the excess functions and any corrections for ordering are unlikely to be important except near critical points. However, in a Lorentz–Berthelot mixture both the random and the correction terms are of the same order and generally of similar size. Such mixtures only are considered here in any detail.

A calculation of the effect of order is made by regarding such ordering as a perturbation of a random assembly. Let $\mathcal{U}$ be the configuration energy of a mixture in a particular configuration and with a particular assignment of molecules to its positions. Again let $\langle \mathcal{U} \rangle$ denote an unweighted average of $\mathcal{U}$ over all assignments. The difference in free energy, δA, between the real mixture and a hypothetical random mixture is given by

$$e^{-\delta A/kT} = \overline{e^{-\delta \mathcal{U}/kT}} \tag{9.57}$$

$$\delta \mathcal{U} = \mathcal{U} - \langle \mathcal{U} \rangle \tag{9.58}$$

where the bar denotes a Boltzmann or canonical average over all configurations, as in Section 8.2. This expression for δA can be expanded, to use the nomenclature of statistical mathematics, either as an expansion of *moments*

$$e^{-\delta A/kT} = 1 - \frac{\overline{\delta \mathcal{U}}}{kT} + \frac{\overline{(\delta \mathcal{U})^2}}{2(kT)^2} - \cdots \tag{9.59}$$

or as one of *cumulants*

$$\delta A = \overline{\delta \mathcal{U}} - (\overline{\delta \mathcal{U} - \overline{\delta \mathcal{U}}})^2/2kT + \cdots \tag{9.60}$$

It follows from (9.58) that $\langle \delta \mathcal{U} \rangle$ and, therefore, $\overline{\delta \mathcal{U}}$ are zero, and so, using the algebra of (8.42)–(8.44)

$$\delta A = -(\langle \mathcal{U}^2 \rangle - \langle \mathcal{U} \rangle^2)/2kT + \cdots \tag{9.61}$$

This elegant expression for the free energy of ordering cannot be related to the thermodynamic properties of a reference substance but may be related to the molecular fluctuation integrals of Section 8.2. The averaging of $\mathcal{U}$ and $\mathcal{U}^2$ over all assignments gives[5]

$$\overline{\langle \mathcal{U}^2 \rangle - \langle \mathcal{U} \rangle^2} = \sum_\alpha \sum_\beta \sum_\gamma \sum_\epsilon \left[\tfrac{1}{2} x_\alpha x_\beta (\delta_{\alpha\gamma} \delta_{\beta\epsilon} - x_\gamma x_\epsilon) \sum_{i,j \neq} \sum \right.$$
$$(\overline{u_{\alpha\beta}^{ij} u_{\gamma\epsilon}^{ij}} - \overline{u_{\alpha\beta}}\,\overline{u_{\gamma\epsilon}}) + x_\alpha x_\beta x_\epsilon (\delta_{\alpha\gamma} - x_\gamma)$$
$$\left. \sum_{i,j,k \neq} \sum \sum (\overline{u_{\alpha\beta}^{ij} u_{\gamma\epsilon}^{ik}} - \overline{u_{\alpha\beta}}\,\overline{u_{\gamma\epsilon}}) \right] \tag{9.62}$$

where $\alpha - \epsilon$ are dummy suffixes for the components, i, j and k denote molecules and $\delta_{\alpha\beta}$ is the Kronecker delta that is equal to unity if α and β are the same species and zero otherwise. For a mixture of Lennard-Jones molecules, this formidable expression clearly involves the molecular fluctuation integrals for pairs $(u^{ij})^2$ and for triplets $(u^{ij}u^{ik})$, but not for quadruplets. The introduction of these into (9.62) gives for δA^E and, to this approximation, for δG^E

$$\delta G^E \simeq \delta A^E = \tfrac{1}{2} A^{(2)}_{ff} \Big[\sum_\alpha \sum_\beta x_\alpha x_\beta (f^*_{\alpha\beta}/f)^2 - 1 \Big]$$
$$+ \tfrac{1}{2} A^{(3)}_{ff} \Big[\sum_\alpha \sum_\beta \sum_\gamma x_\alpha x_\beta x_\gamma (f^*_{\alpha\beta} f^*_{\alpha\gamma}/f^2) - 1 \Big]$$
$$+ A^{(2)}_{fk} \Big[\sum_\alpha \sum_\beta x_\alpha x_\beta (f^*_{\alpha\beta} k^*_{\alpha\beta}/f^2) \Big]$$
$$+ A^{(3)}_{fk} \Big[\sum_\alpha \sum_\beta \sum_\gamma x_\alpha x_\beta x_\gamma (f^*_{\alpha\beta} k^*_{\alpha\gamma}/f^2) \Big]$$
$$+ \tfrac{1}{2} A^{(2)}_{kk} \Big[\sum_\alpha \sum_\beta x_\alpha x_\beta (k^*_{\alpha\beta}/f)^2 \Big]$$
$$+ \tfrac{1}{2} A^{(3)}_{kk} \Big[\sum_\alpha \sum_\beta \sum_\gamma x_\alpha x_\beta x_\gamma (k^*_{\alpha\beta} k^*_{\alpha\gamma}/f^2) \Big] \qquad (9.63)$$

where $A^{(2)}_{ff}$, etc. are the fluctuation integrals of Section 8.2 and $f^*_{\alpha\beta}$, etc. and f are defined by (9.53)–(9.55). This expression is greatly simplified for a binary Lorentz–Berthelot mixture.

To the second order in θ and φ

$$\delta G^E / x_1 x_2 = \tfrac{1}{4} G^{(1)}_{ff} \theta^2_{12} + \tfrac{1}{2} G^{(1)}_{fk} \theta_{12}\varphi_{12} + \tfrac{1}{4} G^{(1)}_{kk} \varphi^2_{12} \qquad (9.64)$$

where $G^{(1)}$ is a convenient abbreviation for

$$A^{(1)}_{\xi\eta} = A^{(2)}_{\xi\eta} + \tfrac{1}{2} A^{(3)}_{\xi\eta} = G^{(1)}_{\xi\eta} = G^{(2)}_{\xi\eta} + \tfrac{1}{2} G^{(3)}_{\xi\eta} \quad (\xi, \eta = f, k) \qquad (9.65)$$

The fluctuation functions $A^{(1)}_{ff}$ and $G^{(1)}_{ff}$ have a simple interpretation as heat capacities at constant volume that arise from fluctuations in the *private energy* of a molecule—that is, the sum of its intermolecular potential energies with all other molecules (see Appendix).

Equations similar to (9.64) can be written for δH^E, δS^E and δV^E, the differences between these functions in the ordered and random assemblies. The complete excess functions are obtained by adding δG^E, etc. of (9.64) to G^E of the random mixture (9.42).

This completes the formal perturbation calculation of the effects of ordering on liquid mixtures. The ordering coefficients of a Lorentz–Berthelot mixture are the functions $G^{(1)}_{\xi\eta}$ that are formed of the molecular fluctuation integrals for pairs and triplets of molecules. Nevertheless, these integrals cannot yet be calculated for fluid systems at any but the lowest densities, and any use of (9.64) depends on finding suitable approximations for $G^{(1)}_{\xi\eta}$. Several recent theories of mixtures can be put into a form where they differ only in the approximations that they suggest for these fluctuation integrals. The approximations are as follows[12].

Random mixture

Here the order is neglected completely, and so the fluctuation integrals are put equal to zero

$$G_{\xi\eta}^{(1)} = 0 \qquad (\xi, \eta = f, k) \qquad (9.66)$$

Both the pair and triplet terms that contribute to $G_{\xi\eta}^{(1)}$ are zero, but the theory is consistent in that it gives the correct value of sums $G_{\xi\eta}$ which are experimentally accessible functions of the reference species. These sums are related to the fluctuations of $\mathscr{U}$ and $\mathscr{V}$, (8.63), (8.70), (8.71) and Appendix. Hence the random mixture ascribes the whole of $G_{\xi\eta}$ to the quadruplet term

$$G_{\xi\eta}^{(2)} = G_{\xi\eta}^{(3)} = 0, \qquad G_{\xi\eta}^{(4)} = G_{\xi\eta} \qquad (\xi, \eta = f, k) \qquad (9.67)$$

The *pair correlation* treatment of Kirkwood and his colleagues[7] leads to (9.66), and so to the neglect of any order in these mixtures.

Lattice model

The lattice model of the liquid state (Section 8.6) is the simplest that yields explicit values of the thermodynamic and statistical properties in terms of the intermolecular potential. It is a reasonable approximation to use this model to calculate $G_{\xi\eta}^{(1)}$. This is a much less drastic approximation than the use of the lattice model to calculate the total excess free energy of a Lorentz–Berthelot mixture—that is, the coefficients in (9.42) as well as in (9.64). Nevertheless, the calculation even of the fluctuation integrals requires some assumption about the correlations of the motions of molecules in neighbouring cells. The simplest is that there is no correlation. It is also convenient to neglect interactions between molecules that are not nearest neighbours.

These assumptions lead[5] to expressions for the pair, triplet and quadruplet integrals that are mutually consistent in that their sum is equal to the thermodynamic coefficient $G_{\xi\eta}$. If, however, these expressions are evaluated for argon at its normal boiling point, then the numerical values satisfy neither (8.86) nor the inequality in the Appendix (A.31). These failures show that the simple cell model and a Lennard-Jones potential cannot give a consistent account of the liquid state. The biggest error is probably the neglect of correlations between the positions of neighbouring molecules. The values of $G_{\xi\eta}^{(1)}$ given by this approximation are

$$G_{\xi\eta}^{(1)} = \frac{1}{2}\left(1 + \frac{1}{z}\right)A_{\xi\eta} \qquad (\xi, \eta = f, k) \qquad (9.68)$$

where z is the co-ordination number of the lattice. The coefficients of ordering of H, S and V may be found by suitable differentiation. The three functions A_{ff}, A_{fk} and A_{kk} are all negative (see Appendix, (8.63) and (8.71)), and so the ordering consequent on a difference in energy and/or size leads to a decrease of the excess free energy from that of a random mixture. This is to be expected.

Semi-random mixture at fixed volume

The term *semi-random mixture* is used here to describe a lattice model in which any given molecule has neighbours chosen at random, that is $(x_\alpha z)$ of species α. This restriction is not quite so drastic as that of the full random mixture of the last Section but can be applied only to a lattice model. The mean energy of interaction of any molecule with a neighbour is now

$$u_\alpha(r) = \sum_\beta x_\beta u_{\alpha\beta}(r) = f_\alpha u_{00}(r/g_\alpha) \tag{9.69}$$

where f_α and g_α are functions of the composition given by

$$f_\alpha = (\sum_\beta x_\beta f_{\alpha\beta} g_{\alpha\beta}^m)^{\frac{n}{n-m}} (\sum_\beta x_\beta f_{\alpha\beta} g_{\alpha\beta}^n)^{\frac{-m}{n-m}} \tag{9.70}$$

$$g_\alpha = (\sum_\beta x_\beta f_{\alpha\beta} g_{\alpha\beta}^m)^{\frac{-1}{n-m}} (\sum_\beta x_\beta f_{\alpha\beta} g_{\alpha\beta}^n)^{\frac{1}{n-m}} \tag{9.71}$$

(compare (9.14) and (9.15) for the random mixture).

It is now necessary to make an assumption that the size of the cell for each molecule of species α is proportional to g_α^3 in order to obtain an explicit expression for the free energy

$$A(V, T, x) = NkT \sum_\alpha x_\alpha \ln x_\alpha$$
$$+ \sum_\alpha x_\alpha [f_\alpha A_0(V/g_\alpha^3, T/f_\alpha) - 3NkT \ln g_\alpha] \tag{9.72}$$

This gives for the coefficient of ordering

$$G_{\xi\eta}^{(1)} = \tfrac{1}{2} A_{\xi\eta} \qquad (\xi, \eta = f, k) \tag{9.73}$$

This approximation has been used by Rice[13], Prigogine and his colleagues[1,2] and Byers Brown[5]. It is seen that the semi-random mixture has the same coefficients of ordering as the lattice model if the co-ordination number of the lattice is put equal to infinity. This equality has been known for many years for earlier lattice theories of mixtures[14].

Semi-random mixture at fixed pressure

The last approximation is perhaps the most straightforward use of a lattice model for the calculation of $G_{\xi\eta}^{(1)}$ but is not in practice the most useful. It is based essentially on a spatially homogeneous lattice of fixed volume. A similar treatment of a deformable lattice (with again plausible but arbitrary assumptions about the sizes of the cells for molecules of different species) led Scott[3] (eqn. 23B–33B) and Prigogine[2] (Sections 10.6–10.8) to an approximation similar to (9.72) but for the Gibbs free energy

$$G(p, T, x) = NkT \sum_\alpha x_\alpha \ln x_\alpha + \sum_\alpha x_\alpha [f_\alpha G_0(pg_\alpha^3/f_\alpha, T/f_\alpha)$$

$$- 3NkT \ln g_\alpha] \quad (9.74)$$

At a fixed zero pressure this gives for the coefficients of ordering

$$G_{\xi\eta}^{(1)} = \tfrac{1}{2} G_{\xi\eta} \qquad (\xi, \eta = f, k) \quad (9.75)$$

The published versions of this treatment[1-3] differ a little from each other and from (9.75) because of slight differences in the assumptions that are needed in any lattice model of mixtures. The numerical values of the coefficients are almost identical.

Bellemans, Mathot and Simon[15] call this approximation 'the second refined version of the average potential model'. They use the name *average potential model* to describe all theories of the kind discussed so far in this Chapter. However, in this book the name is restricted to (9.74) since, in practice, this is the only version that the Brussels School has used extensively in the last ten years.

It is seen that (9.72) and (9.74) differ in structure from the equations for a random mixture, (9.16) and (9.17). In the latter, we choose one hypothetical pure fluid to represent the mixture and assign to its energy and size parameters the values given by (9.14) and (9.15). However, in (9.72) and in (9.74)—the two are not equivalent—we choose as many hypothetical pure fluids as there are components in the mixture, that is, two for a binary mixture. To each of these we assign parameters f_α and g_α, given by (9.70) and (9.71). Here all approximations of this kind are called *two-fluid models* to distinguish them as a group from the *one-fluid models* of which the random mixture is the best known example. This notation is a generalization of that proposed by Scott[3] and will be found useful in the next Section.

The coefficients of the ordering term in G^E are given formally for a Lorentz–Berthelot mixture by (9.64). The two semi-random approximations set out above lead to the following expressions for these fluctuation integrals, which are obtained from the equations in the Appendix.

Coefficients of $\delta G^E/x_1 x_2$ in (9.64)

Semi-random mixture at fixed volume

$\theta^2 \quad -\frac{1}{8}TC_V$

$\theta\varphi \quad \frac{1}{4}(NkT - VT\gamma_V)$

$\varphi^2 \quad \frac{1}{8}\left(\frac{nm}{9}U + \left(\frac{n+m}{3}\right)NkT - \left(\frac{n+m+3}{3}\right)pV + V/\beta_T\right)$

Semi-random mixture at fixed pressure

$\theta^2 \quad \frac{1}{8}(-TC_p + 2pVT\alpha_p - p^2V\beta_T)$

$\theta\varphi \quad \frac{1}{4}(NkT - pV - pVT\alpha_p + p^2V\beta_T)$

$\varphi^2 \quad \frac{1}{8}\left(\frac{nm}{9}U + \left(\frac{n+m}{3}\right)NkT - \left(\frac{n+m-3}{3}\right)pV - p^2V\beta_T\right)$

The coefficients of δH^E, δS^E and δV^E can be found by differentiation.

The coefficients of ordering have been calculated for the three liquids argon, methane and carbon tetrachloride, for which those of a random mixture are shown in *Table 9.1*. The coefficients of δG^E above can be readily calculated from the tables of Chapter 2, but those of δS^E and δV^E for a semi-random mixture at fixed volume cannot be very accurately computed, as they make too great demands on our knowledge of the properties of the three reference liquids. It has been necessary to assume that $T(\partial^2 p/\partial T^2)_V$ is negligible compared with $(\partial p/\partial T)_V$, whereas what little information we have of this second derivative suggests that the ratio of these two functions may be as large as $\frac{1}{3}$. However, neglect of the second derivative leads to the two identities

$$\left(\frac{\partial^2 V}{\partial T^2}\right)_p + 2\left(\frac{\partial p}{\partial T}\right)_V\left(\frac{\partial^2 V}{\partial T\,\partial p}\right) + \left(\frac{\partial p}{\partial T}\right)_V^2\left(\frac{\partial^2 V}{\partial p^2}\right)_T = 0 \quad (9.76)$$

$$\left(\frac{\partial^2 p}{\partial T\,\partial V}\right) = -\left(\frac{\partial p}{\partial V}\right)_T^2\left[\left(\frac{\partial^2 V}{\partial p\,\partial T}\right) - \left(\frac{\partial p}{\partial T}\right)_V\left(\frac{\partial^2 V}{\partial p^2}\right)_T\right] \quad (9.77)$$

The derivatives $(\partial^2 V/\partial T^2)_p$ and $(\partial^2 V/\partial T\,\partial p)$ can be found from $(\partial\alpha_p/\partial T)_p$ and $(\partial\beta_T/\partial T)_p$, respectively and these two equations then give $(\partial^2 V/\partial p^2)_T$ and $(\partial^2 p/\partial T\partial V)$. The results of these calculations are shown in *Tables 9.2* and *9.3*.

A comparison of these coefficients with those of the random mixture (*Table 9.1*) shows that differences in energy alone do not lead to significant departures from randomness. The coefficients of θ^2 in *Tables 9.2* and *9.3* are all small compared with those of *Table 9.1*. However, mixtures of molecules of different size are far from random,

Table 9.2. The coefficients of ordering (9.64) etc., for a semi-random mixture at fixed *volume* of Lorentz–Berthelot molecules

		θ^2	$\theta\varphi$	φ^2
Argon at 87·3 K				
(normal boiling point)	$\delta g^E/x_1 x_2 RT$	−0·10	−1·50	−5·1
	$\delta h^E/x_1 x_2 RT$	0·00	−2·66	−4·5
	$\delta s^E/x_1 x_2 R$	+0·10	−1·16	+0·6
	$\delta v^E/x_1 x_2 v$	0·00	−0·38	+0·03
Methane at 111·7 K				
(normal boiling point)	$\delta g^E/x_1 x_2 RT$	−0·10	−1·63	−4·7
	$\delta h^E/x_1 x_2 RT$	0·00	−1·25	−4·5
	$\delta s^E/x_1 x_2 R$	+0·10	+0·38	−0·2
	$\delta v^E/x_1 x_2 v$	0·00	−0·16	−0·34
Carbon tetrachloride				
at 20°C	$\delta g^E/x_1 x_2 RT$	−0·2	−3·2	−7·9
	$\delta h^E/x_1 x_2 RT$	0·0	−0·7	−6·1
	$\delta s^E/x_1 x_2 R$	+0·2	+2·5	+1·8
	$\delta v^E/x_1 x_2 v$	0·00	−0·35	+0·07

for the coefficients of φ^2 are comparable with those of the random mixture. Ordering at fixed volume reduces the excess free energy by about $\frac{1}{3}$ and at fixed pressure by about $\frac{1}{2}$.

These changes in the excess free energy are of the expected sign but are disappointingly large. They suggest that the theory of the random mixture badly overestimates the excess free energy of mixtures of molecules of different size, and it is shown in the following Sections that this is supported by comparison with experiment.

Table 9.3. The coefficients of ordering, (9.64) etc., for a semi-random mixture at fixed *pressure* of Lorentz–Berthelot molecules

		θ^2	$\theta\varphi$	φ^2
Argon at 87·3 K				
(normal boiling point)	$\delta g^E/x_1 x_2 RT$	−0·45	+0·25	−7·3
	$\delta h^E/x_1 x_2 RT$	+0·08	0·00	−11·6
	$\delta s^E/x_1 x_2 R$	+0·53	−0·25	−4·3
	$\delta v^E/x_1 x_2 v$	+0·03	−0·10	−1·46
Methane at 111·7 K				
(normal boiling point)	$\delta g^E/x_1 x_2 RT$	−0·45	+0·25	−7·2
	$\delta h^E/x_1 x_2 RT$	+0·21	0·00	−11·6
	$\delta s^E/x_1 x_2 R$	+0·66	−0·25	−4·4
	$\delta v^E/x_1 x_2 v$	+0·03	−0·11	−1·43
Carbon tetrachloride				
at 20°C	$\delta g^E/x_1 x_2 RT$	−0·86	+0·25	−12·6
	$\delta h^E/x_1 x_2 RT$	0·00	0·00	−20·2
	$\delta s^E/x_1 x_2 R$	+0·86	−0·25	−7·6
	$\delta v^E/x_1 x_2 v$	+0·05	−0·09	−1·38

9.4 VAN DER WAALS'S APPROXIMATION

The disquieting size of the ordering terms in φ^2 has been noted above. A more serious criticism of the random-mixing approximation and its derivatives is the singular nature of the basic equations for f_x and g_x, (9.14) and (9.15), and for f_α and g_α, (9.70) and (9.71), when the repulsive index of the pair potential, n, approaches infinity. Consider, for example, (9.15). If n becomes infinite whilst m remains finite, then g_x becomes equal to the largest coefficient of the set $g_{\alpha\beta}$ and is independent of composition. That is, we have the absurd result that the single substance chosen to represent the mixture is composed of molecules whose size is that of the largest molecule present, even if the mole fraction of that species is vanishingly small.

This singularity does not affect the first-order terms of (9.25)–(9.29), but its consequences are apparent in those second-order terms that arise from differences of size, (9.36), (9.45), (9.48), (9.51), and in the corresponding ordering terms A_{kk} of (9.73) and G_{kk} of (9.75). If the theories of the last two Sections were applied to a mixture of hard spheres of different sizes, then G^E would be positive infinite. Indeed, it is clear that this must be so, since it is the essence of random mixing that the chance of finding a large molecule in a given molecular environment is the same as that of finding a small one. The replacement of a small molecule by a large one in an already close-packed local configuration must lead to the overlapping of the hard spheres and so to a positive infinite value of $\mathscr{U}$ for that configuration.

Thus the theory of random mixing must be abandoned as a starting point for the discussion of mixtures of hard spheres, and hence also for that of mixtures of real molecules, since these have steep potentials, that is, large values of n. However, it is difficult to choose an alternative starting point that has the same mathematically well-defined basis and is, therefore, open to a systematic improvement, such as that set out in the last Section.

The 'experimental' facts are as follows. Computer simulation of the behaviour of a binary mixture of hard spheres shows that V^E, far from being large and positive, is small and negative as long as the mixture remains in the fluid state[16], that is at a pressure below that of the transition in *Figure 8.4*. Since U^E is zero for hard spheres ($\mathscr{U} = 0$ for all accessible configurations), G^E is related to V^E by the integral

$$G^E(p^*, T^*) = \int_0^{p^*} V^E(p, T^*)\, dp \qquad (9.78)$$

Hence the experimental value of G^E is also small and negative. The contraction on mixing implies that the structure of the mixture differs qualitatively from that of each pure fluid in that there is some degree of microscopic segregation; for example, small spheres may tend to occupy the gaps between the larger. This effect is certainly found in mechanical mixtures of metal balls of different sizes. Such a structure is, of course, the antithesis of a random mixture.

The computer studies[16] show also that V^E becomes large and positive as soon as the mixture enters the solid phase. Here the geometry of the crystal constrains the spheres of different size into a common structure and so makes the system approach more nearly that of their random assignment to the sites of the lattice. These considerations are, however, irrelevant in the fluid phase.

It was shown in Section 8.6 that the Percus–Yevick (PY) theory led to an accurate representation of the fluid branch of the isotherms of a one-component system of hard spheres. The PY equation for a binary mixture was solved by Lebowitz[17], and it has been shown[18] that this solution leads to the same results as those found by computer, namely that V^E, and hence G^E, are small and negative. Unfortunately, the excess functions cannot be obtained explicitly beyond second-order differences in the sizes of the spheres, but the numerical solutions agree well with the computer results. Neither PY theory nor the computer experiments leads to a separation of fluid phases at any density, composition or size ratio. In this they differ radically from the implications of the random-mixture theory as summarized in *Figure 9.1*.

It was shown in Section 8.7 that the structure of real fluids at high densities is, to a large degree, determined by the repulsive forces between the molecules, and that the attractive forces are less specific in their effects. This consideration suggests that the PY result for mixtures of hard spheres might serve as a useful guide for the development of a theory of mixtures of real molecules. The PY results can be brought a little nearer reality by extending them to a mixture of soft spheres, (7.24), by means of the perturbation expansion, (8.210)–(8.214). We have in this potential a common ground on which several theories can be compared, since the equations of the random mixture, (9.14)–(9.17), and of the average potential model, (9.70), (9.71) and (9.74), can also be applied to an assembly of soft spheres. Furthermore, it is a potential in which each molecular interaction is characterized by one parameter only (conveniently a volume, $h_{\alpha\beta}$) and which is, therefore, ideally suited for the study of the specific effects of differences of size upon the excess functions.

Let us consider the excess Helmholtz free energy, $A^E_{T,\rho}$, which is related to a process of mixing in which the temperature and number density are the same for each component before mixing, and also in the resulting mixture. Let the Lorentz rule (7.28) be assumed to apply to each cross-interaction, and let the equation of state of the reference substance be the PY compressibility equation, (8.206), where the reduced number density, ρ, is now that for an assembly of soft spheres. All first-order contributions to $A^E_{T,\rho}$ are eliminated by the Lorentz rule, and so, to the second order, we can write

$$A^E_{T,\rho} = J_n(\rho) NkT \sum_\alpha \sum_\beta x_\alpha x_\beta (h_{\alpha\alpha} - h_{\beta\beta})^2 \qquad (9.79)$$

where the coefficient J is given by the following theories[19].

Percus-Yevick

$$J_n(\rho) = \frac{5}{6} \frac{1 + \rho + \frac{8}{5}\rho^2}{(1 - \rho)^3} - \frac{1}{3} - \frac{1}{2} \frac{(1 + 2\rho)^2}{(1 - \rho)^4} \qquad (9.80)$$

Random mixture

$$J_n(\rho) = \left(\frac{n + 7}{12}\right) \frac{1 + \rho + \rho^2}{(1 - \rho)^3} - \left(\frac{n + 1}{12}\right) - \frac{1}{2} \frac{(1 + 2\rho)^2}{(1 - \rho)^4} \qquad (9.81)$$

Average potential model

$$J_n(\rho) = \left(\frac{n + 11}{24}\right) \frac{1 + \rho + \rho^2}{(1 - \rho)^3} - \left(\frac{n + 2}{24}\right) - \frac{3}{8} \frac{(1 + 2\rho)^2}{(1 - \rho)^4} \qquad (9.82)$$

The coefficient J_n in (9.81) and (9.82) becomes positive infinite if n is infinite. In contrast, the PY expression for J is negative, independent of n, and is always substantially below the other results if $n \sim 12$ and $\rho < 0.6$, the approximate density at which the mixture starts to solidify.

The PY result cannot be applied to mixtures of Lennard-Jones molecules, or to other sets of conformal potentials, without the numerical solution of the integral equation for each particular mixture[20]. However, there is a one-fluid model which leads quite generally to a form of J that resembles closely the PY result, and this is the approximation introduced by van der Waals[21]. In his theory of mixtures he assumed that the parameters a_x and b_x of his equation of state were quadratic sums of the parameters $a_{\alpha\beta}$ and $b_{\alpha\beta}$. This is the only combination that leads to the correct second virial coefficient for the mixture and, as Reid and Leland[22] showed, it can be justified by appeal to the more generalized van der Waals model of Kac (see Section 8.7) in which the attractive potential is weak compared with kT and of long range. Since a is proportional to

$(T^c V^c)$ and b to V^c, the assumption of van der Waals is, in more modern notation[19]

$$f_x = (\sum_\alpha \sum_\beta x_\alpha x_\beta f_{\alpha\beta} h_{\alpha\beta})(\sum_\alpha \sum_\beta x_\alpha x_\beta h_{\alpha\beta})^{-1} \qquad (9.83)$$

$$h_x = \sum_\alpha \sum_\beta x_\alpha x_\beta h_{\alpha\beta} \qquad \text{(where } h = g^3) \qquad (9.84)$$

The complicated average of (9.15) is now replaced by a simple quadratic sum of volume parameters $h_{\alpha\beta}$. These one-fluid equations give A and G for the mixture when substituted in (9.16) and (9.17). The value of $J_n(\rho)$ in (9.79) for the van der Waals approximation is remarkably close to that of the PY result (9.80) and hence to the computer experiments, namely

van der Waals approximation

$$J_n(\rho) = \frac{5}{6} \frac{1 + \rho + \rho^2}{(1 - \rho)^3} - \frac{1}{3} - \frac{1}{2} \frac{(1 + 2\rho)^2}{(1 - \rho)^4} \qquad (9.85)$$

If the PY result is a good discriminant, then it follows that the van der Waals approximation, (9.83)–(9.84), is a better one-fluid model than the random-mixture approximation for mixtures of molecules of different size. It is readily seen that both approximations yield the same simple result if all the sizes are equal (i.e. all $h_{\alpha\beta} = 1$)

$$f_x = \sum_\alpha \sum_\beta x_\alpha x_\beta f_{\alpha\beta} \qquad h_x = 1 \qquad (9.86)$$

If the van der Waals result is cast into the form of (9.42) and (9.64) for a mixture with conformal potentials that satisfy the Lorentz–Berthelot rules, then the coefficients of ordering, $G_{\xi\eta}^{(1)}$, can be extracted. From results published elsewhere[19], and from the equations of the Appendix, we have

$$G_{ff}^{(1)} = 0 \qquad G_{fk}^{(1)} = G_f - G_h \qquad G_{kk}^{(1)} = -Z_{hh} \qquad (9.87)$$

where Z_{hh} is given by (9.36). Only the first of these coefficients is the same as that of the random-mixing approximation, (9.66). The third is large, and is singular if n is infinite. However, this singularity exactly neutralizes that of the random-mixing approximation (9.45) and so gives a total G^E that is not singular. Thus the division of G^E into random and ordering terms is seen to be artificial here.

The merit of the van der Waals approximation is in its more realistic treatment of the contributions to G^E arising from differences of size. However, since $G_{ff}^{(1)}$ is still zero, it does not take into account the small ordering term that arises from differences of energy, which is included in the average potential model by (9.75). This defect can be remedied by considering instead a two-fluid van der Waals approximation which bears the same relation to the average potential model as the one-fluid version does to the random mixture. The equations analogous to (9.70) and (9.71) are[19]

$$f_\alpha = (\sum_\beta x_\beta f_{\alpha\beta} h_{\alpha\beta})(\sum_\beta x_\beta h_{\alpha\beta})^{-1} \qquad (9.88)$$

$$h_\alpha = \sum_\beta x_\beta h_{\alpha\beta} \qquad \text{(where } h = g^3) \qquad (9.89)$$

If these are used in (9.74), then we have the two-fluid van der Waals analogue of the average potential model. The coefficients of ordering are now

$$G_{ff}^{(1)} = \tfrac{1}{2}G_{ff} \qquad G_{fk}^{(1)} = \tfrac{1}{2}G_{fh} + \tfrac{1}{2}G_f - G_h \qquad G_{kk}^{(1)} = \tfrac{1}{2}G_{hh} - Z_{hh} \qquad (9.90)$$

The coefficient $G_{ff}^{(1)}$ is the same as that of (9.75), thus accounting for the ordering effects of the energy differences, whilst $G_{kk}^{(1)}$ still contains the term Z_{hh} which removes the infinity from G^E if n is infinite.

This approach can be carried a stage further and a *three-fluid model* generated in which the preliminary averaging of (9.83)–(9.84) or (9.88)–(9.89) is avoided altogether and A or G is obtained directly from the set of coefficients $f_{\alpha\beta}$ and $g_{\alpha\beta}$. Thus for G we can write

$$G(p, T, x) = NkT \sum_\alpha x_\alpha \ln x_\alpha$$
$$+ \sum_\alpha \sum_\beta x_\alpha x_\beta [f_{\alpha\beta} G_0(pg_{\alpha\beta}^3/f_{\alpha\beta}, T/f_{\alpha\beta}) - 3NkT \ln g_{\alpha\beta}] \qquad (9.91)$$

The coefficients of ordering obtained for this model are such that those for the two-fluid model are the arithmetic means of those for the one- and the three-fluid models. That is, for (9.91)

$$G_{ff}^{(1)} = G_{ff} \qquad G_{fk}^{(1)} = G_{fh} - G_h \qquad G_{kk}^{(1)} = G_{hh} - Z_{hh} \qquad (9.92)$$

This equation can be written more neatly by using those in the Appendix that relate fluctuation integrals with subscripts f and k to those with f and h. This change gives for the three-fluid model

$$G_{\xi\eta}^{(1)} = G_{\xi\eta} \qquad (\xi, \eta = f, k) \qquad (9.93)$$

If this result is compared with that for the random-mixing approximation (9.66) and the average potential model (9.75), then it is seen that the three-fluid model can be regarded as the third member of both the sequences

One-fluid   →   Two-fluid
(random mixing)   (average potential)

Three-fluid

One-fluid   →   Two-fluid
(van der Waals)   (van der Waals)

In fact, the three-fluid model was originally devised by Scott[3] as the natural end of the upper of these two sequences before the development of the lower.

Hence, to summarize, if we take the random-mixing expression for G^E of a Lorentz–Berthelot mixture as our starting point, then we have a potentially exact expression for the second-order coefficients of ordering in (9.64)–(9.65), where the fluctuation integrals are those of (8.62)–(8.83). These are experimentally inaccessible, and the five approximations in the scheme above replace them by the

Table 9.4. Values ascribed to the molecular fluctuation integrals by different theories

Integral	One-fluid models		Two-fluid models		Three-fluid model
	RM	vdW	APM	vdW	
$G_{ff}^{(2)}$	0	0	0	0	G_{ff}
$G_{ff}^{(3)}$	0	0	G_{ff}	G_{ff}	0
$G_{ff}^{(4)}$	G_{ff}	G_{ff}	0	0	0
$G_{fh}^{(2)}$	G_h	G_f	G_h	G_f	G_{fh}
$G_{fh}^{(3)}$	0	0	$G_{fh} - G_h$	$G_{fh} - G_f$	0
$G_{fh}^{(4)}$	$G_{fh} - G_h$	$G_{fh} - G_f$	0	0	0
$G_{hh}^{(2)}$	Z_{hh}	0	Z_{hh}	0	G_{hh}
$G_{hh}^{(3)}$	0	0	$G_{hh} - Z_{hh}$	G_{hh}	0
$G_{hh}^{(4)}$	$G_{hh} - Z_{hh}$	G_{hh}	0	0	0

The function Z_{hh} is the only one which depends explicitly on the form of the potential and becomes infinite as n does.

accessible functions of (9.66), (9.75), (9.87), (9.90) and (9.92). Only in the dilute gas or in a one-dimensional mixture of arbitrary density can we evaluate the fluctuation integrals exactly, and in these circumstances the three-fluid model is exact. However, the amount of order in a dense fluid is certainly less than in this model but certainly much more than in the random mixing and average potential models. The one-fluid and two-fluid van der Waals models are probably closer to the truth. The one-fluid version receives strong support from its resemblance to the PY result for mixtures of soft spheres. The two-fluid contains the useful (and probably accurate) ordering term for the energy, $G_{ff}^{(1)}$ in (9.90), and differs little in the coefficient $G_{kk}^{(1)}$ since G_{hh} is only about 2 per cent of the size of Z_{hh} for a (12,6) fluid.

The estimates of the fluctuation integrals provided by each theory can be put into tabular form[19] by converting each to integrals with subscripts f and h (see Appendix). This is shown in *Table 9.4.*

All theories satisfy the following consistency test (see (8.63), etc. and Appendix)

$$G_{\xi\eta}^{(2)} + G_{\xi\eta}^{(3)} + G_{\xi\eta}^{(4)} = G_{\xi\eta} \qquad (\xi, \eta = f, h) \qquad (9.94)$$

where the functions $G_{\xi\eta}$ are thermodynamically accessible. The one-, two- and three-fluid models differ in that they ascribe certain components of $G_{\xi\eta}$ to the four-body, three-body and two-body fluctuation integrals, respectively.

A further test is that provided by Schwarz's inequality (A.31) for the fluctuation integrals $G_{\xi\eta}^{(1)}$ ($\xi, \eta = f, k$). This is amply satisfied by the three-fluid and by both two-fluid approximations because of the large size of Z_{hh}. It becomes an equality for the random mixture for which all the integrals $G^{(1)}$ are zero and fails for the one-fluid van der Waals model on the probably trivial ground that $G_{ff}^{(1)}$ is the only integral to vanish in this approximation.

The integrals of *Table 9.4* take the following values for liquid argon at its normal boiling point and, for Z_{hh}, with the assumption that the potential is (12,6)

$$G_f/RT = -8.05 \qquad G_h/RT = G_k/RT = -1{\cdot}00$$

$$G_{ff}/RT = -3{\cdot}57 \qquad G_{fh}/RT = 0{\cdot}00 \qquad G_{hh}/RT = 1{\cdot}00$$

$$G_{fk}/RT = 1{\cdot}00 \qquad G_{kk}/RT = -58{\cdot}40 \qquad Z_{hh}/RT = 59{\cdot}40$$

9.5 Comparison of Theory and Experiment for Simple Mixtures

The first comparisons to be made are those between the excess properties of the simple binary mixtures of argon, krypton, nitrogen, carbon monoxide and methane (Section 4.6) and the theoretical calculations for four of the theories developed in this Chapter. These are the average potential model of Prigogine and Bellemans, the one-fluid and two-fluid van der Waals models and the three-fluid model. The random-mixing approximation is omitted, since it is uniformly worse than the average potential model and yields much too large values of g^E and h^E for systems with molecules of different size. Scott[3] has shown that it provides an upper bound for the true value of g^E.

The average potential model requires the assumption of a particular form of the pair potential, and here the conventional (12,6) form is used throughout. The Lorentz rule of additive size parameters is retained, and so no great accuracy is expected in the calculated values of v^E, but provision is made for adjusting the energy cross-term f_{12} which often departs significantly from the

Berthelot or geometric mean. To this end, a parameter ξ_{12} is introduced, defined by

$$f_{12} = \xi_{12}(f_{11}f_{22})^{1/2} \tag{9.95}$$

This is trivially related to parameters e_{12} and θ_{12} of (9.37) and (9.38) by

$$e_{12} = 2(\xi_{12} - 1)(1 + \theta_{12})^{1/2} - [1 - (1 + \theta_{12})^{1/2}]^2 \tag{9.96}$$

The first comparisons are made with $\xi_{12} = 1$ (Berthelot's rule), but later it is adjusted to fit one of the excess functions.

The parameters for the like interactions are derived from T^c and p^c (Section 8.4), since all six substances conform quite well to a common principle of corresponding states. The configurational thermodynamic properties of the reference substance are derived from those of argon, krypton, nitrogen, carbon monoxide and methane. Bellemans, Mathot and Simon[15] obtained the following expressions for the configurational functions G and H and for the total molar volume, v, by smoothing reduced plots of the appropriate functions

$$G/NkT = 3.558\ 774 - 8.379\ 308/\tilde{T} - 4.597\ 179 \ln \tilde{T}$$
$$+ 2.301\ 041\tilde{T} - 0.806\ 469(\tilde{T})^2 - \ln h \tag{9.97}$$

$$H/NkT = 4.597\ 179 - 8.379\ 308/\tilde{T}$$
$$- 2.301\ 041\tilde{T} + 1.162\ 938(\tilde{T})^2 \tag{9.98}$$

$$v/(32.4\ \text{cm}^3\ \text{mol}^{-1}) = h[0.952\ 596 - 0.705\ 204\tilde{T} + 0.834\ 608(\tilde{T})^2] \tag{9.99}$$

where

$$\tilde{T} = T\ \text{K}/(123.2f) \tag{9.100}$$

and f and h are energy and volume parameters based upon argon as the reference substance. These are listed in *Table 9.5* and, together with the Lorentz–Berthelot rules and the reference equations (9.97)–(9.100), yield the results shown in *Table 9.6*.

There are two systems in this Table, $Ar + O_2$ and $N_2 + CO$, for which the energy and size differences of the pure components are

Table 9.5. Energy and volume parameters for 6 simple substances[19]

Substance	f	h
Argon	1.000	1.000
Krypton	1.387	1.225
Nitrogen	0.836	1.198
Oxygen	1.022	0.988
Carbon monoxide	0.881	1.225
Methane	1.266	1.327

Table 9.6. Calculated values of the equimolar excess properties; g^E and h^E are in J mol^{-1} and v^E in cm^3 mol^{-1}. APM = average potential model; vdW = van der Waals models (Lorentz–Berthelot rules)

System		Experiment	APM*	vdW		3-fluid
				1-fluid	2-fluid	
Ar + Kr	g^E	+84	+140	+38	+53	+68
116 K	v^E	−0·53	+0·08	−0·78	−0·54	−0·28
Ar + N$_2$	g^E	+34	+80	+40	+27	+15
84 K	h^E	+51	+105	+42	+27	+13
	v^E	−0·18	−0·07	−0·32	−0·26	−0·20
Ar + O$_2$	g^E	+37	+1	+1	0	0
84 K	h^E	+60	+2	+1	0	0
	v^E	+0·14	+0·01	0·00	0·00	0·00
Ar + CO	g^E	+57	+70	+26	+16	+8
84 K	v^E	+0·10	+0·10	−0·20	−0·17	−0·14
Ar + CH$_4$	g^E	+74	+170	−19	+6	+5
91 K	h^E	+103	+240	−52	−11	−8
	v^E	+0·17	+0·72	−0·31	−0·23	−0·15
Kr + CH$_4$	g^E	+28	+18	+15	+13	+10
116 K						
N$_2$ + O$_2$	g^E	+43	+65	+50	+35	+19
78 K	h^E	+46	+85	+53	+35	+17
	v^E	−0·3	−0·11	−0·32	−0·25	−0·19
N$_2$ + CO	g^E	+23	+2	+1	+1	+1
84 K	v^E	+0·1	−0·01	−0·02	−0·01	−0·01
CO + CH$_4$	g^E	+115	+105	+75	+74	+74
91 K	h^E	+105	+80	+23	+43	+64
	v^E	−0·32	−0·50	−0·84	−0·60	−0·35

* The APM calculations for Ar + N$_2$, Ar + O$_2$, Ar + CH$_4$, N$_2$ + O$_2$ and CO + CH$_4$ are those of Bellemans, Mathot and Simon[15] and are based on parameters that differ slightly from those of *Table 9.5*. The differences so introduced are small.

so small that all theories predict that the mixtures should be almost ideal if they conform to the Lorentz–Berthelot rules. In fact, the systems are not ideal, and so ξ_{12} of (9.95)–(9.96) must be less than unity. To obtain agreement for g^E, we require

$$\text{Ar} + \text{O}_2 \qquad \xi_{12} = 0\cdot988 \quad \text{or} \quad e_{12} = -0\cdot024$$

$$\text{N}_2 + \text{CO} \qquad \xi_{12} = 0\cdot991 \quad \text{or} \quad e_{12} = -0\cdot018$$

Hence the experimental results prove conclusively that the 1–2 energies are here weaker than the geometric means by about 1 per cent.

In the system $CO + CH_4$ the size difference $\varphi_{12} = .h_{11} - h_{22}$ is 0·102, and here the value of g^E predicted by APM is almost correct, whilst the other approximations are low by 40 J mol^{-1}. These discrepancies could well be due to a departure from Berthelot's rule similar to that found for $CO + N_2$. To bring about agreement for the van der Waals models, we need here

$$CO + CH_4 \qquad \xi_{12} = 0·986 \qquad \text{or} \qquad e_{12} = -0·028$$

If this interpretation is correct, then the good agreement with APM (using Berthelot's rule) is due to a spuriously large contribution to g^E that arises from the 10 per cent difference in volume. $Kr + CH_4$ is almost ideal.

Table 9.7. Parameters for $CH_4 + CF_4$, determined from the second virial co-efficient[23]

Interaction	f	h
CH_4–CH_4	1·000	1·000
CH_4–CF_4	0·917	1·451
CF_4–CF_4	1·017	1·916

The remaining five systems have large size differences, $\varphi_{12} > 0·2$, and here it is seen that the APM leads uniformly to values of g^E that exceed the experimental results. Agreement could be enforced by choosing ξ_{12} to be greater than unity, e.g. 1·017 for $Ar + Kr$, but a 1–2 energy that is 2 per cent stronger than the geometric mean is unlikely in so simple a system. It is more probable that the APM leads to too large values of g^E when $\varphi^2 > 0·01$.

The van der Waals results for these five systems are, on the whole, lower than the experimental values, the discrepancies being greatest for $Ar + CH_4$. To obtain agreement for g^E of $Ar + Kr$, the one-fluid version requires $\xi_{12} = 0·986$ and the two-fluid version $\xi_{12} = 0·991$. That is, they require a 1–2 interaction which is 1 per cent less than the geometric mean rather than 2 per cent higher as on APM. There is some direct evidence from the second virial coefficient that ξ_{12} is, in fact, about 0·987 (Section 7.3).

A more critical test is provided by the system $CH_4 + CF_4$ (Section 5.3), since there is here not only a large size difference ($\varphi = 0·916$), but also the strength of the 1–2 energy is known experimentally from a recent study of the second virial coefficient[23]. The independently determined values of these parameters (relative to CH_4–CH_4) are shown in *Table 9.7*, the most striking feature of which is the weakness of the 1–2 energy that is so characteristic a feature of the hydrocarbon–fluorocarbon systems. The comparison of theory and experiment is now free from the uncertainty of unknown parameters and is shown in *Table 9.8.*

These results show clearly the excessively large values of g^E obtained on the random mixing hypothesis and, to a lesser degree, on the average potential model. Both van der Waals models are in good agreement with experiment.

A more exaggerated if more qualitative test even than $CH_4 + CF_4$ is provided by recent measurements by Marsh[24] on the system carbon tetrachloride + octamethylcyclotetrasiloxane. The latter molecule is roughly spherical and its surface is formed of methyl

Table 9.8. Calculated values of equimolar excess properties, based on the parameters of *Table 9.7* (conventions as in *Table 9.6,* with RM = random mixture)

System		Experiment	RM	APM	vdW	
					1-fluid	*2-fluid*
$CH_4 + CF_4$	g^E	$+360$	$+1260$	$+870$	$+280$	$+350$
111 K	v^E	$+0·88$	$+14$	$+7·1$	$+0·90$	$+1·07$

groups. Its volume is about 3·2 times that of CCl_4, and there is no reason to suppose any unusual attractive force between the two components. Nevertheless, g^E and v^E are both negative, about -160 J mol^{-1} and $-0·26$ cm^3 mol^{-1} in the equimolar solution at 45°C, as is required by the van der Waals approximations. Here the earlier theories would yield large positive excess functions.

The results of this Section show the superiority of the van der Waals approximations when the size differences are large. The three-fluid model almost certainly leads to too much order and so, generally, to too low a value of g^E. It is less easy to distinguish between the one-fluid and two-fluid versions of the van der Waals approximation, although probably the second is to be preferred, both on the basis of the results in the tables above and because of its reduction to APM rather than to RM when the sizes are all equal.

These conclusions carry the strong implication that it is the rule rather than the exception for the 1–2 energy to fall a little below the geometric mean. This is shown in *Table 9.9* which presents a consistent picture in that the 1–2 energy is generally about 1 per cent below the geometric and 2 per cent below the arithmetic mean for this set of simple molecules. Previously the systems $Ar + O_2$ and $N_2 + CO$ had been thought to be anomalous. If the interpretation of this Section is correct, the anomaly disappears and the only unusual feature of these systems is that the components have similar molar volumes, so leading to agreement between all

Table 9.9. Values of ξ_{12} (or e_{12}) required to obtain agreement between experiment and the two-fluid van der Waals approximation

System	ξ_{12}	e_{12}
Ar + Kr	0·991	−0·053
Ar + N$_2$	0·996	−0·014
Ar + O$_2$	0·988	−0·024
Ar + CO	0·985	−0·031
Ar + CH$_4$	0·979	−0·064
Kr + CH$_4$	0·995	−0·014
N$_2$ + O$_2$	0·997	−0·016
N$_2$ + CO	0·991	−0·017
CO + CH$_4$	0·987	−0·063
Means	$\overline{0·990}$	$\overline{−0·033}$

the theories. In the other systems differences in volume led, on the older theories, to spurious contributions to g^E which counterbalanced, and often overbalanced, the effects of the choice $\xi_{12} = 1$.

Few of the mixtures discussed in Sections 4.7–4.9 have potentials that are close to the conformal pattern of (9.11). The much-studied mixtures of n-alkanes certainly do not conform, and discussion of these is deferred to Section 9.7.

However, eight systems have reasonably spherically molecules, and for these a comparison of theory and experiment is made in *Table 9.10* by using carbon tetrachloride as the reference substance and eqn. (9.42) and (9.64). Unfortunately, there is only one mixture here that contains two aliphatic hydrocarbons and for which we can be sure that the Lorentz–Berthelot rules are at least approximately correct. This system, neopentane + cyclohexane, is one of

Table 9.10. Comparison of the experimental values of the equimolar excess free energy with those calculated for Lorentz–Berthelot mixtures (conventions as in *Table 9.6*)

System	θ	φ	Experiment	APM	vdW	
					1-fluid	2-fluid
Aliphatic + aliphatic						
CMe$_4$ + c-C$_6$H$_{12}$ (0°C)	0·215	0·009	+184	+160	+180	+160
Aromatic + aliphatic						
Bz + CMe$_4$ (0°C)	0·231	−0·175	+570	+400	+350	+250
Bz + c-C$_5$H$_{10}$ (25°C)	0·100	−0·055	+620	+ 60	+ 70	+ 50
Bz + c-C$_6$H$_{12}$ (25°C)	0·015	−0·184	+320	+260	− 30	− 20
PhMe + c-C$_6$H$_{12}$ (20°C)	0·073	0·036	+400	+ 20	+ 30	+ 20
Halides						
CCl$_4$ + CMe$_4$ (0°C)	0·220	−0·111	+320	+260	+280	+210
CCl$_4$ + c-C$_6$H$_{12}$ (25°C)	0·005	−0·120	+ 70	+110	− 5	− 3
CCl$_4$ + Bz (25°C)	0·010	−0·064	+ 82	+ 32	+ 2	+ 1

large energy but small size difference. Hence all theories lead to similar results that, moreover, agree well with experiment and, therefore, confirm the Lorentz–Berthelot rules. The excess entropy (not shown in the Table) is negative for this system and, as for $CO + CH_4$ above, this result is also predicted by all the theories. The aromatic–aliphatic interaction does not obey Berthelot's rule, as shown e.g. by the second virial coefficient of benzene + cyclohexane[25] and by the critical temperatures of the mixtures (see next Section). Hence agreement with experiment is not to be expected in this part of *Table 9.10*. This expectation is most strongly confirmed by the mixtures of similar size, namely benzene + cyclopentane and toluene + cyclohexane. In both, the experimental results are an order of magnitude larger than all the theoretical and indicate a weakness of the 1–2 energy of about 3 per cent ($e_{12} = -0.06$). Presumably this weakness is present also in the other systems, as implied by the van der Waals models, but is disguised in the average potential model when the sizes are substantially different. Similar conclusions can be drawn from the results for the last three systems.

The fluorocarbon + hydrocarbon systems (Section 5.3) provide the clearest examples amongst non-polar molecules of systems for which the first-order term in e_{12} is dominant. The very large excess functions suggest that e_{12} lies between -0.16 and -0.20, that is, the 1–2 energies fall below the geometric mean by up to 10 per cent. The ratio of excess heats to excess free energies is no larger than 1·7, which suggests that a lack of balance of the non-central forces is not here a serious contribution to the excess functions.

The large errors in some of these theories for mixtures of molecules of different sizes make it interesting to compare them with the more empirical treatment of Lorentz–Berthelot mixtures due to Hildebrand and Scatchard[26]. Their expression for $G^E/x_1 x_2$ (or, more correctly, for a similar function with volume and not mole fractions) is

$$\frac{G^E}{x_1 x_2} = \left(\frac{V_1 + V_2}{2}\right)\left[\left(\frac{\Delta H_1 - NkT}{V_1}\right)^{1/2} - \left(\frac{\Delta H_2 - NkT}{V_2}\right)^{1/2}\right]^2 \quad (9.101)$$

where ΔH_1 is the latent heat of evaporation of component 1.

Now $(\Delta H_1 - NkT)$ is approximately proportional to $(N\epsilon_{11})$ and equal to $-U$ for a conformal liquid, and V_1 is proportional to $(N\sigma_{11}^3)$. The values of $G_{\theta\theta}$, etc. can be obtained by expanding in powers of the differences θ and φ. These are compared in *Table 9.11* with the

Table 9.11. Simplified coefficients of (9.42) for 6 theories of mixtures

	Random mixture	Average potential model	van der Waals models 1-fluid	van der Waals models 2-fluid	3-fluid model	Hildebrand and Scatchard[26]
$G_{\theta\theta}$	$-\frac{1}{4}U$	$-\frac{1}{4}U$	$-\frac{1}{4}U$	$-\frac{1}{4}U$	$-\frac{1}{4}U$	$-\frac{1}{4}U$
$G_{\theta\varphi}$	0	0	$+\frac{1}{2}U$	$+\frac{1}{4}U$	0	$+\frac{1}{2}U$
$G_{\varphi\varphi}$	$-2U$	$-U$	0	0	0	$-\frac{1}{4}U$

simplified coefficients of the last two Sections obtained by putting p, T and C_p equal to zero. It is seen that, subject to this simplification, the treatment of Hildebrand and Scatchard gives the same $G_{\theta\theta}$ as the more sophisticated theories, a large negative cross-term $G_{\theta\varphi}$ as in the van der Waals models and a much smaller value of $G_{\varphi\varphi}$ than the random mixture or the average potential model. The successes of the Hildebrand and Scatchard treatment must be due to a great extent to this realistic estimate of the difficulty of packing together molecules of different sizes.

9.6 CRITICAL POINTS

The results set out in Chapter 6 make it desirable to treat all types of critical points in a binary mixture by one comprehensive theory, since there is no absolute distinction between critical solution points and gas–liquid critical points. However, no attempt has yet been made to use the theories of Sections 9.3 and 9.4 to account, say, for the variety of behaviour summarized in *Figure 6.23*. There is little doubt that the van der Waals approximations of Section 9.4 could usefully be applied to this problem in view of the preliminary results obtained by Scott for a more restricted class of van der Waals systems. These results are summarized briefly at the end of this Section.

However, the more simple behaviour shown in *Figure 6.20* has been discussed at some length. Here there are two critical lines, one of which may be called unambiguously a line of upper critical solution temperatures, the other a gas–liquid critical line.

The U.C.S.T. have generally been studied at low reduced pressures and temperatures and the application to them of any theory of mixtures is quite straightforward. It is not discussed here, as the theoretical determination of a U.C.S.T. is entirely equivalent to that of the excess free energy.

The gas–liquid critical line can also be related to the intermolecular parameters. It was shown above, (9.18), that the equation of state of a random mixture was that of the equivalent substance for that composition, and that both were related to the equation of state of the reference substance by the principle of corresponding states. Hence, for the equivalent substance

$$T_x^c = f_x T_0^c, \qquad V_x^c = g_x^3 V_0^c, \qquad p_x^c = (f_x/g_x^3)p_0^c \qquad (9.102)$$

The functions f_x and g_x are defined by (9.14) and (9.15). They are functions of both $f_{\alpha\beta}$ and $g_{\alpha\beta}$, and so T_x^c is not solely one of the energy parameters and V_x^c is not solely one of the volume parameters, as a simple analogy with the reference substance might suggest. Nevertheless, it is useful to write f_x for a binary mixture as an explicit function of the three f parameters and as an expansion of the volume parameters in powers of $(g - 1)$. If this is done, and if the Lorentz relation is used to eliminate g_{12}, then the first non-vanishing term of the expansion is

$$f_x = x_1^2 f_{11} + 2x_1 x_2 f_{12}\left(1 - \frac{nm}{72} \varphi_{12}^2\right) + x_2^2 f_{22} \qquad (9.103)$$

where φ_{12} is the volume difference between the two pure species. T_x^c is therefore primarily a function of the energy parameters but depends in some degree on the size parameters in a random mixture. The coefficient of φ_{12}^2 is halved when allowance is made for ordering.

The one-fluid van der Waals model leads again to (9.102), but V_x^c is now a function only of the volume parameters according to (9.84). The equation equivalent to (9.103) is

$$f_x = x_1^2 f_{11} + 2x_1 x_2 f_{12}(1 + \tfrac{1}{4}\theta_{12}\varphi_{12}) + x_2^2 f_{22} \qquad (9.104)$$

The critical point of the equivalent substance is not, however, the same as that of the mixture, as the former is determined by the conditions of mechanical and the latter by those of material stability. The second are the more restrictive conditions, as was shown in Chapter 6. The difference between T^c and T_x^c must be calculated before any use can be made of (9.103) and (9.104). Bellemans, Mathot and Zuckerbrodt[27] have shown that this difference is zero to the first order in those of f and g parameters. However, it is not zero in the important class of mixtures in which θ^2 and φ^2 cannot be neglected. For these, the difference has been calculated by Bellemans and Zuckerbrodt and by Byers Brown[4], whose treatment is followed here.

The two equations whose solution gives the classical critical point of the mixture are

$$\frac{1}{m}\left(\frac{\partial^2 G}{\partial x^2}\right)_{p,T} = \frac{RT}{x(1-x)} + \frac{1}{m}\left(\frac{\partial^2 G_x}{\partial x^2}\right)_{p,T} = 0 \qquad (9.105)$$

$$\frac{1}{m}\left(\frac{\partial^3 G}{\partial x^3}\right)_{p,T} = \frac{RT(2x-1)}{x^2(1-x)^2} + \frac{1}{m}\left(\frac{\partial^3 G_x}{\partial x^3}\right)_{p,T} = 0 \qquad (9.106)$$

where there are m moles in the system and x is the mole fraction of, say, the second component. These equations are more useful if written in terms of $A_x(V, T)$ than of $G_x(p, T)$, since the derivatives of the latter have singularities at the critical point of the equivalent substance. The second and third derivatives of G_x can be converted to derivatives of A_x by using (6.26), (6.34) and (6.35). The two equations above then reduce to

$$\left(\frac{\partial p_x}{\partial V}\right)^c_{x,T} + x(1-x)\left[\frac{(\partial p_x/\partial x)^2_{V,T}}{RT}\right]^c = 0 \qquad (9.107)$$

$$3\left(\frac{\partial p_x}{\partial V}\right)^c_{x,T}\left(\frac{\partial^2 p_x}{\partial V \partial x}\right)^c_T - \left(\frac{\partial p_x}{\partial x}\right)^c_{V,T}\left(\frac{\partial^2 p_x}{\partial V^2}\right)^c_{x,T} = 0 \qquad (9.108)$$

when the molecular energies and sizes are reasonably close. The differences between T^c and T^c_x and V^c and V^c_x are small, and so the derivatives of p_x with respect to volume at the critical point of the mixture are given by the Taylor expansions

$$\left(\frac{\partial p_x}{\partial V}\right)^c_{x,T} = (T^c - T^c_x)\left(\frac{\partial^2 p_x}{\partial V^2 \partial T}\right)^c_x \qquad (9.109)$$

$$\left(\frac{\partial^2 p_x}{\partial V^2}\right)^c_{x,T} = (T^c - T^c_x)\left(\frac{\partial^3 p_x}{\partial V^2 \partial T}\right)^c_x + (V^c - V^c_x)\left(\frac{\partial^3 p_x}{\partial V^3}\right)^c_{T,x} \qquad (9.110)$$

Hence, from (9.107) and (9.108),

$$T^c - T^c_x = -x(1-x)\left[\frac{(\partial p_x/\partial x)^2_{V,T}}{RT(\partial^2 p_x/\partial V \partial T)_x}\right]^c \qquad (9.111)$$

$$V^c - V^c_x =$$

$$(T^c - T^c_x)\left[\frac{3\left(\frac{\partial^2 p_x}{\partial V \partial T}\right)_x\left(\frac{\partial^2 p_x}{\partial V \partial x}\right)_T - \left(\frac{\partial p_x}{\partial x}\right)_{V,T}\left(\frac{\partial^3 p_x}{\partial V^2 \partial T}\right)_x}{\left(\frac{\partial p_x}{\partial x}\right)_{V,T}\left(\frac{\partial^3 p_x}{\partial V^3}\right)_{x,T}}\right]^c \qquad (9.112)$$

The derivative of p_x with respect to x may be eliminated by differentiating (9.18)

$$\left(\frac{\partial p_x}{\partial x}\right)_{V,T} = \frac{f'_x}{f_x}\left[p_x - T\left(\frac{\partial p_x}{\partial T}\right)_{V,x}\right] - \frac{h'_x}{h_x}\left[p_x + V\left(\frac{\partial p_x}{\partial V}\right)_{T,x}\right] \qquad (9.113)$$

whence

$$\left(\frac{\partial^2 p'_x}{\partial V \partial x}\right)_T = \frac{f'_x}{f_x}\left[\left(\frac{\partial p_x}{\partial V}\right)_T - T\left(\frac{\partial^2 p_x}{\partial V \partial T}\right)_x\right]$$
$$- \frac{h'_x}{h_x}\left[2\left(\frac{\partial p_x}{\partial V}\right)_{T,x} + V\left(\frac{\partial^2 p_x}{\partial V^2}\right)_{T,x}\right] \qquad (9.114)$$

where f'_x is the derivative of f_x with respect to x.

These equations may be simplified at the critical point by putting $(\partial p_x/\partial V)_{T,x}$ and $(\partial^2 p_x/\partial V^2)_{T,x}$ equal to zero, and the resulting expressions substituted in (9.111) and (9.114). These equations then give $(T^c - T_x^c)$ and $(V^c - V_x^c)$ in terms of accessible functions of the equivalent substance. Numerical values of these differences can be calculated only by assuming an explicit equation of state for the reference, and so for the equivalent substance. The simplest choice is van der Waals's equation which leads to

$$\frac{T^c - T_x^c}{T_x^c} = x(1 - x) \left[\frac{3f_x'}{4f_x} - \frac{h_x'}{4h_x} \right]^2 \qquad (9.115)$$

$$\frac{V^c - V_x^c}{V_x^c} = -2x(1 - x) \left[\left(\frac{3f_x'}{4f_x} \right)^2 - \left(\frac{h_x'}{4h_x} \right)^2 \right] \qquad (9.116)$$

$$\frac{p^c - p_x^c}{p_x^c} = \frac{T^c - T_x^c}{T_x^c} \left(\frac{\partial \ln p_x}{\partial \ln T} \right)_{V,x}^c = 4 \left(\frac{T^c - T_x^c}{T_x^c} \right) \qquad (9.117)*$$

It is seen from these equations that T^c is always greater than T_x^c and p^c is greater than p_x^c. The relative difference is largest for the critical pressure and, indeed, it is a well-known fact that the critical pressures of apparently normal non-polar mixtures show large maxima (see *Figure 6.13a*). These are presumably the consequence of this difference between p^c and p_x^c. It is seen that the critical ratio $(pv/RT)^c$ is not the same for the mixture as for the equivalent substance and the pure components. The derivatives f_x' and h_x' $(= (g_x^3)')$ are expressed most readily[4] in terms of the starred parameters of (9.53)–(9.56). They are given very simply for a Lorentz-Berthelot mixture of molecules of equal size by

$$f_x' = -\theta_{12} = -\frac{T_1^c - T_2^c}{T_0^c}, \qquad h_x' = 0 \qquad (9.118)$$

whence

$$\frac{T^c - T_x^c}{T_x^c} = \frac{9}{16} x(1 - x) \left(\frac{T_1^c - T_2^c}{T_x^c} \right)^2 \qquad (9.119)$$

This difference is often small. For example, for toluene ($T^c = 594$ K) + cyclohexane ($T^c = 553$ K), whose molecules are almost the same size, the maximum value of ($T^c - T_x^c$) is 0·4 K. For a Lorentz–Berthelot mixture of molecules of equal energy

$$f_x' = 0, \qquad h_x' = -\varphi_{12} = -\frac{V_1^c - V_2^c}{V_0^c} \qquad (9.120)$$

whence

$$\frac{T^c - T_x^c}{T_x^c} = \frac{1}{16} x(1 - x) \left(\frac{V_1^c - V_2^c}{V_x^c} \right)^2 \qquad (9.121)$$

* The logarithmic slope of the critical isochore is about 6 for the inert gases, a value appreciably larger than given by van der Waals's equation.

Thus for benzene ($v^c = 260$ cm^3 mol^{-1}) + cyclohexane ($v^c = 308$ cm^3 mol^{-1}) the maximum value of ($T^c - T_x^c$) is 0·2 K. Neither of these figures is appreciably affected by the departures of these two mixtures from the Lorentz-Berthelot equations.

In simple mixtures, experiment shows that T^c is close to a quadratic function of x that can be represented[28]

$$T^c - x_1 T_1^c - x_2 T_2^c = x_1 x_2 t_{12}^E T_0^c \qquad (9.122)$$

where T_0^c is the critical temperature of a reference substance, taken in this Section to be the arithmetic mean of T_1^c and T_2^c. From the equations above, (9.104) and (9.115), the parameter t_{12}^E can be related to e_{12} (9.37) by

$$e_{12} = t_{12}^E - \tfrac{1}{2}\theta_{12}\varphi_{12} - (\tfrac{3}{4}\theta_{12} + \tfrac{1}{4}\varphi_{12})^2 \qquad (9.123)$$

The second and third terms on the right-hand side are of second order in the differences of energies and sizes but are rarely negligible compared with the first-order difference, e_{12}. The second term arises from the one-fluid van der Waals approximation for f_x (9.104), and the third from the difference between T^c of a mixture and that of a hypothetical pure substance equivalent to it. The coefficients of this last term are probably inaccurate, since they are based on van der Waals's equation of state for the reference fluid—a much more drastic approximation than the use of (9.104). Hence measurements of critical temperatures, that is, of t_{12}^E, can be used to obtain values of e_{12} only when the second and third terms of (9.123) are, at worst, no larger than the first.

The critical temperature is known as a function of composition for all 10 binary mixtures formed from argon, nitrogen, oxygen, carbon monoxide and methane (Chapter 6), but only four of these have sufficiently small values of θ and φ to satisfy the criterion of the last paragraph. For these we can derive values of e_{12} which can be compared with those obtained above from g^E, etc. of the liquid mixtures at low temperatures. This comparison is made in *Table 9.12*. The agreement is satisfactory in view of the uncertainty in the third term of (9.123).

A similar but cruder analysis[28] of the critical temperatures of hydrocarbon mixtures confirms the conclusion of *Table 9.10* that the aliphatic–aromatic interaction is significantly weaker than the geometric mean of the like interactions. Four systems containing molecules of dissimilar type but of approximately equal size are benzene + n-hexane, benzene + cyclohexane, toluene + n-hexane and toluene + cyclohexane. For these the mean value of e_{12} is $-0·04$, whilst for the two like mixtures, n-hexane + cyclohexane and benzene + toluene, it is 0·00.

343

Table 9.12. A comparison of the values of the energy differences e_{12} obtained from the critical temperatures with those obtained from excess free energies

System	Critical temperature		Free energy
	t_{12}^E	e_{12}	e_{12}
$Ar + O_2$	$-0{\cdot}018$	$-0{\cdot}018$	$-0{\cdot}024$
$Ar + CO$	$-0{\cdot}028$	$-0{\cdot}020$	$-0{\cdot}031$
$N_2 + CO$	$-0{\cdot}012$	$-0{\cdot}014$	$-0{\cdot}017$
$O_2 + CO$	$-0{\cdot}023$	$-0{\cdot}010$	—

The critical temperatures of two systems containing fluorine compounds show even more clearly the effects of weak forces between the unlike molecules. There are pronounced minima in the T^c graphs, and the derived values of e_{12} are

sulphur hexafluoride + propane $\qquad\qquad e_{12} = -0{\cdot}19$

perfluoro-methylcyclohexane + methylcyclohexane $\quad e_{12} = -0{\cdot}23$

These agree well with the values of e_{12} of $-0{\cdot}16$ to $-0{\cdot}20$ derived from the excess properties of fluorocarbon systems at low reduced temperatures. The molecular volumes of sulphur hexafluoride and propane are almost the same, and so the value of e_{12} for this system is quite soundly based.

Kreglewski[29] claims that the change of T^c and p^c with composition can be explained satisfactorily for hydrocarbon and hydrocarbon–fluorocarbon mixtures by making the approximation that f_{12} is equal to the smaller of f_{11} and f_{22}, that is, in the notation of this Chapter, $e_{12} = -\theta_{12}$. This is not dissimilar from some of the values above, when θ is small, but it seems unlikely that the rule is a general one.

The only recent attempt to account for the complete range of critical behaviour of *Figures 6.18–6.28* is that of Scott and van Konynenburg[30]. With the aid of modern computers they have continued the work that van der Waals started in his last years but which he was never able to complete satisfactorily. They have solved simultaneously the two equations (9.105) and (9.106) for a system in which G_x is obtained from the free energy of the reference substance, G_0, by the one-fluid van der Waals approximation, and for which G_0 is itself obtained by assuming that the reference substance obeys van der Waals's equation of state. The results so far available are confined to binary mixtures of molecules of equal size. Their reduced properties are specified by two independent ratios of molecular parameters, for example, f_{12}/f_{11} and f_{22}/f_{11}. Here, however, the differences e and θ are used again and the reference substance is defined to have molecular parameters that are the arithmetic mean of 1–1 and 2–2. That is, the binary mixtures discussed by Scott and van Konynenburg are specified by the two independent parameters

$$e_{12} = (2f_{12} - f_{11} - f_{22})/\tfrac{1}{2}(f_{11} + f_{22}) \quad \theta_{21} = (f_{22} - f_{11})/\tfrac{1}{2}(f_{11} + f_{22})$$
$$\text{where } f_{22} \geqslant f_{11} \quad (9.124)$$

These clearly satisfy the inequalities

$$e_{12} \geqslant -2 \quad 0 \leqslant \theta_{21} \leqslant 2 \quad (9.125)$$

and *Figure 9.2* shows the phase behaviour over all parts of the (e, θ) area that are of interest. The full lines divide the area into six

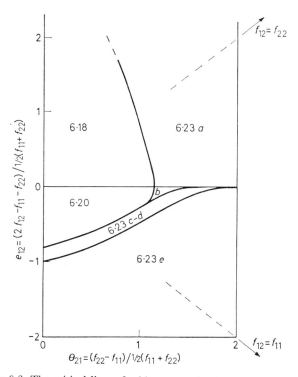

Figure 9.2. The critical lines of a binary van der Waals mixture of molecules of equal sizes (after Scott and van Konynenburg[30]). Each mixture is specified by the two independent parameters e_{12} and θ_{21} (9.124). The figure is divided into six regions, in each of which the critical line (or lines) is of one of the types shown in *Figures 6.18, 6.20* and *6.23a–e*

regions in each of which the critical lines conform to one of the six main types, namely those shown in p, T projection in *Figures 6.18, 6.20* and *6.23a–e (Figures 6.23c* and d have qualitatively the same type of critical line). These six main regions can be further subdivided according to the presence or absence of azeotropy. The conditions for azeotropy in this model are

$$\text{positive:} \quad f_{12} < f_{11} \qquad \text{negative:} \quad f_{12} > f_{22}$$

and are shown on the diagram as dashed diagonal lines. These lines should be produced back to the origin, but only the outer parts are drawn to avoid confusing the remainder of the diagram.

This figure shows how small positive values of e_{12} and θ_{21} are associated with 'normal' behaviour, i.e. *Figure 6.18*, and how a liquid–liquid U.C.S.T. appears (*Figure 6.20*) as soon as e_{12} becomes negative. Since the van der Waals equation of state does not lead to a solid state, a U.C.S.T. (at $T = 0^+$) appears as soon as e_{12} reaches 0^-. In practice the upper limit on e_{12} would be lower than this, i.e. a non-zero negative number, if the U.C.S.T. is to lie above the eutectic point.

If θ_{21} is large, then we obtain the set of critical lines shown in *Figure 6.23*, and it is particularly noticeable that the range of e and θ parameters that lead to the variant *6.23b* is unusually small. This explains why until recently only one example of such behaviour was known outside the field of polymer solutions. Scott and van Konynenburg[30] have recently found four more, one of which, methane + 3,3 dimethyl pentane, is notable since both components are aliphatic.

No quantitative conclusions can be drawn from so crude a model, but the variety of behaviour that it reveals augurs well for more realistic calculations which use the one-fluid van der Waals approximation to calculate the parameters f_x and h_x of the equivalent substance but do not require the latter to conform to van der Waals's equation of state.

9.7 MIXTURES WITH NON-CENTRAL FORCES

The theory of mixtures outlined above is restricted to spherical molecules with conformal potentials. This theory is the extension to mixtures of the principle of corresponding states for pure substances that was set out in Section 8.4. Deviations from this principle by pure substances whose molecules had non-central forces were discussed in Section 8.5.

These results may readily be extended to mixtures. Consider, first, an assembly of Lennard-Jones (12,6) molecules each of which has a weak point dipole at its centre. The extension of (8.143)–(8.159) is straightforward[31] for a mixture in which all but the first-order differences in f and g are neglected. Balescu[32] (see Prigogine[2]) has further extended this treatment to mixtures in which the higher-order differences are important, as for example, a Lorentz–Berthelot mixture with point dipoles. However, neither treatment is given here, as there is no clear example of a mixture of spherical or almost spherical molecules in which the excess functions are determined mainly by the dipole–dipole interactions and, furthermore, as Balescu's treatment is not entirely correct[33].

Perhaps the most obvious suggestion for a mixture of this kind is chloroform + carbon tetrachloride, where the treatment of Balescu (after correction) suggests that about $\frac{1}{3}$ of the excess functions are a consequence of the dipole–dipole energy of the chloroform molecules[33]. In all the other systems in *Tables 9.6* and *9.10* the dipole–dipole contributions to the excess functions are outweighed by those from the central forces and from such non-central forces as arise from the change with orientation of the repulsive and London forces.

It was shown in Section 8.5 that the most simple treatment of the variation of the London forces with orientation led to a hypothetical molecular potential which was conformal with the averaged spherical potential but was a function of the temperature, (8.171). The Helmholtz and Gibbs free energies and the equation of state of the assembly of non-spherical molecules were formally related, at each temperature, to those of a reference assembly of spherical ones by the principle of corresponding states, (8.172)–(8.174).

The free energies of a mixture of molecules of parameters $f_{\alpha\beta}$, $g_{\alpha\beta}$ and $\delta_{\alpha\beta}(T)$ can be calculated in a similar way[34], as a hypothetical assembly of spherical molecules of energy parameters $(f_{\alpha\beta} + 2\delta_{\alpha\beta})$ and linear size parameters $(g_{\alpha\beta} - \delta_{\alpha\beta}/3)$, or volume parameters $(h_{\alpha\beta} - \delta_{\alpha\beta})$. This approximation is correct only to the first order in the differences of f, g and δ and cannot be extended to higher orders of the differences in δ because of the limitations of the perturbation method used in Section 8.5. It should be noted, however, that δ itself is already a 'second-order' term, (8.170). The excess free energy of a binary mixture is given by the first two terms of (9.40) where e_{12} is now a difference between composite parameters $(f_{\alpha\beta} + 2\delta_{\alpha\beta})$ and s_{12} between parameters $(h_{\alpha\beta} - \delta_{\alpha\beta})$. Thus, on substitution for G_f and G_h (see Appendix)

$$G^E/x_1 x_2 = U[e_{12} + 2d_{12}(T)] + (pV - NkT)[s_{12} - d_{12}(T)]$$
$$(9.126)$$

where

$$d_{12}(T) = 2\delta_{12}(T) - \delta_{11}(T) - \delta_{22}(T) \qquad (9.127)$$

347

For convenience, the difference

$$\Delta_{12}(T) = \delta_{11}(T) - \delta_{22}(T) \qquad (9.128)$$

is also introduced and defined here.

Thus there are two kinds of contribution to G^E, first the terms in e_{12} and s_{12} that arise from a lack of balance of the central part of the total potential, and secondly the terms in d_{12} that arise from a lack of balance of the non-central part of the potential. A measurement of G^E of the mixture at one temperature would not show to which of these two causes the non-ideality was to be ascribed. However, the dependence on temperature of the two terms is different, since d_{12} is proportional to $(1/T)$, (8.170). If U is independent of T and $(pV - NkT)$ is negligible, then a central-force model (all $\delta_{\alpha\beta} = 0$) or a non-central force model with $d_{12} = 0$ leads to

$$H^E = G^E, \qquad TS^E = 0 \qquad (9.129)$$

and a mixture in which the whole of the non-ideality is caused by a lack of balance of the non-central forces (that is, $e_{12} = 0$) to

$$H^E = 2G^E, \qquad TS^E = G^E \qquad (9.130)$$

These last equations are the analogue of (8.142) for a mixture and were first derived by Pople[35]. They show the large contributions to the excess heat and entropy made by the non-central forces. They depend, however, on the arbitrary assumption that U is independent of temperature. If, instead, U is taken as the experimental configuration energy of, say, carbon tetrachloride at 20°C, then the equations above become

Spherical molecules (all $\delta_{\alpha\beta} = 0$) or *non-spherical molecules* with $d_{12} = 0$

$$H^E = (1 - TC_p/U)G^E = 1 \cdot 51 G^E \qquad (9.131)$$

$$TS^E = (-TC_p/U)G^E = 0 \cdot 51 G^E \qquad (9.132)$$

Non-spherical molecules $(e_{12} = 0)$

$$H^E = (2 - TC_p/U)G^E = 2 \cdot 51 G^E \qquad (9.133)$$

$$TS^E = (1 - TC_p/U)G^E = 1 \cdot 51 G^E \qquad (9.134)$$

These results may be compared with those for a random mixture of Lorentz–Berthelot molecules where the non-ideality can arise from a difference in molecular energies and/or sizes. The two limiting cases are

$\theta \neq 0, \varphi = 0$

$$H^E = \left[\frac{1 - TC_p/U - 2T^2(\partial C_p/\partial T)_p/U}{1 - 2TC_p/U} \right] G^E = 0.75G^E \quad (9.135)$$

$\theta = 0, \varphi \neq 0$

$$H^E = (1 - TC_p/U)G^E = 1.51G^E \quad (9.136)$$

There are two well-known systems for which the ratio H^E/G^E is less than unity, namely carbon monoxide + methane (0·96) and carbon tetrachloride + neopentane (0·97). Both of these are close to Lorentz–Berthelot mixtures in which the non-ideality arises from the large difference θ in the molecular energies. Nitrogen + oxygen (1·53), carbon tetrachloride + benzene (1·34) and toluene + cyclohexane (1·5) are mixtures in which the departures from the Lorentz–Berthelot relations determine the size of the excess functions. Three systems have the ratio equal to two or more— benzene + cyclohexane (2·56), chloroform + carbon tetrachloride (2·15) and cyclohexane + carbon tetrachloride (2·11). In all these it is very probable that there is a significant lack of balance of the non-central forces.

The importance of the latter is made clear by calculating the conditions for azeotropy in a mixture in which all but the first-order differences in f, g and δ may be neglected. The condition is obtained by equating the chemical potentials (9.52) in the gas and liquid phases at a given pressure and temperature, and then putting equal the compositions of the two phases in these equations. The algebra is tedious[4,34,36] and not given here. The result is simple for a binary azeotrope of non-spherical molecules

$$2x_1 - 1 = \frac{\Delta U(\theta_{12} + 2\Delta_{12}) + p\Delta V(\varphi_{12} - \Delta_{12})}{\Delta U(e_{12} + 2d_{12}) + p\Delta V(s_{12} - d_{12})} \quad (9.137)$$

where the differences d_{12} and Δ_{12} are functions of the temperature and are defined by (9.127) and (9.128). The differences ΔU and ΔV are the latent energy and volume change on isothermal evaporation of the reference substance.

An azeotrope is formed whenever the modulus of the right-hand side of this equation is less than unity, as it then has a solution for a meaningful value of x_1, the mole fraction of the first component in the azeotropic mixture. The terms $p\Delta V$ may often be neglected, since the ratio $(p\Delta V/\Delta U)$ is only about 0·15–0·20 at the critical point and decreases with falling temperature.

With the omission of these terms

$$2x_1 - 1 = (\theta_{12} + 2\Delta_{12})/(e_{12} + 2d_{12}) \qquad (9.138)$$

This equation gives the simple, and plausible, result that a positive azeotrope is formed whenever the effective energy parameter $(f_{12} + 2\delta_{12})$ is less than both $(f_{11} + 2\delta_{11})$ and $(f_{22} + 2\delta_{22})$, and that a negative azeotrope is formed whenever it is greater than both. The f parameters are true molecular constants and so a mixture of spherical molecules (all $\delta_{\alpha\beta} = 0$) either forms an azeotrope at all temperatures, that is, *absolute azeotropy*, or else at none. However, the δ parameters change with temperature and so a mixture of non-spherical molecules can show either *absolute* or *limited* azeotropy. Thus a model that takes account of the non-central forces is necessary for the discussion of any of the many cases of limited azeotropy. The results in Section 6.2 show that limited azeotropy is particularly common in mixtures containing one polar component.

On this simple model azeotropy arises from energy differences between the molecules. The first-order terms in the size differences, s_{12} and φ_{12}, have little influence in (9.137). A better theory would include the second-order terms in θ_{12} and φ_{12}, and could be achieved by combining the methods of Section 8.5 with those of 9.2, as Balescu[32] (see Prigogine[2]) did for the case of a dipole interaction. However, the first-order terms are adequate for the discussion of the azeotropy of the binary mixtures formed from carbon dioxide, nitrous oxide, ethane, ethylene and acetylene (see Section 6.2). These form the simplest set of substances whose mixtures have been adequately studied and in which there is extensive azeotropy.

This arises in many of the mixtures from the large quadrupole–quadrupole energies of carbon dioxide and acetylene. These energies are manifest in the large values of δ for these substances (*Table 8.3*). The reduction of all non-central forces to one parameter, δ, disguises the fact that the signs of the quadrupoles are different in these two molecules, as the oxygen atoms in carbon dioxide carry a partial negative and the hydrogen atoms in acetylene a partial positive charge. The parameters $f_{\alpha\beta}$, $g_{\alpha\beta}$ and $\delta_{\alpha\beta}(T^c)$ for all interactions in these mixtures may be determined[34] from the vapour pressures of the pure substances (see *Table 8.3*) and from the critical temperatures and pressures of the mixtures. These properties determine unambiguously f_{11}, g_{11}, δ_{11}, f_{22}, g_{22}, δ_{22}, g_{12} and either f_{12} or δ_{12}. That is, the deviation of the (T^c, x) graph from linearity can be explained either by a lack of balance of the central forces $(e_{12} \neq 0, d_{12} = 0)$ or of the non-central forces $(e_{12} = 0, d_{12} \neq 0)$. The equation for T^c is an obvious extension of

(9.122)–(9.123) with the neglect of the second-order terms in θ and φ

$$T^c = T_0^c\{x_1^2[f_{11} + 2\delta_{11}(T^c)] + 2x_1x_2[f_{12} + 2\delta_{12}(T^c)]$$
$$+ x_2^2[f_{22} + 2\delta_{22}(T^c)]\} \quad (9.139)$$

Calculations based upon $e_{12} \neq 0$ are called here Calculation 1, those based upon $d_{12} \neq 0$ are Calculation 2, and those based on the assumption that all molecules are spherical (all $\delta_{\alpha\beta} = 0$) are

Table 9.13. The composition of azeotropes. The calculated values are for mixtures of spherical (Calculation 0) and of non-spherical molecules (Calculations 1 and 2). The mole fraction is that of the first component. A dash shows that the experimental behaviour is not known

System	Critical point		Normal boiling point			
	Experiment	0, 1, 2	Experiment	0	1	2
$CO_2 + N_2O$	none	none	—	see below*		
$CO_2 + C_2H_6$	0.7	0.7	0.5	0.6	0.4	0.4
$CO_2 + C_2H_4$	0.42	0.32	none	0.2	none	none
$CO_2 + C_2H_2$	none	none	0.33†	none	none	0.94†
$N_2O + C_2H_6$	0.7	0.7	—	0.6	0.3	0.4
$N_2O + C_2H_4$	none	none	—	none	none	none
$C_2H_6 + C_2H_4$	none	none	none	none	none	none
$C_2H_6 + C_2H_2$	0.5	0.5	0.6	0.5	0.6	0.7
$C_2H_4 + C_2H_2$	0.8	0.8	none	0.8	none	0.9
$CO_2 + N_2O + C_2H_4$	none	none	—	none	none	none
$CO_2 + C_2H_6 + C_2H_4$	—	none	none	none	none	none
$C_2H_6 + C_2H_4 + C_2H_2$	none	none	none	none	none	none

* The Calculation 0 predicts no azeotrope and requires the vapour pressure of N_2O to be substantially less than that of CO_2 at all temperatures. Calculations 1 and 2 predict a crossing of the vapour-pressure curves and, therefore, azeotropy. There is, in fact, no crossing but the vapour pressure of CO_2 exceeds that of N_2O by only 4 per cent at the triple point of CO_2, and so there is probably a positive azeotrope.
† There is here a definite disagreement of theory and experiment. The observed azeotrope is negative, presumably a consequence of the opposite signs of the linear quadrupoles of the two molecules. The azeotrope calculated from the critical properties of the mixture is positive, as the (T^c, x) graph is concave upwards.

Calculation 0. The composition of the azeotrope is obtained from these parameters and the properties of the reference substance (chosen to be carbon dioxide) by using (9.137).

The results of the three calculations[34] are shown in *Table 9.13.* All give the same result at the critical point, as is clearly necessary if the critical properties are used for fixing the parameters. The calculations differ, however, at temperatures well removed from the critical. Calculation 0 predicts little variation of the composition with temperature. The small changes shown arise from the change with temperature of the ratio $(p \, \Delta V/\Delta U)$. Calculations 1 and 2 do not differ greatly from each other and predict pronounced changes with temperature of the azeotropic composition. In several cases these calculations and the experimental observations show limited azeotropy. The results for the system carbon dioxide + ethylene are shown in *Figure 9.3*.

The absence of azeotropy in the three ternary systems is not very helpful. No ternary azeotrope is formed, as far as is known, and none of the calculations predicts one. However, it has been found possible[34] to calculate from the two-body parameters, $f_{\alpha\beta}$, $g_{\alpha\beta}$ and

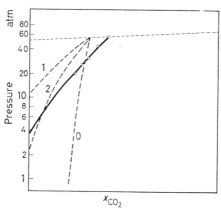

Figure 9.3. The mole fraction of carbon dioxide in the azeotrope of the system carbon dioxide + ethylene. The points and the full line are the experimental results (Section 6.2). The dashed curves are those calculated for a mixture of spherical molecules (Calculation 0) and of non-spherical molecules (Calculations 1 and 2)

$\delta_{\alpha\beta}$, the critical temperatures and pressures and the liquid–vapour equilibrium curves of the system carbon dioxide + nitrous oxide + ethylene. There are no new disposable parameters in the calculation of the properties of a ternary system.

The treatment above is based on a replacement of true non-spherical temperature-independent potentials by spherical but temperature-dependent potentials with parameters $(f + 2\delta)$ and $(h - \delta)$. Leland and his colleagues[22] have introduced shape factors more general than δ for use with the one-fluid van der Waals approximation. Their definition is empirical and in terms of macroscopic properties but has an analogous molecular form, namely, for a pure substance

$$f_{\alpha\alpha}(T)\, T_0^c = \Theta_{\alpha\alpha}(T_\alpha^R)\, T_\alpha^c \qquad (9.140)$$

$$h_{\alpha\alpha}(T)\, V_0^c = \Phi_{\alpha\alpha}(T_\alpha^R)\, V_\alpha^c \qquad (9.141)$$

Thus the temperature-dependent f parameter is divided into two factors: a constant (T_α^c/T_0^c) which is primarily an energy factor, and a shape factor $\Theta_{\alpha\alpha}$ which is a universal function of the reduced temperature $T_\alpha^R = T/T_\alpha^c$. The volume parameter h is divided similarly. In this way they can discuss departures from the principle of corresponding states both for pure substances and, with the van der Waals approximation, for multicomponent mixtures.

There is one class of non-polar substances whose departures from spherical symmetry is so extreme that the perturbation method used for pure substances in Section 8.5 and for mixtures in this Section is quite inadequate for their discussion. This class is that of the long-chain hydrocarbons and, in particular, the series of n-alkanes. Nevertheless, the regular progression in these series as successive —CH$_2$— groups are added to the chain is necessarily reflected in a regular progression of the macroscopic properties, and it is natural to attempt to bring such series within the scope of some theoretical model. To this end, a modification of the principle of corresponding states has been developed.

At an early stage of Chapter 8 it was necessary to factorize the total distribution function for a group of h molecules, $f^{(h)}$, into the product of the internal molecular partition functions and a positional or configurational function $n^{(h)}$. This factorization is justified for simple molecules and is used in the derivation of the usual principle of corresponding states in Section 8.4. However, in chain molecules this division is, strictly, impossible since a flexible chain can rotate either as a whole or in groups of segments. The latter motions cannot be classified as wholly internal or wholly external, since they clearly affect the energy of interaction of the molecule with its surroundings. Any division of the degrees of freedom into molecular and configurational is necessarily empirical and to be judged by the success of its macroscopic predictions.

The extension of the principle of corresponding states to chain molecules was made first by Prigogine and his colleagues[2,37] on the basis of a cell model and is now a much-tilled field of statistical thermodynamics. No detailed account of this work is given here, since much of it, in both inspiration and application, arose from a desire to understand the behaviour of polymer solutions.

A principle of corresponding states is developed by regarding a chain molecule as a series of quasi-spherical segments whose interaction with the segments of neighbouring chains is characterized in the usual way by an energy, ϵ, and a distance, σ. (The segments may be of more than one kind, e.g. CH$_3$– and –CH$_2$–, each with its appropriate ϵ and σ for like and unlike interactions.) The chain is specified, first, by the number of segments, conventionally denoted

r, secondly, by the number of external contacts that these make with other segments, qz (where z is a coordination number of about 10) and, thirdly, by that of external degrees of freedom, $3c$. Clearly q and c increase with r, and it is often assumed that $q = r$, so that the ratio (c/r) or (c/q) becomes a measure of the flexibility of a chain. The ratio is unity for a monomer and often falls to about 0·3 in the infinite chain.

It is reasonable, and can be supported by plausible but not rigorous arguments, that r, q and c should serve as reduction parameters for obtaining the reduced volume, energy and entropy, respectively, of a chain molecule[38,39]. Thus a reduced volume $\tilde{V}$ at a reduced temperature of

$$\tilde{T} = (c/r)(kT/\epsilon) \tag{9.142}$$

is defined by

$$\tilde{V}(\tilde{T}) = V_n(T)/rN\sigma^3 \tag{9.143}$$

where $V_n(T)$ is the orthobaric liquid volume of the alkane C_nH_{2n+2}. The energy U_n and the entropy S_n are reduced similarly

$$\tilde{U}(\tilde{T}) = U_n(T)/qN\epsilon \qquad \tilde{S}(\tilde{T}) = S_n(T)/cNk \tag{9.144}$$

The extension of the principle of corresponding states is, therefore, the assumption that there is for all alkanes a single reduced equation of state which, for example, gives $\tilde{U}$ as a function of $\tilde{T}$ (or of $\tilde{V}$ and $\tilde{T}$ off the orthobaric line).

In this treatment the chain molecule is replaced by a set of segments. The predicted properties of the fluid do not change if some of these segments are imagined to be moved from one molecule to another, since such a move changes neither the total number of segments nor that of molecules. Hence the properties of a mixture of alkanes should depend only on the mean chain length and not upon the individual lengths, and so this principle of corresponding states formally includes the older, and more empirical, *principle of congruence* put forward by Brønsted and Koefoed[40] in 1946. This states that the thermal properties of a multicomponent system of alkanes are determined not by the individual chain lengths but by the mean $n = \sum_{\alpha} x_\alpha n_\alpha$. Thus the properties of *congruent mixtures* (mixtures with the same value of n) differ only in the ideal entropy of mixing. This principle and its verification[40] have been the motive behind much of the work on alkane mixtures summarized in Section 4.7. Some of the unusual features of these systems, such as the negative values of V^E, are consistent with the principle of corresponding states of Prigogine. (The negative volumes are a simple consequence of the fact that the curve that represents $\tilde{V}$ as a function of $\tilde{T}$ is concave upwards.) Other features, notably the change of H^E from positive to negative as the temperature rises, are not derivable from Prigogine's cell model and only qualitatively in accord with the wider principle of congruence[38,39,41].

Clearly there is no need to be committed to a particular equation of state of the reference substance in this field, since a theory of mixtures is usually held to have fulfilled its function if it describes accurately the properties of the mixture in terms of the properties of the pure substances and a set of intermolecular parameters. However, many recent efforts have been attempts to set up model configurational integrals which describe the reference substance. Amongst the most successful of these is that of Flory and his colleagues[42]. Patterson, in his recent papers[41,43], has reviewed critically this and other similar attempts and has shown that the thermodynamic consequences of each model are very sensitive to the particular assumptions made. The details are too complex to be summarized here.

9.8 CONCLUSIONS

The theory of mixtures did not at first share in the burst of development which transformed that of pure liquids between 1960 and 1964, nor in the development of perturbation theories that has been so characteristic a feature of work on liquids since 1964. The starting point of all serious work on mixtures in the decade after 1956 was the concept of the random mixture. We have seen that this is unrealistic if the molecules in the mixture are of different sizes, but there was no other concept whose relation to the exact configuration integral was so well defined.

It has, therefore, been particularly fortunate that the Percus–Yevick equation, which played so large a part in the renaissance of the theory of pure liquids, is soluble for a mixture of spheres of different sizes. This solution and the experimental work on computers with the same systems have revealed how inappropriate a concept the random mixture is for molecules with steep potentials. The Percus–Yevick solution leads to small negative values of the excess volume and free energy for mixtures of molecules of different size and with steep intermolecular potentials, of which the hard sphere is the limiting case. This result is almost certainly applicable to more realistic model potentials which have strong negative regions, and hence also to real mixtures. The confidence with which this extension is made is based on the recent appreciation of the fact that in a pure liquid it is the repulsive part of the potential that primarily determines the structure, and that the attractive part is much less specific in its action. It is this truth that has been responsible for the recent interest in perturbation theories: its enunciation was probably van der Waals's most enduring contribution to the theory of fluids.

The developments described in Section 9.4 show how these ideas can be applied to mixtures of simple molecules whilst the comparison with experiment in Section 9.5 demonstrates their superiority to earlier theories. However, there is no reason to suppose that these developments are the only or the best way of using these ideas. Rather it is to be hoped that they will be as fruitful as was the concept of the random mixture in begetting healthy offspring.

References

[1] Prigogine, I., Bellemans, A. and Englert-Chwoles, A. *J. chem. Phys.* 24 (1956) 518

[2] Prigogine, I. *The Molecular Theory of Solutions*, Amsterdam (North-Holland) 1957

[3] Scott, R. L. *J. chem. Phys.* 25 (1956) 193

[4] Byers Brown, W. *Phil. Trans.* A250 (1957) 175

[5] Byers Brown, W. *Phil. Trans.* A250 (1957) 221

[6] Salsburg, Z. W., Wojtowicz, P. J. and Kirkwood, J. G. *J. chem. Phys.* 26 (1957) 1533

[7] Wojtowicz, P. J., Salsburg, Z. W. and Kirkwood, J. G. *J. chem. Phys.* 27 (1957) 505

[8] Chaundy, T. W. and McLeod, J. B. *Q. Jl Math.* 9 (1958) 202

[9] Longuet-Higgins, H. C. *Proc. R. Soc.* A205 (1951) 247

[10] Prigogine, I., with Garikian, G. *Physica* 16 (1950) 239; with Mathot, V. *J. chem. Phys.* 20 (1952) 49; with Bellemans, A. *Discuss. Faraday Soc.* 15 (1953) 80

[11] Byers Brown, W. and Longuet-Higgins, H. C. *Proc. R. Soc.* A209 (1951) 416

[12] Byers Brown, W. *Proc. R. Soc.* A240 (1957) 561

[13] Rice, S. A. *J. chem. Phys.* 24 (1956) 357; 29 (1958) 141

[14] Guggenheim, E. A. *Mixtures*, p. 42, Oxford Univ. Press, 1952

[15] Bellemans, A., Mathot, V. and Simon, M. *Adv. chem. Phys.* 11 (1967) 117

[16] Smith, E. B. and Lea, K. R. *Nature, Lond.* 186 (1960) 714; Alder, B. J. *J. chem. Phys.* 40 (1964) 2724

[17] Lebowitz, J. L. *Phys. Rev.* 133 (1964) A895

[18] Lebowitz, J. L. and Rowlinson, J. S. *J. chem. Phys.* 41 (1964) 133

[19] Leland, T. W., Rowlinson, J. S. and Sather, G. A. *Trans. Faraday Soc.* 64 (1968) 1447; with Watson, I. D., 65 (1969) 2034

[20] Throop, G. J. and Bearman, R. J. *J. chem. Phys.* 44 (1966) 1423

[21] van der Waals, J. D. *Die Kontinuität des gasförmigen und flüssigen Zustandes*, Vol. 2, Ch. 1, Leipzig (Barth) 1900

REFERENCES

[22] Reid, R. C. and Leland, T. W. *A. I. Ch. E. Jl* 11 (1965) 228; 12 (1966) 1277; Leach, J. W., Chappelear, P. S. and Leland, T. W. 14 (1968) 568

[23] Douslin, D. R., Harrison, R. H. and Moore, R. T. *J. phys. Chem.* 71 (1967) 3477

[24] Marsh, K. N. *Trans. Faraday Soc.* 64 (1968) 883

[25] Rowlinson, J. S. *Nature, Lond.* 194 (1962) 470

[26] Hildebrand, J. H. and Scott, R. L. *The Solubility of Nonelectrolytes*, Ch. 7, New York (Reinhold) 1950

[27] Bellemans, A., with Mathot, V. and Zuckerbrodt, P. *Bull. Acad. r. Belg. Cl. Sci.* 42 (1956) 631; with Zuckerbrodt, P. *ibid.* 643

[28] Partington, E. J., Rowlinson, J. S. and Weston, J. F. *Trans. Faraday Soc.* 56 (1960) 479; Jones, I. W. and Rowlinson, J. S. 59 (1963) 1702

[29] Kreglewski, A. *J. phys. Chem.* 71 (1967) 2860; 72 (1968) 1897, 2280

[30] Scott, R. L. and van Konynenburg, P., private communication

[31] Barker, J. A. *J. chem. Phys.* 19 (1951) 1430

[32] Balescu, R. *Bull. Acad. r. Belg. Cl. Sci.* 41 (1955) 1242

[33] Rowlinson, J. S. *Molec. Phys.* 1 (1958) 414

[34] Rowlinson, J. S. and Sutton, J. R. *Proc. R. Soc.* A229 (1955) 271, 396; with Weston, J. F. *Thermodynamic and Transport Properties of Fluids*, p. 10, London (Instn mech. Engrs) 1958

[35] Pople, J. A. *Discuss. Faraday Soc.* 15 (1953) 35

[36] Cook, D. and Longuet-Higgins, H. C. *Proc. R. Soc.* A209 (1951) 28; Cook, D. A219 (1953) 245

[37] Prigogine, I., Trappeniers, N. and Mathot, V. *Discuss. Faraday Soc.* 15 (1953) 93

[38] Delmas, G., Patterson, D., with Somcynsky, T. *J. Polym. Sci.* 57 (1962) 79; with Böhme, D. *Trans. Faraday Soc.* 58 (1962) 2116; Bhattacharyya, S. N., Patterson, D. and Somcynsky, T. *Physica* 30 (1964) 1276

[39] Hijmans, J. *Physica* 27 (1961) 433; Holleman, Th. and Hijmans, J. 28 (1962) 604; 31 (1965) 64; Holleman, Th. 29 (1963) 585; 31 (1965) 49

[40] Brønsted, J. N. and Koefoed, J. *K. danske Vidensk. Selsk.* (*Mat. Fys. Skr.*) 22 (1946) No. 17

[41] Patterson, D., Bhattacharyya, S. N. and Picker, P. *Trans. Faraday Soc.* 64 (1968) 648

[42] Flory, P. J., with Orwoll, R. A. and Vrij, A. *J. Am. chem. Soc.* 86 (1964) 3507, 3515; with Abe, A. *ibid.* 3563; Flory, P. J. 87 (1965) 1833; Abe, A. and Flory, P. J. *ibid.* 1838; Höcker, H. and Flory, P. J. *Trans. Faraday Soc.* 64 (1968) 1188

[43] Patterson, D. *Rubb. Chem. Technol.* 40 (1967) 1

APPENDIX

The configurational Helmholtz and Gibbs free energies of a family of conformal substances are related by

$$A(V, T) = fA_0[V/h, T/f] - NkT \ln h \qquad (A.1)$$
$$G(p, T) = fG_0[ph/f, T/f] - NkT \ln h \qquad (A.2)$$

The derivatives of A and G with respect to the parameters f and h ($= g^3$) are widely used in Chapters 8 and 9 and are collected here, together with some related functions. Each derivative is evaluated for the reference substance, that is, at $f = h = 1$, and all thermodynamic functions are configurational.

$$A_f = G_f = U \qquad (A.3)$$
$$A_h = G_h = pV - NkT \qquad (A.4)$$
$$A_{ff} = -TC_V \qquad (A.5)$$
$$A_{fh} = pV - VT\gamma_V \qquad (A.6)$$
$$A_{hh} = V/\beta_T + NkT - 2pV \qquad (A.7)$$
$$G_{ff} = -TC_p + 2pVT\alpha_p - p^2V\beta_T \qquad (A.8)$$
$$G_{fh} = -pVT\alpha_p + p^2V\beta_T \qquad (A.9)$$
$$G_{hh} = NkT - p^2V\beta_T \qquad (A.10)$$

Other functions may be obtained by suitable differentiation with respect to p, V or T. For example

$$V_f = (\partial G_f/\partial p)_T \qquad \text{etc.} \qquad (A.11)$$

The differences between the derivatives of A and those of G are given by

$$G_{\xi\eta} - A_{\xi\eta} = -V_\xi V_\eta/V\beta_T \qquad (\xi, \eta = f, h) \qquad (A.12)$$

These functions are closely related to those introduced in Section 8.2 to describe the fluctuations of $\mathscr{U}$ and $\mathscr{V}$ of a Lennard-Jones assembly

$$A_{fk} = A_{fh} - A_h = A_{fh} - A_k \qquad (A.13)$$
$$G_{fk} = G_{fh} - G_h = G_{fh} - G_k \qquad (A.14)$$
$$A_{kk} = A_{hh} - Z_{hh} \qquad (A.15)$$
$$G_{kk} = G_{hh} - Z_{hh} \qquad (A.16)$$
$$Z_{hh} = -\frac{nm}{9}G_f + \left(\frac{n+m-3}{3}\right)G_h = \overline{\mathscr{W}} - \overline{\mathscr{V}} \qquad (A.17)$$

(see 8.58 and 9.36).

Hence

$$G_{\xi\eta} - A_{\xi\eta} = -V_\xi V_\eta / V\beta_T \qquad (\xi, \eta = f, k) \qquad (A.18)$$

The functions with subscripts f and k are related to the molecular fluctuation integrals by (8.63)–(8.83). Those with subscript f and h are related to similar fluctuation integrals.

$$A_{\xi\eta} = A_{\xi\eta}^{(2)} + A_{\xi\eta}^{(3)} + A_{\xi\eta}^{(4)} \qquad (\xi, \eta = f, h \text{ or } f, k) \qquad (A.19)$$

$$A_{fh}^{(2)} = A_{fk}^{(2)} + A_h \qquad (A.20)$$

$$A_{fh}^{(3)} = A_{fk}^{(3)}, \qquad A_{fh}^{(4)} = A_{fk}^{(4)} \qquad (A.21)$$

$$A_{hh}^{(2)} = A_{kk}^{(2)} + Z_{hh} \qquad (A.22)$$

$$A_{hh}^{(3)} = A_{kk}^{(3)}, \qquad A_{hh}^{(4)} = A_{kk}^{(4)} \qquad (A.23)$$

These are related to the corresponding functions of G by

$$G_{\xi\eta}^{(2)} = A_{\xi\eta}^{(2)}, \qquad G_{\xi\eta}^{(3)} = A_{\xi\eta}^{(3)} \qquad (\xi, \eta = f, h \text{ or } f, k) \qquad (A.24)$$

$$G_{\xi\eta}^{(4)} = A_{\xi\eta}^{(4)} - A_{\xi\eta} + G_{\xi\eta} \qquad (A.25)$$

The functions $A_{\xi\eta}^{(1)}$ and $G_{\xi\eta}^{(1)}$ are related to fluctuations in the 'private' energies and virials of the molecules.

$$A_{ff}^{(1)} = A_{ff}^{(2)} + \tfrac{1}{2}A_{ff}^{(3)} = -\sum_i \frac{\overline{(\mathscr{U}_i - \overline{\mathscr{U}}_i)^2}}{2kT} \qquad (A.26)$$

$$A_{fk}^{(1)} = A_{fk}^{(2)} + \tfrac{1}{2}A_{fk}^{(3)} = -\sum_i \frac{\overline{(\mathscr{U}_i - \overline{\mathscr{U}}_i)(\mathscr{V}_i - \overline{\mathscr{V}}_i)}}{2kT} \qquad (A.27)$$

$$A_{kk}^{(1)} = A_{kk}^{(2)} + \tfrac{1}{2}A_{kk}^{(3)} = -\sum_i \frac{\overline{(\mathscr{V}_i - \overline{\mathscr{V}}_i)^2}}{2kT} \qquad (A.28)$$

where

$$\mathscr{U}_i = \sum_j{}' u_{ij}, \qquad \mathscr{V}_i = -\tfrac{1}{3}\sum_j{}' v_{ij} \qquad (A.29)$$

where the prime denotes the omission of the term $i = j$.

From the equations above

$$G_{\xi\eta}^{(1)} = A_{\xi\eta}^{(1)} \qquad (\xi, \eta = f, k) \qquad (A.30)$$

These fluctuations, like those of $\mathscr{U}$ and $\mathscr{V}$ in Section 8.2, must satisfy Schwarz's inequality

$$G_{ff}^{(1)} G_{kk}^{(1)} - (G_{fk}^{(1)})^2 \geqslant 0 \qquad (A.31)$$

REFERENCE

Byers Brown, W. *Phil. Trans.* A250 (1957) 175, 221; *Proc. R. Soc.* A240 (1957) 561

GENERAL INDEX

INDEX OF SYSTEMS

Systems are of one, two or three components, and are in the alphabetical order of the group of chemical elements that denote the first component. There are no cross-references. Components are named if they have isomers. Unnamed paraffins and perfluoroparaffins are the n-alkanes. The alphabetical order is subject to three conventions:

(*1*) inorganic components precede organic;
(*2*) carbon is placed first in organic components and is followed immediately by hydrogen (if present);
(*3*) substances with one carbon atom, etc. precede those with two, etc.